HUGH YOUNG

A Surgeon's Autobiography

BOOKS BY HUGH HAMPTON YOUNG

HYPERTROPHY AND CANCER OF THE PROSTATE

YOUNG'S PRACTICE OF UROLOGY

UROLOGICAL ROENTGENOLOGY

GENITAL ABNORMALITIES, HERMAPHRODITISM AND RELATED AD-
RENAL DISEASES

HUGH HAMPTON YOUNG

After a portrait by Sir William Orpen

HUGH YOUNG

A Surgeon's Autobiography

WITH OVER 100 DRAWINGS BY

WILLIAM P. DIDUSCH

AND THREE COLOR PRINTS

hb

HARCOURT, BRACE AND COMPANY

NEW YORK

TO

*My master, William Stewart Halsted, whose influence
in surgery is everlasting*

*My associates and the graduates of the Brady Urolog-
ical Institute who after long years of training have
gone forth to add luster to Mr. Brady's foundation*

*My children—Frances Young Rienhoff, Frederick
Colston Young, Helen Young Crain, and Elizabeth
Young Starr*

PREFACE

WHY WRITE of my life? Some ten years ago I dictated for my children a brief story of my experiences as a boy on a Texas ranch, and also told them of those fighting men, their grandfathers. Mr. and Mrs. Alfred Harcourt happened to read this purely personal document, and gave me no rest thereafter until I began this autobiography.

But when I came to write about my life, I asked, "What about the medical work on which I have spent most of my time and effort?" My friends as well as my publishers advised me to tell the complete story. They urged that developing my specialty of urology was too important a part of my life to be omitted. That would be sacrificing the true picture. A generation ago a free discussion of my medical work in a book of this sort might have been unacceptable, but today public enlightenment on matters of health has aroused great general interest in all phases of medicine. Subjects that were taboo are now freely discussed by the laity. My work has been largely with afflictions about which there is still much ignorance; they are some of the deadliest of diseases. The part that I have played in the evolution of methods for their control or cure by surgical operations has absorbed much of my life. And so I tell the most important happenings in my medical career. In order to make the story easily understandable I have illustrated it with anatomical and surgical drawings properly labeled. Unessential details and intricacies of technique have been omitted.

I was glad of the opportunity to tell of Mr. James Buchanan Brady's great foundation, and what has been accomplished here in his memory.

I was glad of an opportunity to acknowledge my indebtedness to General John J. Pershing, and to tell what was done by the Division of Urology A.E.F., of which he appointed me director. The widespread interest in venereal diseases has emboldened me to speak frankly of those great scourges as they affected the health and efficiency of our troops. The remarkable results obtained in the A.E.F. show what can be accomplished in the civil population by a program of far-reaching scope. "The war years" occupy several chapters in my book.

Early in my career it was my good fortune to have as patients many men prominent in public life. Intimate friendships, thus formed, made it possible for me to secure important medical legislation through their influence. As a result I have been put on the legislative committees of state and national societies. I have recounted my experiences with the General Assembly of Maryland and the Congress of the United States.

Other chapters have given me a chance to tell of the fine time I have had not only in my professional life with a splendid group of confreres and assistants, but also enjoying outdoor sports with boon companions.

In the preparation of the manuscript and the correction of the proofs, I have received the frank criticism of many friends. I wish to express my appreciation of the interest that has been shown and the advice offered by Mr. Henry L. Mencken, Dr. and Mrs. Morris I. Fishbein, Dr. and Mrs. William M. Dabney, Dr. and Mrs. John B. Whitehead, Mrs. Esther Colston Coale, Drs. Charles R. Austrian, Austin H. Wood, Hugh J. Jewett, Miss Isabel Ely Lord, and particularly Mr. and Mrs. Alfred Harcourt. Their advice has been of incalculable value. Above all I wish to express my gratitude to my secretary, Miss Bertha M. Trott.

HUGH HAMPTON YOUNG

Linkwood
100 West Cold Spring Lane
Baltimore, Maryland

CONTENTS

ILLUSTRATIONS

HUGH YOUNG

A Surgeon's Autobiography

AT THE age of eighteen months I was taken by my father, General William Hugh Young, and my mother, Frances Kemper Young, from San Antonio, Texas, where I was born, to Austin by stagecoach. It was winter, and the black, waxy roads were wet with continuous rains. The stagecoach, drawn by six horses, struggled over these terrible roads, and although relayed every few miles with a fresh string of animals, arrived at Austin late in the night. Mother and Father, wet, bedraggled and tired, put up at the hotel, and while they prepared to retire placed me on the big double bed. A large whisky toddy was prepared by Father, enough for himself and Mother, and this he placed on the table beside the bed. Attracted by the amber color of the liquid, I seized it with my baby hands and tossed off the larger part of it, according to the story I have heard recounted many a time. My parents, busy in their preparations to go to bed, did not notice what I had done until almost all of their refreshment had disappeared, and then were horrified at the thought of what might happen. But nothing did happen, except that I became uproariously drunk, refused to go to sleep, continued to keep up a perfect carnival of noise and merriment throughout the night, and prevented my parents from getting any sleep. Strange to say, I didn't get sick, and the next day was none the worse for having imbibed what was thought to be enough for my father and mother.

This inoculation against the effect of whisky probably has stood me in good stead many a time.

Early in life, I was placed in the tender care of my grandfather, Colonel Hugh Franklin Young. To me he was a heroic character, over six feet tall, straight as an Indian, handsome, and fearless. He had had thrilling experiences fighting white men, red men, and Mexicans, and I usually refused to go to sleep until he told me a story.

Grandfather was a huntsman and frequently went out for big game. One of his bedtime stories told how he and a friend went out with their rifles to kill a bear. They came to a large canebrake and separated, agreeing to rejoin on the other side of the brake. After going a short distance, Grandfather saw two beautiful cubs nestling at the foot of a tree and, fascinated by them, he decided to take them home. Pretty soon there was a crashing in the canebrake that announced the rapid approach of the mother bear. Dropping the cubs, he took a steady aim at the onrushing furious mother and fired. She continued to come on, and as Grandfather had had only one bullet in his rifle, his only hope of escape was to run. He was going well until suddenly across his path he saw a huge log barring the way. His only chance was to mount the log and jump across. As he landed on the other side he slipped and fell into the soft mud, and before he could get on his feet the bear was on him and chewing at the back of his neck. In a short time a stream of blood, which ran down over his cheek and accumulated on the ground, convinced him that he was rapidly bleeding to death. He was preparing for another world when a shot rang out, the bear toppled over, and his companion appeared at his side. Quickly dragging Grandfather out of the mud, he wiped the clotted blood from his face and said, "Get up." Grandfather muttered that he was too weak from loss of blood, at which his friend exclaimed, "That's not your blood, it's the bear's." Grandfather had broken the bear's jaw with his shot, and this prevented her from biting him.

Grandfather often told me about the buffalo hunts in which he

HUGH FRANKLIN YOUNG AT SEVENTY

WILLIAM HUGH YOUNG AT TWENTY-SIX
Brigade Commander, Confederate Army

FRANCES MICHIE KEMPER
AT EIGHTEEN

MRS. GEORGE WHITFIELD KEMPER
AT FIFTEEN

took part. Between Austin and San Antonio he would frequently see from a hilltop great valleys completely black with buffalo. While out hunting one time, he lost his way. After two or three days, the water gave out, and his thirst was so great that he feared for his life. Having frequently killed and butchered a buffalo, he remembered that the animal had a supernumerary stomach which was filled with water and newly cropped hay. Hastily killing an animal, he opened this stomach with his bowie knife. He compressed the hay in the stomach with the buffalo's tail, so the water would rise to the surface, and greedily drank the liquid, which he assured me was pure and palatable.

These and many other exciting tales were the bedtime stories of my early youth—tales that often had the opposite effect desired for the modern bedtime story. They were far from soporific, and frequently after Grandfather left me I lay on the bed trembling with fear, and later awakened from a horrible dream, during which I had been in fearful fights with savages or beasts.

Grandfather was born in Rockbridge County, Virginia, not far from the Natural Bridge. His great-grandfather, who was born in Ireland, killed an Indian who had murdered his only brother, so that fighting Indians came naturally to him. The name Hugh is traditional, as it appears in practically every generation of our family for nearly two hundred years. There were sixteen children in his grandfather's family and eight in his father's. At the age of sixteen Grandfather decided that there were too many in the family to give him any chance for success in Virginia. So he quietly decamped and made his way through the mountains of Virginia and Tennessee and on into Mississippi, where he led an adventurous life. He soon joined the constabulary engaged in fighting the Mississippi River bandits and pirates who infested Mississippi and Louisiana.

One of Grandfather's prominent characteristics was fondness for dress. I never remember seeing him except in a frock coat and a high silk hat. Apparently such were his habits, even in the frontier towns of Mississippi in the eighteen-twenties. I recall well his describing how one night he went to a ball with a beautiful girl. He was careful to have in each hip pocket a pistol beneath the tails of his "clawhammer coat," as he called it. During the dance someone told him that a certain bad man was outside with a pistol, saying that he would get him before the evening was over. Grandfather took the young lady to her mother, explaining that he had something important to attend to, but that he would be back very soon. With a cocked pistol in each hand, he hunted for the bandit, but failed to find him. The dance was then resumed.

Grandfather married Frances Hampton Gibson at Clarksburg, Tennessee, in 1836. She was descended from William Hampton, who came to Jamestown in 1620. Wade Hampton was her cousin. From her I get my middle name. Grandfather's roving disposition, however, did not permit him to rest, and he took his bride across the Mississippi to Booneville, Missouri, which only a few years before had been part of the Louisiana Territory that Jefferson got from Napoleon.

In this frontier country my father was born. He had a sister eighteen months younger than he. She died in infancy a result of falling from the shoulders of her Negro nurse. In 1840 the family was again on the move, when Grandfather took his wife and my father, two years old, into the wilds of northern Texas, crossing the dangerous Indian territory to make a new home in Clarksville, near the Red River. Here my grandmother died at the age of twenty-four, leaving the little boy alone, with a roving huntsman for a father.

At that time Texas was in the throes of the war for freedom from Mexico. The first ray of hope had come to the Texans in their glorious defeat of Santa Anna at San Jacinto, but the war was not over, and the frontiersmen who had come to Texas had to organize for self-protection against both Indians and Mexicans. Grandfather joined the Texas militia and was soon enrolled with a group of men who formed the celebrated Snively Expedition. In the spring of 1843 the Republic of Texas discovered that the Mexicans had purchased huge stores of merchandise in St. Louis, and had assembled a train of prairie schooners, each with its large team of mules, to transport these supplies by the Santa Fe Trail from Missouri across the present panhandle of Texas to the old Spanish city of Santa Fe. Colonel Jacob Snively was commissioned by President Sam Houston to assemble a force and intercept the rich wagon train as it crossed from the United States into Texas. He was instructed to remain on Texas soil. As the men had to equip themselves with horses, clothes, and arms, they were offered, as a prize, one-half the spoils. Volunteers were asked to meet on the Red River. Grandfather, one of the hundred and seventy-five adventurous spirits who gathered there, has left an interesting diary.

This little command started west through wild country inhabited only by Indians, many of whom were on the warpath. The expedition followed Indian trails until it had passed the western boundaries of the United States along the Red River, then proceeded north in the panhandle of Texas, and on May 27, 1843, reached the Santa Fe Trail, south and west of the Arkansas River near Fort Leavenworth. Here they waited for news of the precious wagon train. Their scouts brought word of the approach of a body of Mexican troops marching east from Santa Fe across the northern part of Texas to meet the wagon train when it left the United States. The scouts reported that there were about a hundred men in the party, and the Texans, dismounting, engaged them. The entire force of Mexicans was captured with the exception of two. On the ground lay thirty-six dead and wounded, evidence of the wonderful marksmanship of Snively's men.

"Grandfather," said I, "did you kill any of those Mexicans?" "I do not know, my boy, that I ever killed anybody, but I do remember that I saw one man stick his head from behind a tree.

I fired. Shortly afterwards the Mexicans ran and I found a dead Mexican with a hole in his forehead, but I'm not sure it was I who killed him."

The Texans waited some days. Learning from the captives that General Armijo, with a force of over seven hundred Mexicans, was following them, Colonel Snively pushed on to attack them, but found they had turned tail and run. With all fear of a Mexican attack removed, Colonel Snively returned along the Santa Fe Trail, liberated the captives, even furnishing mounts for the wounded. They passed the scene of their engagement a few days before, where the bodies of some twenty-five dead Mexicans lay.

Snively then encamped in the forest along the southwest shore of the Arkansas River, and waited for the approach of the Mexican train. In the meantime, seventy-five homesick men had left. Game was scarce, and to keep from starving it was necessary to send hunters across the river into the territory of the United States, where buffalo were plentiful. Game was free to everyone— white men, Indians, bandits, Mexicans—according to the law of self-preservation on the prairies.

One day two of the huntsmen returned in great haste, crossed the river, and informed Colonel Snively that United States Dragoons, accompanying the caravan, had come upon them and would soon be there. Looking upon them as friends, the Texans did not attempt to leave. The Dragoons soon arrived on the opposite bank. There were two hundred cavalry accompanied by two pieces of artillery. A United States officer came to the river's edge and informed Colonel Snively that he was invited by Captain Philip St. George Cooke, who commanded the Dragoons, to cross the river and visit him. The officer said he was authorized to guarantee safe passage back. Colonel Snively went over with one of his men. According to Grandfather, Colonel Snively was informed by Captain Cooke that the Texans were on United States soil and that he was compelled to disarm them. Snively protested that he felt sure he was west of the 100th meridian boundary line, and as the line between the United States and Texas never had been surveyed, this was at best disputed territory. Captain Cooke was inflexible, and gave the Texans an hour to lay down arms, asserting that if any attempted to escape he would immediately fire. Without giving Colonel Snively a chance to return to his force, Captain Cooke crossed with his command, surrounded the Texans, and disarmed them. Colonel Snively protested the inhumanity of depriving them of their arms in a country infested with thousands of hostile Indians, so Captain Cooke gave back ten of the rifles and offered to allow as many as wished to accompany him back to Missouri. Grandfather and thirty-nine others had been able to conceal their rifles beneath birchbark, which strewed the ground, and gave up captured Spanish *escopetas* (short rifles) in their stead. Captain Cooke then recrossed the Arkansas, accompanied by some of the Texans.

Colonel Snively moved a few miles up a creek. His force was now reduced to about fifty. Twice they fought off attacks by Indians, losing a few men and a good many horses. However, they decided to attempt to intercept the wagon train. Two scouts, sent forward, were killed by Indians; others were sent out and reported that the train had crossed the river into Texas a few days before, and had gone on its way.

After they had followed the Santa Fe Trail for several days, discontentment again arose among Snively's men, and they began dropping out of line until only ten were left to continue the pursuit. In Grandfather's diary he remarks:

We ten were overwhelmed with disappointment and chagrin. A march of four days would have sufficed to put the wagon train in our power. With reluctance we followed the others. In a short time we were surrounded by five hundred Comanche and Kiowa warriors. We received them with galling fire and emptied a number of saddles, and repulsed the attack. This was our last affair with the Indians. The last four days of our march we had nothing to eat.

The Texas Government made an earnest protest at Captain Cooke's action, which Grandfather attributed to Mexican bribes.

The United States finally paid $18.50 for each of the guns taken from the Texans, but failed to acknowledge that Captain Cooke had invaded the territory of Texas.

Captain Cooke's action stirred up a tempest in Texas, which was taken up by newspapers in the United States. It played an important part in fanning the flames that two years later resulted in war with Mexico. Historians who have written of these times report having conferred with Grandfather and read his diaries.

After Texas joined the United States, Grandfather became a colonel in the militia, and served in the Mexican War. He subsequently became a judge, and had much to do with the development of that part of the country.

At an early age, Father was sent to McKenzie College, a frontier school with scandalously bad food and cruel teachers. I remember his telling of the fearful times the boys had until eventually they rebelled and threw rotten hams out of the windows.

From McKenzie College father went to Nashville, where he lived with his uncle, Dr. John Young, a prominent physician who subsequently took an important part in politics. While in Nashville, father became a great friend of Henry Watterson, who went to the same school and even at an early age showed evidence of a brilliant mind.

When he was twenty-one, Father appeared at his uncle's home in Staunton, Virginia, on his way to the University of Virginia. There he met Frances Kemper, who was later to become his wife. This sixteen-year-old niece of David Young's wife was on her way to Charlottesville to attend a girls' school. With the sobering experiences of the West, Father appeared very old to the rollicking miss. He often asserted that it was love at first sight on his part. During the next two years at the university father paid court with little success. Frances Kemper had far too many beaux to take any interest in this serious young man. Her brother, George Kemper, was also a student at the university, as was her cousin, Charles Kemper Young, also a first cousin of Father's. Seeing that he was making no progress with the young lady, during his second year Father decided to build a house, and bring her brother and cousin to live with him. Securing a lease from the university for a small plot of ground off the campus, he built a two-story brick house which he called "The Lone Star." The three of them were valeted by father's body-servant, Lee, one of Grandfather's slaves.

With the outbreak of the Civil War, Father remained at the University of Virginia to study military tactics. Two companies of students—the "Southern Guard" and the "Sons of Liberty"— formed the Cadet Corps in the military school organized by the university to train officers for the Confederate Army. Father became the captain of one of these companies, and Robert E. Lee, Jr., son of the General, was captain of the other. Intensive training was given these young men for six months, when they left to become officers in the Southern forces. Armed with a commission to raise a regiment, Father said good-by to his sweetheart and made his way back to Texas, where he found his father serving as brigadier general in charge of recruiting service for northern Texas. Obtaining a horse, Father rode over this sparsely populated region and picked the men for his regiment. From all accounts, it was a fine, high-spirited, sharpshooting body of men who assembled at Dallas and organized the 9th Texas Infantry. On account of his youth, Father was not elected to the command, but only as captain of a company. The early training of the regiment was acquired at Little Rock, Arkansas, after which they joined the Confederate Army of Tennessee.

One of Father's comrades, in writing me, said:

I was with your father's regiment when it joined the army of Albert Sidney Johnston at Corinth, Miss. At dress parade there were some 40,000 men. They were as fine looking soldiers as the country ever produced, but among the officers none showed off to better advantage than your father. From there we marched off to the battle of Shiloh, where we fought one of the bloodiest battles of the war. One of our brigades suffered severely and was fleeing from the enemy. Our regiment was ordered to charge a battery which was supported by infantry. This was a desperate charge and was led

by your father. Many in our company were killed and wounded but the
battery was taken and the enemy repulsed. This was a turning point in the
battle, and from then on the enemy were on the run. The 9th Texas Infantry was reported to have taken nine batteries that day. They were
specially cited and praised by Gen. Bragg, commanding the Division.
After the battle, Col. Maxey, who commanded the 9th Texas Infantry, was
promoted to the command of the brigade and although your father was
only a captain he was promoted over majors and lieutenant-colonels and
became, at the age of twenty-four, colonel of the 9th Texas Infantry.

Father was engaged in nearly all the great battles of the Army
of Tennessee in Kentucky, Mississippi, Alabama, and Georgia.
Many of his horses were wounded or killed, and the principal occupation of Lee, who accompanied him as orderly, was to keep him
in horses and food. In several of these battles Father was severely
wounded, but he always returned to his regiment, and at the age
of twenty-six he was commissioned brigadier general, the youngest,
I am told, in the Confederate Army.

At the great battle of Atlanta when it was so heroically defended
by the Confederates, my father commanded a brigade that lost
heavily in the fierce fighting that has been so romantically described in *Gone with the Wind*. When General Hood assumed
command and decided to evacuate the city and return with his
army to Tennessee, to Father's brigade was assigned the difficult
task of capturing the fort commanding Allatoona Pass, while the
rest of the army escaped into Tennessee. This proved to be my
father's last fight.

His small army of seven thousand men had driven the Union
forces back over mountainous terrain until they made their final
stand at the fort towering above Allatoona Pass. The desperate
condition of the Union defenders was signaled to General Sherman
on Kennesaw Mountain some ten miles away. Back came the
signal "Hold the fort, for I am coming," a message that has been
immortalized in the Union war poem of the same name. The battle
raged most of the day, and the Confederates with consummate
dash carried all before them. Father was following his men closely,

and the capture of the fort seemed imminent when a shell fragment struck him down. With a badly splintered leg, Father was put in an ambulance and carried off the field. Lee was close by. Slowly they made their way over mountain roads to reach a line of evacuation, Lee bringing the two horses, one of which he rode. Other wounded were encountered, and at Father's orders Lee dismounted and put these Confederates into the saddles and led the horses. Suddenly from around a hill appeared a troop of Union cavalry. The ambulance had taken the wrong road. As Father had been in command of the Confederate forces, his captors thought him so valuable a prisoner that, although severely wounded, he was carried over many miles of rough roads up to the top of Kennesaw Mountain into the presence of General Sherman, who, in his memoirs, has described their interview.

Two years ago, accompanied by Judge Shepard Bryan and Mr. Wilbur G. Kurtz, a Georgia historian, I went from Atlanta to Allatoona Heights. On the way we passed Kennesaw Mountain, headquarters of General Sherman during part of the campaign. The Western & Atlanta Railroad passes through Allatoona Pass in a low mountain range, at the summit of which are the defensive works of the old fort. We were able to go only a short distance in our motorcar. Then we took a mountain road, finishing the ascent by a rocky path. Although small, the fort with its high embankment evidently was a very strong position. In every direction was rough mountain country, rough hills covered with dense scrub timber. Mr. Kurtz, who has made a great study of the military campaigns in this region, said it had hardly changed at all since the Civil War. As I viewed the field of my gallant father's last fight, I was amazed at the splendid courage of the Confederates who were able to drive a strong force across these rugged hills up to the very embrasures of the fort itself.

After days of suffering and lack of medical attention, Father finally reached a hospital. By that time the shattered left leg, with splintered bones and a large flesh wound, had become gangrenous. Fortunately, he fell into the hands of an intelligent young surgeon who told him that the only thing that would save his life was to burn out the "proud" flesh with pure nitric acid. Father told how he was strapped to a stretcher and, without anesthesia, nitric acid was poured into the rotting flesh, which crackled until the smoke reached the ceiling. This heroic treatment was effective, the sepsis was routed, before long the slough was thrown off, and his life was saved. When in swimming with Father I often saw the large depression in his leg. But this was not the only mark of battle, as I remember clearly a depression in his chest from a bullet that entered beneath the collarbone and came out through the shoulder blade, penetrating the lung and missing (I know not how) the heart and the great vessels. There were also wounds in thigh, arm, neck, and scalp.

When Father was captured, Lee, although long since freed by Lincoln's proclamation, begged to go to prison with him; when this was not allowed, he remained near by and day by day brought food that he secured by foraging the countryside. One night Father was suddenly entrained for another hospital and Lee was not at hand. Father tried frantically to reach him but, not succeeding, disconsolate, left Lee behind. It was not until several years after the war that master and servant met at Atlanta, where Lee still waited for his return, and gave Father his sword that he had salvaged.

This family of slaves, attached only by the bonds of love, stayed with us, supported by my father and employed around our home, until they died off, one by one—fine examples of those loyal bondsmen who formed such an important part of the households of the South; men and women who took care of the Missus and the children while father and sons went off to fight for what they thought was right.

From his old comrades, I got thrilling stories of Father as a fighter. Major Frank Spencer told me how they were lying in a trench, with the "Yankees" several hundred yards in front of them. Sniping was going on incessantly. One of the men in Father's regiment was caught in an effort to escape to the rear. Father appeared on the scene, lectured the man about the enormity of his action, and, feeling certain he was really not a coward but overcome by the emotion of the moment, decided to do something to inspire confidence and bravery in the timid soldier. Ordering some privates to secure the man, he mounted the breastworks with them and placed him astride a branch of a tree immediately in front of the works and in plain sight of the Northern army. Grasping the man's legs, Father stood there while he ordered the others back to the trench. Major Spencer said that for five minutes it looked as if the whole Union Army was blazing away at the man on the tree and Father below, but neither was hit, and soon they scurried back to the trenches. The lesson had been effective. A few minutes later the Confederates were ordered to charge, and as they sprang over the breastworks and crossed the intervening space the one who led them was the man who had been held by Father on the limb of the tree.

While my father was heavily engaged in the Army of Tennessee, my mother's two brothers, George and William Kemper, were captains in Stonewall Jackson's regiment, which had been recruited in the Valley of Virginia. They were with him in the celebrated campaigns in the valley, during which Jackson had his headquarters at the home of my mother's father, just outside Port Republic at the headwaters of the Shenandoah River. It was while Jackson and his troops were in the region of Port Republic that three Union armies coming from different directions converged upon Jackson in the hope of defeating and capturing him. Instead, Jackson managed to meet them separately and defeat them. The first engagement was at Port Republic. Jackson's troops were stationed along the river to prevent its crossing by the Union troops. Mother's two brothers were with their companies, which were ranged along the riverbank. Suddenly one of Jackson's staff saw a woman among the soldiers; riding up, he discovered my mother. "What are you doing here, Miss Fannie Kemper?"

said he. "My two brothers are over there," said she, "and I guess I have got a right to be here too." "You certainly have not," said the young officer. Calling upon two privates to assist, he grabbed the young woman and put her on an artillery caisson. With a soldier on each side to hold her, the horses galloped off and took her to her home half a mile away.

During the rest of the war the home of her father and also the ancestral home of her mother, known as Bogota, a few miles away, were frequently raided by the Northern troops after Jackson left the valley and joined Lee in the great campaign around Chancellorsville. At the Battle of Chancellorsville, where Jackson received the wound that ended fatally, my mother's brother George was killed. A year later, at the Battle of the Wilderness, Captain William Kemper also met his death. This left mother only one brother, who was then about fifteen. Chafing at not being allowed to enter the army, Brother Johnny, as she called him, made his escape and followed Jackson's army some distance before he was seen by one of Mother's friends, who recognized his extreme youth and had him sent home.

In 1865 Grandfather was joined by my father, who had been released from the prison on Johnson's Island in Lake Erie. He had made his way to Texas, not knowing where his father was, as he had been without news for many months. By making diligent inquiry, he finally discovered that he was in San Antonio, and the two generals—father and son—went to live together. Along with Father came numerous other Confederates, many of whom had known Grandfather as Colonel Young after the Mexican War, and as it proved confusing to have two General Youngs living under one roof, Grandfather was forced by common consent to retire to the title of Colonel and Father continued to be known as General Young by his comrades in arms, who formed the principal men of San Antonio.

Grandfather's seventy-five slaves had been emancipated, his

plantations in northern Texas, with no laborers, had to be sacrificed, and when he arrived in San Antonio it was to start life anew. Enterprising and energetic, he soon amassed considerable means.

Father had intended to study law after getting his M.A. at the university, but this plan had been cut short by the war. He determined to study law in the office of one of the best law firms in San Antonio, but his military reputation and rank led to his being treated so deferentially by his instructors that his study of law and admission to the bar came much too easily and he was not as well grounded as he should have been (so he said).

One of the enterprises in which Grandfather was engaged was the organization of the first transportation system between San Antonio and Monterrey, Mexico. Great wagon trains of prairie schooners, each drawn by a team of about fourteen mules, traveled across the prairies in groups of one hundred for self-protection. My father's half-brother Newton told me of an exciting time he had when captaining one of these trains. Smoke rising over a hill warned him that Indians had attacked and set fire to wagons preceding him. Uncle Newton threw his wagon train into a circle with the teams inside and the wagons abutting each other. Boxes and bales were thrown beneath the wagons to form a barricade, and a post of command was similarly made in the center. Before long some five hundred Comanches surrounded them, but as a good number of the Indians were killed, they kept at a respectful distance, and finally disappeared without charging the circle of wagons.

After some years there was a good deal of money owing, and Father was sent to Mexico to collect it. His diary of the trip is interesting, particularly his description of the officers of Maximilian, who then ruled Mexico. The debts, amounting to $20,000, were paid in gold dust and nuggets. Father had been directed to take this to a United States mint. Realizing the dangers of such a trip with so much money, he wrapped his precious bundle of gold in some soiled linen, put it in an old carpetbag, and started for Denver, Colorado. He treated the bag with indifference, and the rough characters he met did not suspect its value.

At Denver he struck the first railroad and started east. Before long the train stopped to take on wood and water. A short distance ahead were thousands of buffalo on one side of the railroad embankment. Taking his rifle, father hurried along the other side until he reached the buffalo and then, rising up on the track, picked out a bull with a fine head and fired. The next thing he remembered was "coming to" in the baggage car of the train, with his face covered with blood. As the train had pulled out from the station, the engineer had seen a human form on the track, stopped, and taken him aboard. Father's first thought was for the bag of gold. He was much relieved when he found it hanging on a peg in the car where he had left it. Examination of the rifle, which had been salvaged by the trainman, showed that it had burst, and pieces of the steel had gashed father's forehead. Continuing on by train, father reached Chicago, where he turned in the gold to the mint and received credit for $20,000.

From there he went to Virginia, where, on November 3, 1869, he and mother were married at the home of her father, Dr. George Whitfield Kemper, Madison Hall, an old house built by the brother of President Madison near Port Republic.

The trip back to San Antonio was a trying one for the bride. The railroads in the South, still suffering from the effects of the war, were bad. At New Orleans they took a boat for Galveston. The ship was small and the trip rough, but nothing like so terrible as the travel by stagecoach from Galveston to San Antonio, two hundred and fifty miles distant across the soggy prairie. The young couple joined grandfather in a home on Soledad Street and the three lived together until the old man died. There I was born on September 18, 1870. It has always been a matter of regret to me that I had no brothers or sisters.

When I was four years old, I clearly remember playing on the bank of the San Antonio River back of our home with my chum, George Dashiell, and Della, a Negro girl who looked after us. We had started to run up the bank toward the house when I slipped on pebbles and plunged into the river. Della, terrified, tried to fish me out with a stick; failing, she ran to the house and called Mother, who dashed down, and when she arrived at the river, saw me whirling by in the rapids below the quiet hole into which I had fallen. Mother dived into the swirling tide, succeeded in grasping my clothes, and was carried down herself until stopped by a wooden post, the remains of an old bathhouse lower down the river. To this she clung until we were rescued by neighbors. I am told that I was apparently lifeless, but they held me up by my heels, a gallon of water ran out of my mouth, and I was given artificial respiration and covered with hot blankets. Father was so overjoyed at our rescue that he placed a stained-glass window in St. Mark's Cathedral, depicting Pharaoh's daughter fishing Moses out of the water.

Dean Richardson of St. Mark's was our closest friend, a man with a large round head and a flowing beard, and a belly that shook like a bowl of jelly when he told funny stories. Father was his senior warden and superintendent of the Sunday school at St. Mark's for thirty-five years. These men, both soldiers and proud of the old South, were to me the beau ideal of Southern chivalry.

Soledad Street, on which we lived, was only a few blocks from Main Plaza, which was surrounded by innumerable saloons, gambling-houses, a variety theater, and other rough joints. Rich Mexicans and cowmen, lured by the white lights, came to San Antonio in great numbers, and also bandits. I remember one night in which a great fusillade of shots was heard soon after supper. Father rushed down to Main Plaza and found that the proprietor of the Variety Theater and gambling house, Jack Harris, and several of his gang had been killed by a noted outlaw, Ben Thompson, and his men, who had ridden into the theater on their horses and shot it up.

A few months afterwards, when Ben Thompson had the temerity to come again and walk with his gang into the theater, he met with a bloody reply from a group of Harris's friends, who rose from their hiding-place behind the orchestra screen and poured a deadly volley into Thompson's men.

San Antonio was then the liveliest of Western towns, the meeting-place of every type of man, drawn there by the fabulous tales of riches to be made from cattle-raising or mining in Mexico. It was bad form to ask anyone where he came from, or why, because many had been run out of their home states. The Civil War had liberated great numbers of soldiers who would not live under the carpetbaggers in the South. Many still refused to swear allegiance to the United States, and entered the army of Maximilian.

In the back yard of our home were Negro quarters occupied by those who had been slaves before the war. There was Mammy, now an old woman, who had nursed my father's mother, Father, and me. She was a privileged character and freely expressed her opinion of all of us. Once, when Cousin John Young, a distinguished divine from the East, was at our house, after dinner Mammy was brought in to meet him. "Mammy," said Cousin John, "what kind of a looking baby was the General?" Whereupon Mammy replied, "Law, Marse John, you ought to have seed him. He was so tiny we could have put him in a quart cup and he was as hairy as a 'possum." Mammy's daughter, Mandy, was the cook, and what a wonderful cuisine she provided! One eye was gone and the other very defective, but that didn't prevent her putting together the most delicious things in her marvelous menus. She had a brood of children, Henry, Della, Molly, and Lou. They were my boon companions, and the envy of my young days on account of their greater agility in and facility for games. Mandy was a sister of Lee, Father's orderly during the war.

When I was five, I was sent to a kindergarten conducted by a Miss Larner, a delightful woman, who amused us with games, handiwork, and drawing. I feel sure that my fondness for mechanics and love of art had its inception in these early days with Miss Larner. One of my proud possessions is a small desk my grandfather gave me for having stood at the head of the spelling class for a month, but my prowess as a speller did not last.

Being of an adventurous type, Father never seriously stuck to law, but soon was engaged in great schemes of irrigation and land development. He had the profoundest admiration for Texas as a state, and western Texas in particular he thought a country of rich promise. The Nueces River Irrigation Company and the Young Valley Ditch were his creations. Into his office were brought minerals from distant localities, and I remember, when I was a small boy, his saying that rich deposits of oil, asphalt, and so on were present in some of his properties that would, some day, be worth millions. This neighborhood is now one of the great oil fields of the West. By the time I was six, Father had acquired some thousand acres of land within the limits of the City of San Antonio and numerous ranch properties farther out.

About this time there appeared a persuasive cousin from the East, John Lyle, who bought the *San Antonio Express*, the only newspaper in that portion of the West, and preceded to squander money. He was soon bankrupt. Appealing to Father for assistance, he got generous aid and, before long, all of Father's property was mortgaged in an attempt to save the *San Antonio Express*. After a year or two Father found himself the possessor of the paper. In his efforts to rehabilitate it he lost many more thousands and in so doing mortgaged all his lands at 12 per cent interest. His faith in the future was so unbounded that rather than sell property that he thought would be extremely valuable someday, he continued to pay this crushing interest yearly. Although he made a great deal of money and was a big factor in the development of that part of Texas, these heavy debts eventually ended in his complete undoing, but not until he had sent me through the University of Virginia, the medical school, and the hospital. Then, for the first time, I learned of his troubles and the sacrifices he had made to educate me.

At the age of six I had a sweetheart. Mary McCleary was the lovely child of a brilliant lawyer who lived a few hundred yards from us. The boys used to tease me with a song, some of the words of which were "kissed a girl through a fence for a stick of candy." I can still hear my tormentors.

When I was seven, I had the misfortune to come down with typhoid fever and two fearful complications, first diphtheria and then scarlet fever. I lay sick in Mother's room for many months. On a door frame a long series of high temperatures were recorded, and they remained there for several years. During this illness, in which my life was despaired of, I am told that a knock was heard on the door and Mother found Mary McCleary, who asked, "Mrs. Young, is Hugh going to die?" To which mother replied, "I don't know, Mary." "Well, put this little ring on his finger and maybe he will get well." This ring, a pretty circlet with blue enamel forget-me-nots, now adorns the finger of my granddaughter Betsy. Whether the amulet was responsible or not, I began to improve at once, 'tis said.

Each year at the Sunday-school picnic the children voted a "king" and "queen" of the festival. On one occasion Mary and I won the honor, and were the proudest mortals in San Antonio. We gathered at St. Mark's Cathedral and took omnibuses for a suburban park. Father, as superintendent of the Sunday school, managed the affair, and he delegated to me the collection of 10 cents from each pupil for bus fare. Arriving at the picnic grounds, we all headed for the merry-go-round. Mary took the greatest delight in grabbing for a ring each time we circled around, hoping to get the brass one that fetched a prize. As we rode around time after time my own slender supply of money was soon exhausted, but as Mary was keen to continue, I dipped into the Sunday-school money, and before long this too had almost vanished. After the picnic was over, Father asked me for the bus money and, shamefacedly, I admitted that I had spent most of it.

I was inspired one Easter Sunday to present Mary with a large chocolate egg filled with candy. We went to the same Sunday school, and I hoped to see her when the class was dismissed but, much to my regret, she stayed for the services in the cathedral. Concealing the Easter egg in the folds of my coat, I waited until Mary left the church just before the sermon. As she left her pew, I left ours, but being unwilling to be seen following Mary, I went out one door while she went out another. Father saw me disappear and asked one of my pals why I had left. My comrade, wishing to protect me, said he thought I had gone to see about our horse, which was hitched to a tree outside. Father rushed out, expecting to find me struggling with the horse, but instead found me presenting the Easter egg to Mary. It took some time to live that down.

Mary's father was made chief judge of the Federal Court of Montana and the McLearys left San Antonio. I saw nothing of Mary for several years, but I continued to think of her as my sweetheart until, a student at the University of Virginia, I received a letter from home telling me that Mary was engaged to be married. A little later I got a note saying she was in Washington on her way to Europe with an aunt and would like to see me. I hastened up, and if I had not been an impecunious undergraduate with no immediate prospects, something might have happened even then.

When I was eight years old, a client of Father's gave me a pony, Nellie. One day she disappeared and was gone for a month. I was brokenhearted. Finally some cowboys found her living with a bunch of wild mustangs ten miles from home. There were many such packs of wild horses on the prairies, each led by a dashing stallion.

My early years on Soledad Street were very delightful and adventurous. The river teemed with snakes and waterfowl. My slingshot and "nigger-shooter" became very effective weapons. With traps that I constructed from sticks I learned how to catch birds and rabbits. It was necessary to forage in order to secure material for better implements of the sport. In our back yard was a shed in which the washing was done. It was covered with long cedar shingles that made excellent material for traps and triggers. Many times I have climbed to the top of this shed and stolen shingles, then hidden beneath the bank of the river while they were cut into strips and a trap or a kite was constructed. So expert did I become that frequently I was able to sell the products of my handiwork to other boys. One of the forays I made upon the roof of the wash shed almost ended fatally. Having secured some shingles, I was making for the ladder when I fell through a large hole in the roof. Mother was aroused by my cries and, hastening to the shed, found me hanging some twelve feet in the air. Seeing no ladder at hand, she attempted to make use of a barrel, but it was filled with water. With a huge effort the barrel was turned over and Mother grabbed me just as I let go. I remember to this day the terror that filled me as I hung there watching Mother try to turn over the barrel.

When I was ten, Father and Mother decided it would be well to move to the country, presumably for Grandfather's health, but perhaps because the family had become greatly alarmed over the fact that the seventy-year old warrior was deeply enamored of a seventeen-year-old blonde, the daughter of Judge Devine, one of the most distinguished lawyers in that section. She apparently was much taken with Grandfather. Although the old gentleman had been married three times before, he was still quite keen to marry a fourth wife, but about this time the move to the country was made, and the marriage never took place.

Grandfather used to ride out on horseback every day and stayed with the workmen, thus rapidly regaining his health. When we moved out, I found the house perched on top of a hill on a ranch that was owned by Father. It was a veritable wilderness of brush, but the soil was fertile and the ground covered with the wonderful mesquite grass of western Texas that has made that country such a fine stock-raising area. This grass has the most wonderful tenacity of life. Subjected to dreadful droughts, which often last for months, it withers and apparently dies. On the first good rain it springs to life as if by magic. During the severe droughts the mesquite trees bring forth long beans on which the stock can live, and the prickly pear, which is abundant, is also ravenously eaten by the hungry livestock. The prickles are usually burned off by the stockmen, lest the muzzles of the cattle get covered with these formidable thorns, which sometimes kill them.

It was necessary to clear the wilderness for a garden and a small farm, and to build fences, stock pens, stables, chicken yards, and barns.

In my wanderings around the ranch I was followed by my faithful Irish terrier Don, who had been noted as a rat-killer in town and also as a killer of the snakes that infested the river. One day I almost stepped on a large rattlesnake coiled ready to strike. Don's success along the riverbank had engendered supreme contempt for all snakes, and in he dashed. Out sprang the huge snake. With a sharp cry of pain, Don retreated, and from his muzzle two huge drops of blood exuded. The snake, fully six feet long, had struck him square in the nose. Poor Don drooped at once, and showed no desire to attack the snake again, even when I had killed it with a stick. Back to the house we went, and Don soon sank into a stupor on the porch. When Father arrived, Don was gasping for breath. He seemed about to die when Father brought forth a cup of hot oil heavily charged with whisky, and while I held Don's mouth open Father poured the mixture down his throat. Soon Don was revived, but it was weeks before he was himself again. Never again did he dare to rush in on a rattlesnake until I had thrown a rock and made the snake strike and leave his coil; then, whether the snake had been injured or not, in Don would rush, grab him back of the neck, and thresh him to death. Don soon learned to recognize the rapid prairie snake, the chicken snake, and other harmless reptiles, and would kill them as quickly as he had the water snakes of the city, but he was careful of all rattlers. Finally he became incautious, and one day a huge rattler buried his fangs in Don and he died in a few hours. The death of my faithful dog was my first bereavement, one from which I did not recover for many a day. He and I had been on many a scouting expedition together. He had always slept on my bed and been my constant companion.

In the afternoons, on Saturdays, and particularly during the long summer vacations, there being no other boys within miles, I had to amuse myself as best I could. I often took to the hills on my pony, with a long spear in my hand. I had fashioned it after those of the Indians and I used it in spearing cactuses and other objects while running at full speed, thus trying to enact an Indian's life as I imagined it.

Grandfather had an old ten-bore shotgun that weighed at least ten pounds. I often looked at it longingly. One day a huge hawk settled on a tree a short distance from the house and, although I was only ten, I seized the gun, crawled on my stomach a hundred yards until I was close to the hawk, rested the heavy fowling piece on a stump, and took aim. The stock was so long that I could not reach the trigger, so I put the butt in my armpit and hugged it to my side. When I pulled the trigger, the big hammers came back at me and tore a gash in my cheek. But I was up and after the hawk and followed it for half a mile. One leg and one wing had been broken, but it was still full of fight and when I rushed in upon it, it seized my hands with its beak and claws and we had a terrific fight until I choked the hawk to death. Returning to the house, I proudly showed my conquest to my horrified mother, who was greatly upset at seeing my bleeding face and hands. This incident caused me to be forbidden to use the gun, but I could not resist the temptation and used to slip out and kill meadow larks and doves, which were plentiful on the ranch. I have always been sorry that my parents did not give me a light shotgun. Until I left Texas I never had anything but this piece, which I could hardly raise to my shoulder, and therefore never learned, early, to shoot on the wing, something that I have always regretted.

Rabbits were plentiful, and I used to catch them in snares. These had to be constructed most skillfully in order to entice these wary animals to nibble at the bait, which was attached to a trigger that released the noose by which the rabbit was strung up and hung. There were many jack rabbits, and they were so speedy that no dog could catch them. The cowboys said that when an ordinary dog chased a jack rabbit, he would run on three legs and every now and then would sit down and wait for the dog to catch up, but when a greyhound got after him, the rabbit really let himself out and one saw a streak of jack rabbit half a mile long.

During the spring, instead of riding my Nellie I went back and forth to the city with Father. I had about three hours after school let out in which I hung around Father's office. This got very boring, and I asked him to allow me to sell newspapers. At first he demurred, but on my insistence finally gave in. The *San Antonio Light*, which is still being published, had its presses in a back room near the San Antonio River. About thirty newsboys would collect there in the yard, and while waiting for the presses to start frequently would go swimming. There was a large pecan tree, the big branches of which swept over the river. We would shinny out on this like monkeys and drop off into the water. We had a wonderful time ducking each other until a shout announced that the presses had started. Dripping wet, we slipped into our clothes and made a beeline for the room where we were allowed to get the papers right off the press. There was a lot of jostling in our efforts to get close to the distributor, and as soon as we were given our fifteen or twenty papers, up the street we would dash for Main Plaza, about five blocks away, where the principal hotels of San Antonio were located. Here the wealthy stockmen sat around on benches and chairs swapping stories and whittling sticks. The boys who got there first would immediately dispose of all their papers, and not infrequently when the buyer handed over a quarter he would say, "Keep the change, buddy." The spirit of rivalry to get there first was great, and as we ran down the street many a pedestrian was knocked into the gutter and quite a few accidents came from collisions with carriages.

One day a big boy, fully sixteen years old and very rough in his ways, appeared at the pressroom. Shoving his way up to the front, he asked for two hundred papers. Awe-struck, we looked at each other, wondering how in the world he could sell so many. We soon discovered that he had subsidized eight boys to work for him, and as soon as he distributed the papers they dashed off to the prize territory ahead of the rest of us. Big business was just as unpopular with us as it is today with the proletariat. Whether by his natural aggressiveness or by corruption, Jim Hosack succeeded day after day in getting his large number of papers first, and indignation mounted higher and higher among us regulars. One day, while we were all on the riverbank watching some boys disporting themselves in the water, Jim came close to the edge. The disgruntled newsboys rushed at him and pushed him into the water. The rest of us were barefooted, and with howls of joy we watched him struggle to climb up the slippery bank with his shoes on.

During my second summer on the ranch a small boy named Tommy Rail arrived to keep me company. He was the son of one of my father's clients who had become divorced from his wife, and the boy had been put in an orphanage, where Father found him so pale and thin that he invited him to come out and spend the summer with us. I shall never forget the first dinner that Tommy had with us. He ate like a famished animal, and later he was amazed at the softness of his bed. Tommy never returned to the orphanage, but stayed with us for seven years. His father was in the army and disappeared within a year or so, so Tommy became a ward of the family and received the same advantages that I did. Tommy's father had been in the cavalry, and Tommy's love was so centered on horses that when he was sixteen he refused to go to school any longer and took a job in a stable.

Tommy was a great little companion, and many a fine time did we have together. He and I were "licked" impartially by Father for various acts of deviltry. If anything, I caught the worst of it. Tommy and I rode home from school together. One day Tommy pointed out a boy driving a butcher's cart and told me that this boy had struck him. Filled with righteous indignation, I rode up to the cart and demanded what he meant by striking a boy so much smaller than he. He jumped to the ground and said if I would get off my horse he would lick me too. He promptly proceeded to do it. In a minute I was on my back with the butcher's boy on top. Tommy was so terrified that he did not come to my rescue, so I got one of the best drubbings I have ever had.

When I was twelve, Mother took me to Virginia, and I made the acquaintance of my grandfather's workshop. Grandfather Kemper, although a busy physician and surgeon, was a wonderful mechanic, and whenever he had a moment would be in his shop making all sorts of articles for the house and amusing things for me. I took a great interest in what he was doing, and he taught me how to use the tools. Before the summer was over I had learned to use saws, planes, and chisels, and to make fairly difficult things. Interest in mechanics, thus started, has had a deep influence upon me throughout life.

Shortly after this I went to visit my cousin Captain Henry Clay Michie, in Albemarle County, Virginia. His son Frank, just my age, was also crazy about mechanics. Frank and I constructed a railroad line across the orchard and built cars for it, upon which we transported the girls of the family, with ourselves as the motive power. We took great pride in this equipment, but pushing the girls back and forth almost worked us to death. Nevertheless, it was a valuable experience.

Grandfather Kemper gave me a fine set of tools, with which I started a workshop on the ranch. I soon wanted to enlarge it by the addition of a scroll saw and a turning lathe, but Father insisted on my making these for myself. Although I bitterly deplored his refusal to buy these machines for me, having to construct them stimulated my ingenuity. Mother used to get me to make things for the house, my most important contribution being a formidable bookcase, which I made at the age of fifteen. Shortly after that I built a new body for an old hunting-cart. Before long I was commissioned by another boy to make him a buggy body. He had the wheels, axles, shafts, and springs, but the body was missing. When asked to estimate how much I would charge, after much figuring I offered to complete the job, painting and varnishing the buggy, for $6.50.

This offer was promptly accepted. I bought my materials, which cost $6, worked two weeks continuously on the job, and then never collected a cent. The owner used to exasperate me by driving by the house with other boys in the buggy body I had made and thumbing his nose at me. He was bigger than I was and I could not lick him, so I put my account in the hands of a lawyer friend, but never recovered. This was my first experience with the deceits of business.

A little later a family of Nortons built an attractive house on an adjacent ranch. There were three boys, varying between the ages of Tommy and myself. We had a grand time together, riding all over the country, racing our young mustangs, scurrying off to the river—stealing watermelons on the way down—and swimming for hours in the San Antonio River. In order to cool the watermelons we would take them in with us, swim on them, and carry on all sorts of antics until they were thoroughly chilled, then devour them on the riverbank. We often took off our saddles and rode the ponies into the water, carrying out all sorts of stunts from their backs, much to the terror of the ponies.

Another most amusing companion in the form of a Negro boy, Dave, just my age, arrived with his father and mother, who worked the farm. Dave could do everything better than I could and was my constant admiration and despair. Besides being remarkable at wrestling, running, and jumping, Dave was full of native Negro melody, could sing, whistle, play the Jew's harp, and do a magnificent clog dance, all of which I vainly tried to learn.

The old Goliad Road, over which Santa Anna had led his army to attack San Antonio and capture the Alamo, passed within a hundred yards of our home. It was the great road along which traveled thousands of horses and cattle from the ranches of Mexico and western Texas to the great markets in San Antonio. Often I would sit on my pony and watch the herds go by, "passing the time of day" with the jovial, long-necked, skinny stockmen who rode, gracefully lounging in their Mexican saddles, on their broncos. One day I saw a beautiful little colt lagging behind and asked the boss cowboy to give it to me, saying that I felt sure it would die in the stock pens of San Antonio. He was a bighearted fellow, and said he would give me the colt if I could lasso it. This I did, and proudly took the colt home, where she frantically neighed for her mother and refused to eat or drink, being still of the suckling age. After she had starved for a day, I took a pan of milk and, with the assistance of farm hands, forced the colt's head down into the milk, into which I had inserted two fingers and turned them up to simulate her mother's teat. In a short time the little beauty learned how to suck my two fingers projecting from the pan of milk to get nourishment, and before long learned that the fingers were not necessary and greedily drank from the pan alone. Soon she was eating with the rest of the stock.

I acquired other colts in a similar manner, and each one I "broke" by myself. All were mustangs, and even though brought up in captivity and as gentle as house pets, they would frantically try to throw off anybody who mounted them. It was necessary to proceed by easy stages, just as the cowboys do in breaking animals taken wild from the plains. I had many a hard fall, but it was excellent training, and in a few years I had no difficulty holding my own in roundups. By the time I was fourteen I had eight ponies, and rode them by turns to school.

When I was fifteen my Uncle John gave me a lovely yellow mare, which I named Bessie. She was very fast, and when the Norton boys, who lived on an adjacent hill, and I started down the one-mile lane that bordered our ranch on the north, on our customary morning race, I was always able to outdistance them when astride Bessie. These races were run even when the road was soft with mud, and often I narrowly escaped breaking neck or limb. It was excellent training and fine exercise. As a result, I forged ahead in athletics, such as running, jumping, and football. My feet then seemed always better than my hands.

Until I was fifteen I attended the public schools, going through the subjunior class in high school, having skipped the eighth grade by studying during one of the summers. The San Antonio Academy was then started by Dr. William B. Seeley. He had been associate professor of Greek at Princeton and had come to San Antonio because of pulmonary tuberculosis. Full of enthusiasm and inspiration, he instilled in me a real liking for Latin and Greek, which he taught with consummate skill.

My love of athletics also grew apace. At football, which the whole school played in an adjacent park, my natural fondness for running was given full play. We had wonderful times together during the noon-hour recess, taking little or no time to eat anything. During one of our hard football matches I came to blows with one of my fellow students, Ed Lowry, who insulted me by calling me a coward. We were hustled back into school and I sat clenching my fists the rest of the afternoon. As soon as we were dismissed I rushed up to Lowry and told him that if he would come out with me, I would show him whether I was a coward or not. As there was no convenient place to stage the fight near the school, we decided to repair to a secluded place along the river. As we made our way there, each surrounded by his group of friends, and followed by the rest of the school and the rag, tag, and bobtail of the city, who joined us on our half-mile march to the river, it was a motley procession. Arriving at the battle ground, we decided to strip to the waist and to conduct the fight according to the Marquis of Queensberry rules. Seconds and a referee were appointed. The rounds were of two-minute periods, with one-minute interval, and without gloves. The fight continued for round after round. Lowry was taller than I was and battered my head, while I concentrated principally on his middle. I was thinking the fight would never end, and in fact that I would probably get licked, when Lowry suddenly said to me, "Young, I have decided that you are not a coward, and if it is all right with you we will call it square." With the blood streaming down my face, one eye closed, and my lips battered, I hastily assured him that I was perfectly willing to have the fight ended. The boys called it a technical victory for me, but during the week it took me to recover I was dubious of the honors that they insisted on giving me.

While out on the ranch, Grandfather's health had been very good. He used to manage the place attired in his frock coat and high silk hat. As it was difficult to secure labor, the job of milking the cows was assigned to me, and for three years I milked five or six cows every morning before breakfast, and also before dinner. Tommy Rail's job was to drive up the horses. On one occasion I was unable to get any milk from a cow. Grandfather, in disgust, said, "I'll show you how to do it." Putting his silk hat on the ground and his head to the flank of the cow, he started milking, but the cow, being wild, kicked the bucket, and the milk landed in the old gentleman's hat, much to my delight.

Life on the ranch was dreary for my mother. The roads were terrible, especially in winter. It was almost impossible for her friends to get out to see her and she had a lonely time, so Father decided to build a house in the city. Mother and I drew up the plans, largely from some books on modern houses. The specifications and working drawings were made by an architect, and in a few months the brick house with stone trimmings, which contained twelve rooms and cost only $6500, was finished. Such a house now would cost $30,000. Common laborers then received less than $1 a day and worked ten hours, and carpenters and bricklayers got only $2 a day. In order to build this house, Father had to go into debt, and it was necessary for me to pitch in and help construct the various outhouses and fences. With my own hands I did a great deal of heavy carpenter work.

Since I was brought up on the stirring stories of both Grandfather's and Father's military experiences, it is hardly surprising that I had a great desire to go into the army. I begged Father to let me go to West Point, but the war had not been over long enough; he could not reconcile himself to the thought of his son in a "Yankee" uniform.

The urge to be soldiers led me and some other youths to organize a military company that we called the Maverick Rifles. As this company was being formed my enthusiasm knew no bounds, and when a committee was named to secure funds to buy uniforms I raised over half the money alone. We equipped two platoons of striplings who made up in ardor what we lacked in physique. The State of Texas had no guns to give us, so we spent weary months in setting-up drills and field maneuvers. I secured a copy of Upton's *Tactics* and studied it night and day until I almost knew it by heart. Coming to the "Manual of Arms," I decided to learn it by myself, so, with the old double-barreled shotgun, and the book open on the bed, I practiced the "Manual" as best I could before a long mirror. After a few weeks I had the temerity to let the captain of the company know what I was doing. He came over and almost exploded at some of my efforts in the "Manual of Arms." My interpretations had not been accurate, but he was so much impressed by my ardor that when his second lieutenant resigned I got his place, and was one of the proudest sixteen-year-olders in these United States.

Grandfather's health began to fail, and he died the next year, nearly eighty years of age. To the very last he was as straight as an Indian, full of interesting anecdotes about his experiences in pioneer days and during the wars against Indians, Mexicans, and Yankees. His funeral was attended by many Texas and Confederate veterans and the militia companies of San Antonio. My comrades in the Maverick Rifles acted as special guard of honor and furnished the pallbearers. This, the first funeral in our family, depressed me greatly, as I adored my grandfather.

It was decided to send me off to school. Mother's uncle, Charles Kemper, had started a home school on his farm in Louisa County, Virginia. Here at the Aspinhill School were gathered together about twenty boys of various ages. My uncle was a distinguished mathematician and a great engineer, who had retired temporarily to this farm and organized the school in order to educate his boys. As there was no place in the dormitory for me, I was given a small room immediately over that of my Uncle Charles, who, finding that I was fond of mathematics, took a great interest in me. He would frequently wake me during the night to show me some problem that he had solved, often after months of effort. He taught me surveying and took me on numerous engineering expeditions, thus arousing in me great interest in this work.

His wife, a daughter of Dr. Pendleton, was of an entirely different mold, a great linguist and with the literature of the world at her fingertips. She sat at the head of our long dining-room table and convulsed us with her amusing narratives. Her literary interest caused her to neglect her household duties and her own toilet, so that she looked little different from the cook. Life at Aspinhill was an eye-opener to a boy from the wilds of Texas, and I had a wonderfully good time.

About three miles away Captain William Pendleton maintained a home school for girls. His daughter, who was a year or two younger than I, was a black-eyed little beauty. Six other girls were assembled there under the tutelage of a young vamp of a schoolteacher, very little older than they and just as pretty. We boys were confined at Aspinhill until Saturday morning, when we promptly begged, borrowed, or stole all the horses and mules we could obtain in the neighborhood and rushed for Captain Willie Pendleton's home school, where we and the girls had a marvelous time until midnight, when we were forcibly ejected by Captain Pendleton. We returned after church the next day. How the charming Captain, who had little money, was able to feed the hungry youngsters who crowded around his hospitable board morning, noon, and night, I know not. Occasionally a terrific storm arose during the evening, making it impossible for us to return to our school, and on such occasions we usually slept on the floor. I remember having spent one night on the grand piano.

On Sunday mornings we met the girls at Gilboa Church, which was of the Campbellite denomination. I was in a mixed class of boys and girls, the lessons being held in a large box pew such as the Colonial churches of Virginia are provided with. One morning on my way to Sunday school I stopped by a spring to get a drink and discovered a small, inoffensive green snake swimming in the water.

Quickly capturing it, I stuck it in my pocket, buttoned it down, and went on to church. I had long since forgotten about it when a howl from one of the girls called our attention to the snake, which had escaped from my pocket and was crossing her lap. The ten boys and girls in the class jumped over the top of the pew in record-breaking speed. The panic became contagious and the entire Sunday school cleared out in short order. I was reprimanded by my teacher, the assistant superintendent, the superintendent, and the preacher, and was in bad repute for several weeks.

During this year George Kemper and I published a school news-paper that we called *The Crescent*. It was only a four-page affair, but we soon secured enough advertisers and subscribers to make it, as we thought, a profitable venture. We had it printed at the Louisa Courthouse about ten miles away, but the expenses soon became so great that when the time came for the final number, which we had assured our readers would describe the school commencement adequately, we were already much in debt. George and I then determined to set up the type and print the paper ourselves. The good-natured printer allowed us to come into his shop and get out this final edition. George was a pretty good typesetter and I ran the press.

In the same shop the weekly newspaper of Louisa Courthouse was published. It had recently been sold by its owner, Colonel Bibb, to a stranger who had recently come into town. There had been some hard feeling over the transaction. Colonel Bibb stopped to see how George and I were getting on with our printing, and was offering to show me how to fix my forms in the press when the new pro-prietor said something uncomplimentary to the Colonel, who ripped out an oath and drew a pistol on him. George and I disap-peared headlong out of a window. The Colonel was promptly arrested and George and I were taken to the courthouse as witnesses, much more scared than the Colonel, an old Confederate officer, who seemed quite unperturbed. I forget what the verdict was, but I know that George and I scurried back to the shop, wrote up a sensational account of the affair, and soon appeared on the streets with an extra edition, which we sold at a great profit, completely wiping out our deficit.

In the fall of 1889 I was forced to go to another school, Uncle Charles having accepted the professorship of mathematics at the University of Kentucky. The Staunton Academy, which I attended that year, was presided over by a remarkable character, a huge man who sat with a black skullcap on a bald, eczematous head and surveyed the thirty culprits of all ages who filled the one schoolroom. Major Owens was a ripe classical scholar. He was a jovial soul, and in order to impress the youngsters who constantly flunked before him, would sing out the rule that had been violated in a funny sing-song which would be taken up by the entire school. The ditty began, "The object of a verb is put in what case?" intoned by the Major, and the refrain, "Put in what case, put in what case," sung by the entire school. It was a hilarious place, and very little order was preserved, but the Major inspired us all with a love for the classics. I boarded with the aunt of both my mother and father, Mrs. David Young. Aunt Betty was a charming old lady, who occupied the room immediately beneath mine. Harry Blackburn, my roommate, and I had bought a pair of boxing gloves, and one day when we were engaged in a sparring match Harry caught me under the chin and I went down so hard that the plaster was jarred loose from the ceiling below and landed on Aunt Betty, who was dozing in a chair before the fire. The terrified old lady rushed out, thinking an earthquake had shaken the house. Harry and I were in bad odor for some time.

During the spring of 1890 the whole of Virginia was aflame with land development. New townsites, with building lots carved out of farm lands, were being laid out along the whole length of the Shenandoah Valley. Enough lots were actually sold to house the population of New York City. A movement was on foot to build another new town near the home of my grandfather along the south fork of the Shenandoah River. At the end of the school term I was

told I could get a fine job with an engineering corps, in which my
mother's brother Albert had secured work. Dr. Humphreys, professor of engineering at the Washington and Lee University, who was
in charge of this work, decided that he would make this an epoch-
making piece of engineering. A square mile was first laid out, one
side paralleling the railroad track. The base line along the track was
to be exactly one mile in length. Preliminary surveys were made,
in which the levels were taken, and then cedar posts, sawed off exactly two feet from the ground, were placed every hundred yards.
On the top of each post was a copper plate, and at every twentieth
foot a stake, which carried a hook suspended from a nail on the side
of the stick, was planted. At night, when the temperature had
become stable, about thirty of us accompanied the Professor and his
assistants to the spot. A steel tape, which had been corrected by the
Bureau of Standards, was used. A pull of exactly twenty pounds
was put upon it, while every twenty feet the tape was suspended
from the intervening stakes. When the pull was exact, an engraver
marked on the copper plate the exact position of the three-hundred-
feet mark. The temperature of the atmosphere at that moment was
recorded, and the entire gang then moved on to the second three-
hundred-feet hub and repeated the procedure. In this way the end
of the base line exactly one mile long was engraved upon the final
hub.

But this was not sufficient for the Professor. The same procedure
must be carried out at least ten times. After two weeks had been
consumed in this example of supreme accuracy, the statistics were
turned over to the office force of engineers, who made due allowance
for temperature changes and levels, finally determined just where the
end of this perfectly accurate mile was, and engraved the plate
accordingly. This took about four weeks. Another fortnight was
spent in determining absolutely accurate right angles from the
two sides that joined this perfect base line, and the lengths of the
other three lines were then determined with equal accuracy. Almost
two months was consumed in establishing this perfect one-mile

square. Not until then were the ordinary engineers allowed to lay the street lines and the lot subdivisions. In the meantime, so much time had been lost that the boom burst, and the company went to the wall. Our scientific work went for naught. The town site became a farm again.

Professor Humphreys was kind enough to put me in the office, where I was commissioned to make a composite map of five hundred pieces of property that were included in the immense townsite. Many of the surveys from which this map had to be constructed had been made over a hundred years before, and with very crude instruments. During this time the magnetic needle had moved westward several degrees. To put together this huge map, which was like a crazy quilt, from the old surveys was one of the most interesting occupations I have ever had. At the end of the summer Professor Humphreys advised me to become an engineer and offered to put me in charge of a transit party with a squad of men under me at the munificent salary of $75 a month. I was overcome with joy. The idea of making that much a month was overwhelming. I communicated my delight by telegram to my father and demanded that I be allowed to stay and go into engineering. In reply I received a brief wire: "Resign at once and go to the University of Virginia."

CHAPTER 2. AT THE UNIVERSITY

OF VIRGINIA

WHEN I got to the university, I met two young men who were standing examinations for scholarships, so I decided to have a try at them myself. I was lucky enough to be successful, and thus saved $500 on my first year's tuition. The University of Virginia at that time had no entrance examinations. It was run on the elective system, and a student could enter any class that he thought he could make. Each school in the academic department had a junior, an intermediate, and a senior class. I had been told by my father to enter courses leading to the Master of Arts degree. Having had a lot of Latin and mathematics, I was able to enter senior Latin, senior and intermediate mathematics, and intermediate Greek. These were the same classes that my father, thirty years before, had taken.

It was soon evident that I was not nearly as well prepared for these senior classes as some students from Virginia, many of whom had studied calculus before they arrived at the university and had even read much of the university work in senior Latin and Greek. It was a hard year, but there were some charming and inspiring boys in the classes, and the professors, all of whom had been officers in the Confederate Army, were delightful men and brought out the best we had in us. At the end of a year I had the good luck to pass in all my classes. No marks were ever given at the University of Virginia. To make one's "tickets" was honor enough. In fact, only a

40

small number did pass, not more than 20 or 30 per cent in most classes.

Living-conditions were very primitive. We had no bathrooms. Under my bed I had a washtub, which a Negro boy filled with hot water on Sunday morning. It took a long scrub to make up for the absence of bathing during the week. We lived at mess halls that were remarkably inexpensive, varying in cost from $14 to $16 a month, and with really very good Southern cooking at that. During the spring I found sufficient time to go out with the track team, and succeeded in coming in first in one race, second in another (220 yards), and a third in another (100 yards). The next year my track-work brought me invitations to try for the football team. I only weighed a hundred and thirty pounds and was never heavy enough to make the varsity team, but played halfback against them in practice games. I was elected captain of the academic team, and we succeeded in beating both the law and the medical teams that year. During my second year I graduated in senior Greek, in senior and junior natural philosophy, and in Spanish, which I took because I expected to return to Texas and probably to settle along the Mexican border.

This year I took over the editorship of the varsity newspaper, *College Topics*. My experience in newspaper work at Aspinhill stood me in good stead. On the board of editors was an enterprising chap from Baltimore named Bob Leach, who said that our paper was entirely too staid and uninteresting and that he could double the subscription list by patterning it after *Town Topics*, the ribald social sheet published in New York. We decided on this course, and Leach was our prize scandalmonger. We got together each week a lot of very personal matter that was read with much amusement by our subscribers.

Our circulation grew rapidly. But it kept the editor in chief constantly in hot water. One day a fellow student arrived at my room and said: "As editor in chief of *College Topics* you are responsible for the articles which appear in it. You have insulted my two cousins, the Misses Moran, of Charlottesville, and I am going to try my best to lick you." Whereupon he took off his coat. It required much explanation on my part to dissuade him from carrying out his threat. This and numerous other similar occurrences made the job of editor in chief, while Leach was associate editor, a highly adventurous career.

During the summer I returned home and Father asked me for the first time what profession I wanted to take up as my lifework. "Father," said I, "I believe I would like to go into journalism. They say that I have made a success of the college newspaper and I think I would like to follow this as a career." "All right," said he. "I will take you down and introduce you to Colonel Grice, the editor of the *San Antonio Express*." When the Colonel asked me if I had had experience, I proudly stated that I had had some little experience as editor in chief of *College Topics*. He hurt my pride greatly by informing me that I might forget that at once. "But regardless of that," he said, "as I am very anxious to do the General a favor, I will give you a job as reporter on the paper if you will go home and write something, sufficient to fill two columns, which is worthy of publication." During the next week I spent my days and most of my nights trying to find some subject worthy of two columns in the *San Antonio Express*. I ransacked the library, got out the old gray horse and traveled over most of San Antonio, in an effort to discover something that would fill two columns.

After another week, I went to my father and said, "I feel confident that I will not be a success as a journalist; I believe I'd like to go into medicine." "Why?" said he. "Because I believe I would like surgery. I understand that it is quite mechanical and I have an idea that I would like it." "All right," said he, "we will go down and see Dr. Cupples," who was our family physician. Dr. Cupples discouraged me by saying that medicine was a very unsatisfactory profession, that he had practiced it for fifty years and was still in debt, but that if I insisted he would be glad to take me around in his buggy while practicing in the homes and hospitals of San Antonio. But he thought I had better take home some books on anatomy and physiology. If, after looking them over, I still felt strongly inclined to go into medicine, I was to come back the next week.

I found the old textbooks fearfully dry and discouraging, but I showed up the next week at his office and for the rest of the summer went around with him while he treated patients from infancy to old age, for every kind of disease. He showed me how to induce chloroform anesthesia and I administered it in a good many simple cases. In others I acted as nurse, orderly, attendant, and general utility man. I had a fine summer and made up my mind that I would like medicine, especially surgery.

On returning to the University of Virginia in the fall of 1892, I had to finish only three "tickets" to graduate as both B.A. and M.A. In comparison with the two previous years, this was too easy, and I therefore asked the registrar to allow me to enter the first of the two years that formed the medical course at that time. He objected strenuously, said I could not possibly take the whole of first-year medicine, which was very heavy, in addition to German, chemistry, and history, which were necessary to get my two academic degrees. When I explained that I simply wanted to attend some of the medical classes in my spare time, he acceded to my request. When the chairman of the faculty arrived a few days later, he demanded that I give up the first-year medical work; but again, by exerting all my persuasive powers, I was allowed to do as I wished. It happened that the medical courses came largely seriatim, and it was possible for me to attend the various medical lectures of the first year without interruption to my academic studies.

I found the medical work so much more interesting than the academic that in a short time I was deeply engrossed by it, so that in early December, when the first final medical examination came, I had no difficulty in passing it. Two or three others came in December and January and they were likewise made with ease. When the academic examinations came, I failed in history. This was a fearful blow, as this examination was necessary for my Master's degree, and it was the first time I had failed in a subject at the university. During the rest of the year I gave more attention to history, as well as to the other academic subjects, to be sure to pass. But medicine still fascinated me, and I decided to make a try at all the examinations. When the session ended and the results were posted, we found that I had not only made my three academic subjects necessary for the Master's and Bachelor's degrees, but also had had the good luck to pass the ten subjects that formed the first-year course in medicine. I had the good fortune to be one of the nine to pass among the one hundred and twenty who took anatomy, a notoriously hard course.

At the university at that time a student was given a diploma for every subject or school in which he had passed during the year. As the various subjects were taken up, the dean would read off the names of the successful men, they formed in line, and the band played as they went up to get their diplomas to the accompaniment of applause. It was a long program. I received ten diplomas in medicine and three for the academic subjects and, in addition, the degrees of Bachelor of Arts and Master of Arts, making it necessary to go up fifteen times. Before long my name became quite a joke, causing much hilarity among the audience whenever it was read out. But the fact that I had passed all these courses did not mean that I was a creditable scholar in each of the classes. In some I had just "skimmed through."

The next year I had little difficulty in completing the second of the two years in medicine and in getting my medical degree. I am told this is the only time that anyone has made the degrees of B.A., M.A., and M.D. in four years.

In the early nineties, medicine was poorly taught in America. Some of the schools had two six-month sessions, but most of the others had three, also of six months each. The University of Virginia had two full sessions of nine months, so that the didactic work was as good as any in the country. The professors of anatomy, chemistry, histology, and pathology were full-time men who devoted themselves exclusively to teaching and investigation; they were not engaged in private practice. These subjects were thoroughly taught. No one was allowed to pass unless he made at least 80 per cent, and many failed. In most of the other medical schools all the teachers were practitioners who devoted only part of their time to teaching. At the university the clinical branches were taught by practitioners, but they were men of fine standing. They also gave very exhaustive didactic lectures and required 80 for a passing mark. Only a small percentage of those applying for the medical degree passed; the remainder went to other medical schools where the marking was less severe. One of my friends who entered the medical school when I first went to the university found chemistry very difficult and failed to pass it. The second year he came back and took chemistry over again and failed. He repeated chemistry his third year and again failed. He had completed all other subjects but, intent on graduating, he returned his fourth year, and although he got 79 on his examination, he was again failed and had to return the fifth year to take chemistry once more—and finally got his medical degree.

Those who did graduate in medicine at the University of Virginia had little difficulty in later examinations, and stood high before the examining boards of the army, the navy, and the hospitals of New York and other great centers, to which nearly all men from Virginia went for practical experience. Our medical school was one of the early ones and maintained its high rank until, with the development of fine hospitals in great cities, other schools outstripped it in clinical advantages.

At the university we had no hospital—only a small dispensary for outpatients—and the only surgery I saw was performed by Dr. William C. Dabney, father of my closest friend, Dr. William M. Dabney of Baltimore. Although Dr. Dabney was professor of medicine, he was also an excellent surgeon, but had to do his work in the homes of his patients. I was invited to see a few of his operations. When I got my degree, although crammed full of science and book learning, I knew next to nothing about the practice of surgery.

During my last three years at the University of Virginia, I was a member of the Chi Phi Fraternity. Our chapter contained a delightful bunch of fellows. One was the son of Professor Minor, three were sons of Colonel Marshall, General Lee's aide and secretary. My roommate was a Keith of Virginia and another classmate was a descendant of the Masons, celebrated in Revolutionary times. Bob Ballantine, son of the distinguished New Jersey brewer, furnished much amusement and lent us money. On Saturday nights we had a wonderful frolic over a case of beer, during which we all got slightly tight.

Greek-letter fraternities are inspiring, especially the ritual, filled with high ideals and protestations of undying love for fraternity and brothers. The closely knit friendship between members, many of whom were boys of fine quality, was, I believe, one of the best influences of my college career, in many ways more valuable than the dry studies over which I had labored so hard. The spirit of comradeship and learning how to take care of one's self in contests with quick-witted fellows were excellent preparation for the world at large.

CHAPTER 3. STARTING TO PRACTICE MEDICINE

AFTER saying good-by to the people of Albemarle County, who had been so kind to me at the university, I sold my old furniture and returned to my home in San Antonio. The newspapers had carried an account of the graduation and had even stressed the three degrees acquired in four years, but no one guessed how little practical medicine I knew. One of my old friends told me that a friend of his had something wrong with her and he wanted me to make an examination and operate. He remarked that he would not trust the old fogies in San Antonio to do the operation, but that he would trust her to me with my modern, scientific knowledge of surgery. Fully aware of my shortcomings and that San Antonio had excellent surgeons, still I could not bring myself to tell him the truth.

After seeing the patient and palpating the uterus, I made out that the lower portion was greatly enlarged and should be cut off, but what the proper operation was I hadn't the slightest idea. I told them a surgical operation was necessary and that I should be glad to take charge of the case, but as I was just starting in practice, it would be better for all concerned if I called in Dr. Cupples, just to prevent criticism. Asserting that he saw no reason for bringing in an old-timer, my friend consented. Dr. George Cupples had graduated at the universities of Edinburgh, London, and Paris, but on account of a tuberculous sister had left Europe and come to West Texas, hoping that the dry climate would cure her. He had done some of the first great surgical operations in the United States. Examining the patient, Dr. Cupples said, "This is a case for Schroeder's operation, which, as you know, removes this enlarged uterine neck obliquely and, by an excellent plastic closure, restores the uterus to normal." Simply saying that I agreed with him, I asked whether he would kindly assist me. The old gentleman said, "I wouldn't do this for anyone else, but your father is my dearest friend and I'll do it for his son."

I asked two other distinguished doctors to help at the operation. A knife was handed to me. I held it aloft. Then, saying, "In your august presence, Dr. Cupples, I could not think of doing this operation," I pushed the knife into his hands. He expressed pleasure at my pretty speech and did a beautiful operation. I was saved.

The experience had been a valuable one, because it brought home to me that I must go to one of the great centers and learn the art of surgery, which appealed to me so strongly. Casting about for a place to go, I decided on the Johns Hopkins Hospital, which, although only five years old, had already risen to the front rank. I collected $40 from the patient, and with it bought a ticket to Baltimore.

WHEN I got off the train at Baltimore, I asked a Negro hack-driver if he knew a good hotel and how much he would charge to take me there. He said he would do it for a dollar. I put my bag in the cab and he drove up the incline to the street, crossed Jones's Falls (a small creek), and stopped in front of a hotel. The distance from the station was about a hundred yards, but when I objected to the price, he said that a bargain was a bargain. The hotel was a mediocre one. I met one of my old clubmates the next day. When I told him I was stopping at the St. Charles Hotel, he almost died laughing, and insisted upon my going to his home. I paid dearly for the night I spent with him, because he got me into a poker game and I lost half of the money I had brought to Baltimore.

I went over to the Hopkins Hospital and found that the graduate school would not open for two weeks. My friend Smith Hollins McKim was working in Dr. J. M. T. Finney's dispensary, and through him I heard that Dr. William D. Booker, professor of pediatrics, was looking for someone to relieve the resident of another hospital, who wanted to go off on a vacation. Dr. McKim advised against it, but it seemed to me that as long as the graduate school would not open for two weeks, I could not do better than take the temporary position and try to make a friend of one of the prominent professors at Hopkins.

Dr. Booker, a tall, gruff man, asked me where I had graduated and I told him the University of Virginia. "So did I," said he. "Who was your father?" "General William H. Young of San Antonio." "Was he in the Confederate Army?" "Yes," said I. "I was a major in the medical corps myself," said he. "Who was your mother?" "Frances Kemper." "Any kin to General James L. Kemper?" "A cousin," said I. "I was on General Kemper's staff. I think you'll do. Come around to my house tomorrow morning at eight o'clock with your valise."

It took over an hour to reach St. Agnes Hospital in Dr. Booker's one-horse buggy. Dr. Booker discoursed at length on the Confederate Army, quizzed me about my parents and relatives in Virginia, and then asked me what I wanted to make of myself. I told him that I had always been mechanically inclined and thought I would like surgery. Dr. Booker offered to ask Dr. Finney to give me a place in his surgical dispensary, and Dr. Finney did so.

Dr. Booker showed me numerous interesting cases presenting diseases I had read about but never seen. For the first time I was intimately thrown with patients. I went over their histories carefully, took voluminous notes, and got a lot of valuable experience.

When the graduate school opened, I went to work in bacteriology, followed the rounds of Dr. William Osler in the medical wards, occasionally saw operations by Dr. Halsted and his staff, but spent most of my time in the laboratories when not in Dr. Finney's surgical dispensary. Bacteriology interested me immensely, and I used to carry culture tubes in my pockets so that I could inoculate them from interesting cases. One day a patient with greatly swollen eyelids appeared. Dr. Hobach, assistant chief, decided that an abscess was present and incised the swollen lower lid. Out came a peculiar whitish secretion, not at all like pus, so I took cultures from it. Two days later the media were covered by a heavy grayish growth that immediately suggested the anthrax bacillus. Making a smear from it on a glass slide and staining it, I saw the large rods typical of anthrax. Believing that I had made an important discovery, I carried my cultures and slides to Dr. Simon Flexner, associate in pathology and bacteriology. He said: "It looks like anthrax, but there's never been such a case at the Hopkins; it must be a contamination. You should be more careful in taking cultures." Crestfallen but unconvinced, I decided to look up the patient. I got his address from the record room and found that he lived about six miles from the hospital. I took a horsecar, transferred twice, and found that the patient's address was a large factory that dealt in hides and hair. As the anthrax bacillus is usually brought to this country in hides from South America, I felt confident I was right. In a little house near the factory I found the patient. His face, neck, and lips were markedly swollen and his eyes were closed. His pulse was very rapid and he had a high fever. Realizing that this was a case of very rare edematous anthrax, I telephoned the hospital superintendent, who demurred when he heard how far away I was; but when I informed him of the rarity of the disease, he agreed to send the two-horse ambulance for the patient. It was after sundown when I got my patient to the hospital.

Dr. Osler was called at once and expressed the greatest interest. The patient died the next day. The autopsy, performed by Dr. George Blumer, revealed lesions that had never been described before in cases of anthrax. A little later the pathological report on the organs was made by Dr. Simon Flexner before the Johns Hopkins Medical Society. In his presentation, Dr. Flexner said that the case would be reported in detail by Drs. Blumer and Young in the *Johns Hopkins Hospital Bulletin*. The case was unique in that there was present acute inflammation of the lining membrane of the heart (endocarditis) due to the anthrax bacillus. No other case was present in the literature of a fresh endocarditis developing on a previously normal heart valve. There was also an acute peritonitis due to the anthrax bacillus, and no exactly similar case had been previously described.

These unique pathological conditions interested Dr. Welch, and he talked at length on the subject. Dr. Osler discussed the clinical aspects and the great rarity of the case. It was the first time my name had been mentioned in a medical meeting, and to have these distinguished men commend my enterprise in discovering and bringing the patient to the hospital was most stimulating.

A little later I was approached by Dr. Bolton, associate in bacteriology, who asked me if I would like to go to Philadelphia as an assistant bacteriologist to that city, where he recently had been appointed chief bacteriologist. Examinations were going to be held for two assistants. Herbert Pease, an instructor in bacteriology at the Hopkins, had decided to try for one of the positions. Pease and I went to Philadelphia and took part in a three-day series of examinations in the laboratories of the University of Pennsylvania and the board room of the City Hall. The twenty-seven applicants were given an extensive series of practical and written examinations. When they were over, it was announced that Pease stood first and I second. When the Mayor was informed of the results, he was reported to have said: "If I understand correctly, the new bacteriologist in chief is from the Johns Hopkins. The man who has won first place in the examination is also from the Johns Hopkins; I'll appoint him, but I'll be damned if I appoint this third man— Young—who is also from the Johns Hopkins. With two great medical schools in Philadelphia, I can't afford to take all these bacteriologists from the Johns Hopkins." Crestfallen, I returned to Baltimore, but I have thanked the Mayor many times. Bolton and Pease soon ran counter to the politicians and were dismissed.

A curious aftermath of my Philadelphia experience was that I came down with diphtheria, evidently a result of my breaking a culture tube of the diphtheria bacillus that I accidentally dropped on a table in front of me during the examinations. I was sent to the isolation ward and given intramuscular injections of diphtheria antitoxin. I was one of the earliest patients in Baltimore to receive these injections of diphtheria antitoxin, and my case was one of a small series that was reported by Dr. Blumer in the *Johns Hopkins Hospital Bulletin* for 1895.

My experience with antitoxin came to my help later. In order to make a little money, which I sorely needed, I used to go every Saturday afternoon to one of the suburbs of Baltimore—Canton— and dress two patients with tuberculous hips. I had to carry a large bundle of gauze bandages and plaster of Paris, and the work of removing the old cast and putting on another consumed most of the afternoon. For my work I received $1 from each patient and 20 cents of this went for carefare, but the $1.80 looked very good at the end of each week. One time, while dressing one of my little patients, her mother said: "I'm very much worried over my child of two years who has, according to our family doctor, membranous croup. Would you mind looking at the child?" A glance down the throat showed a very extensive case of diphtheria, which covered the tonsils and the back of the throat. It had apparently spread to the larynx, as the child was breathing heavily. I asked the mother if antitoxin had been used and she said she had never heard of it. At that moment the family physician arrived and the mother introduced him to me. He said he was afraid the child was going to die. When I asked him if he had used antitoxin, he replied: "No, indeed. I know nothing about that newfangled remedy." I suggested that it should be tried in this case, inasmuch as the results with antitoxin had been very encouraging, but he told me that if he were to use it and the child died, it would ruin his practice. The mother, overhearing his remarks, said, "I want this new remedy tried on my child, as you say she is going to die anyhow." The doctor said he would wash his hands of the case and "leave this young fellow to do whatever he wishes." With that he stalked out of the room.

Left with this desperate case of diphtheria on my hands, I telephoned to Dr. J. F. Martinet, Dr. Booker's assistant in pediatrics, and he agreed to bring the antitoxin down. In an hour or so he arrived in his buggy. The injection was given at once. The child seemed to breathe more easily, and I rode back to the city with Dr. Martinet.

We saw the patient the next morning. The breathing was extremely labored and difficult and the child was very blue. Dr. Martinet said that if the child were in a hospital, a tracheotomy or intubation would be indicated, but as we had no instruments and the child would surely die before we could get her to the hospital, there was nothing to be done. I said: "Dr. Martinet, I have a pocketknife with which an operation could be done. Don't you think we could carry out tracheotomy?" He said he thought not, because other instruments were needed, particularly two silver tubes, one inside the other, which are always inserted into the opening made by the knife into the trachea (windpipe). I admitted that I had not only never done such an operation or even seen one, but I knew how it should be done and thought it would not be difficult. Martinet said such an attempt would be foolhardy and would discredit us with the physicians of Baltimore. With that, he left.

Hoping to find a tube of some sort, I asked if a drugstore were anywhere near. They said not, but that a short distance away there was a grocery store which carried some medical supplies. Hurrying there, I inquired if they had any surgical instruments or tubes. I was told the only tubes they had were glass ones used in taking tonics that contained iron. I thought it would be possible to fashion from one of these a makeshift tracheotomy tube. With a kerosene lamp it was possible to heat and bend the tube into the proper curve and round the ends, which I cut off with a file. Fearing that it might break in the child's throat, I wrapped the tube closely with thread. From a piece of cigar box I made a crossbar to which strings were tied to encircle the neck and hold the tube in place. This bar I bound to the glass tube. With this crude tracheotomy tube I rushed back to the house. The child was blue and gasping for breath. Three women held it on a pillow while, with the pocketknife, I opened the throat. There was a gush of air; I slipped the glass tube into the opening, down into the trachea, and fastened it around the neck with the strings. Immediately the blueness began to disappear. The child breathed more freely and soon was asleep. It was possible to remove the tube in a few days, and the wound soon healed.

My next operation was on the toe of Count Ferdinand von Klinkerström. This former officer of the Prussian Army had married a Baltimore girl. He was very proud of his feet, and wore shoes that were much too tight. As a result, his right little toe was drawn back in the form of a hammer and known medically as a hammertoe. On its summit had grown a vicious corn that caused the Count much pain. When told that the only hope of cure was amputation of the toe, he was greatly concerned until I assured him that it would make it possible for him to wear a smaller shoe. The operation was carried out at his home on Charles Street after a few local injections of cocaine. The specimen—bent in a right angle—looked a great deal like the flexed arm so often seen in coats of arms, so I had it mounted with a blue ribbon attached and kept it on my mantle as my only mark of aristocracy. I met the Count at the home of his cousin, Baron von Knobloch, where Douglas Duval and I had gone to live in order to have practice in conversational German.

Another interesting experience during the winter of 1895 was that with a Negro boy who had been working at a tin-clipping machine. He had cut off the middle finger of his left hand just at the base of the fingernail. I asked him what he had done with the amputated portion and he promptly produced it (from his pants pocket), wrapped in a piece of brown paper. An hour had intervened since the accident, but it seemed worth while to attempt to replace the amputated part. After washing it in salt solution, I sewed the severed tip back to the finger with interrupted sutures of fine silk. I was pleased to note on the following day that sensation had already returned to the tip. The wound healed perfectly, and in due time a new fingernail appeared.

Toward the end of our pathological course, Dr. Welch called me to his office and said that there was a vacancy in the chair of pathology at the University of Texas, and he wondered whether I would like to apply for the position. I told him I would, because I felt it would be a great honor to go back to the university of my native state as professor of pathology; but I did not get the position, which went to a much older man in Philadelphia.

Toward spring I decided to apply for an internship in surgery, and wrote Dr. Halsted a letter of application in which I cited my previous work at the University of Virginia, and so on. I received no reply, and a month later, as I happened to meet him in the corridor, I stopped, introduced myself, and said: "You don't know me, Dr. Halsted. My name is Young. I wrote you applying for a postion on the surgical staff." Whereupon Dr. Halsted, in his stiff manner, said, "Oh, yes, Young, I got your letter, but there isn't any place for you."

My disappointment was intense, and when Dr. Booker asked me if I had anything to do for the summer, I told him no. He suggested that I try to get a job on the surgical staff. I told him that I had written to Dr. Halsted applying for a position on his staff. Whereupon Dr. Booker said: "You made a fearful mistake in writing him a letter. No man who writes Dr. Halsted a letter ever gets a position on his staff. I'm very sorry I didn't think to tell you."

Dr. Booker then told me that he needed a bacteriologist and pathologist at the Thomas Wilson Sanitarium and asked me how I would like to come out and spend the summer there. I accepted at once. The sanitarium was devoted entirely to babies suffering from the intestinal infections so common in summer. Dysentery was extremely fatal, and Dr. Booker was engaged in an extensive bacteriological study of the disease. He had made the most comprehensive researches on the bacteria of the intestinal tract and had already described sixty-four varieties of the colon bacillus. A great enthusiast and an inspiring worker, he made my summer a very profitable one. I learned much pathology and bacteriology.

In the early part of September, before the sanitarium closed, I was called on the telephone by Dr. Edmund J. Clark, an intern on the surgical staff at the Johns Hopkins Hospital. He and I had been fellow students in the postgraduate school and were close friends. He asked me whether I would like to come on the surgical staff for a month to substitute for a man who wanted to take a vacation.

I went in at once. Dr. Finney was in charge of the Surgical Service, as Dr. Halsted was on his vacation. I was put in charge of the Negro wards and gave anesthetics in the operating-room. In addition to the clinical we had much laboratory work. We wrote up the pathological reports of the cases operated on and also carried out our own bacteriological examinations. The work was fascinating, and I soon knew that I would like surgery immensely.

Robert L. Garrett was there, also substituting for a man away on his vacation. On October 1 Francis R. Hagner of Washington appeared and said that he had met Dr. Halsted the early part of the summer and was told to come on the first of October, as there would be a place for him on the surgical staff. Two men did leave at this time, but there were the three of us—Hagner, Garrett, and myself— when Dr. Halsted returned. He bowed distantly to Garrett and to me and also to Hagner, who was much disappointed that Dr. Halsted did not speak to him and confirm his appointment. We all wondered what was going to happen, but as Dr. Halsted previously had told me personally that there would be no place for me, I had little hope. I made up my mind, however, to sit tight, say nothing, and stay on until I was told to go. Day after day passed and Dr. Halsted said nothing. The three of us got more and more nervous. As a result of loss of sleep and worry we were on the verge of a breakdown. Finally Hagner and Garrett came to me and said: "There are two vacancies on this staff, and there are three of us here, so one is bound to go. We have been waiting around here for weeks for Dr. Halsted to say something, but he has done nothing but avoid us. It has got on our nerves. We are all good friends, and we think we should decide on a plan of action and all do the same thing. Do you think it is better to write Dr. Halsted, or talk to him personally?" I replied: "Gentlemen, you two are free to do what you want, but as far as I am concerned I shall do nothing. I am going to stay here until I am kicked out." They finally agreed to do as I proposed—nothing. The suspense continued from day to day. Dr. Halsted said not a word. We got up each morning after a sleepless night, did our ward work, gave anesthetics, avoided Dr. Halsted in every possible way and, exhausted, flung ourselves on our beds again at night. This kept up for several weeks until Hagner got sick. It turned out to be typhoid fever, and he lay at death's door for several weeks, his temperature at one time reaching 107°. (During his convalescence he had the good fortune to fall in love with a charming nurse, who is now Mrs. Hagner.) When Hagner returned at the end of the winter, another vacancy had occurred on the staff and Hagner, Garrett, and I all stayed on.

We constantly looked forward to the time when we would be allowed to do an operation. One day Frank Hagner came into the dining-room jubilant because Dr. Bloodgood had told him he could operate on a case of rupture in the groin. He went to the patient's ward and, assuming a very imposing air, said to him, "Tomorrow I shall operate on you." The patient went raving mad, became so violent that he had to be put in a strait jacket, and had to be sent to the state hospital.

When I started my internship at the Johns Hopkins Hospital, there were less than three hundred beds for patients. The operating room was small; it had a wooden floor and inadequate ceiling lights. The operating table, which was of wood, consisted of four legs and a trough two and a half feet wide, six feet long, and six inches deep, with a hole in the center that was closed with a bung. On this wooden table was a stretcher about two feet wide and eight feet long.

The patient was brought from the ward on one of these stretchers, covered with a pad and carefully wrapped with blankets. He went to the anesthesia room, where large straps were placed across his chest and arms, and above his knees. The anesthetist used a cornucopia-shaped cone made of pasteboard covered with oiled silk and toweling. In the cone was a large sea sponge into which the anesthetist poured the ether. The saturated cone was placed over the patient's face. There usually was a considerable struggle before the patient went under. A strong orderly pinned the patient's arms to his sides and the anesthetist struggled with the head to keep the cone in place. From time to time fresh ether had to be added, and often the patient would seize upon that moment to try to free himself.

One day I was giving ether to a burly, six-foot Irishman whose red face gave indication of many years of heavy drinking. These patients are invariably hard to anesthetize, and in some instances ether has very little effect. I filled and refilled the sponge with large dashes of ether. Still the patient could not be got under and fought desperately. Finally, when I took the cone off to add more ether, he seized upon that moment to get away. With one violent movement he raised his knees and broke the strap across them. In another desperate surge with his hands he tossed the orderly over on the floor, and before I could get hold of his head he had tumbled off the stretcher with the board fastened to his back. Regaining his feet, out of the room he dashed, his only covering being the board that was strapped to his back. Down the hall he went in a drunken fury, scattering nurses and patients as he went on his way, and finally ran out into the street, where a policeman caught him.

Another time I was giving ether to a young mulatto girl. She had a stiff knee joint and Dr. Halsted had broken up the adhesions by bending the knee when she was deeply anesthetized. She had taken ether over and over again and was hard to get under. As I took off the cone to add more ether, she rolled her black eyes and said, "Kiss me again, Dr. Young." If only she hadn't said "*again*." I had been on the staff only a short time, and this occurrence worried me no little.

After a patient was under the anesthetic, he was wheeled to the operating-room and lifted on the board from the truck to the operating table, to which he was fastened in the proper position with straps.

Dr. William S. Halsted, professor of surgery, had brought this old wooden table back from Germany. It was a relic of the army hospitals of the Franco-Prussian War. It could not be tilted or turned. If you wanted the foot elevated, the orderly raised the board and put a sawhorse under it, and a block of wood acted as a shoulder rest. To get the patient in a position with the thighs flexed and the legs in the air, two posts were stuck into holes on the side of the board and around these the legs were wrapped. Crude as it was, the finest surgery in America at that time was done on this table. The great trough allowed abundant irrigations of the wound, which were then frequently used.

This was before the days of sterile operating-gowns and rubber gloves. Most surgeons in America and Europe put on short rubber boots, without removing their shoes or trousers. Their sleeves were rolled up, a rubber apron was tied on, and a small sterile towel fastened in front. Dr. Halsted had made a great innovation at the Hopkins by insisting that his staff take off all their clothes, put on white tennis shoes, a duck suit with short sleeves, and a little round skullcap.

Great care was taken in the preparation of the hands, which were scrubbed for five minutes, then passed into a bowl containing a saturated solution of potassium permanganate, then into a saturated solution of oxalic acid, which dissolved off the permanganate; then the hands and arms were immersed for five minutes in a long bowl of 1:1,000 bichloride of mercury.

The patient, anesthetized, was placed on the table. The wet antiseptic towel, which covered his skin, was removed. He was then scrubbed with soap; the soap was removed with ether and then alcohol. Potassium permanganate solution was smeared around the region where the incision was to be made, followed by oxalic acid, and a scrubbing of 1:1,000 bichloride of mercury. Finally when the region was considered clean and sterile, towels were draped around the site of operation. Although the instruments had been boiled for ten minutes, Lister's ideas of infection from the air were still prevalent and the instruments were kept immersed in 1:30 carbolic acid solution. As this was hard on the instrument man's hands, he wore a rough pair of heavy rubber gloves with which he fished the instruments out and shook them before he handed them to the operator. The fear of infection was still great, and the wounds were sometimes doused with a solution of bichloride of mercury.

There were many regions in which the surgeon operated with trepidation. One of these was the knee joint, as infections at such operations usually meant loss of the leg. Up to 1895 few such cases had been operated upon. A Negro woman came to the hospital with fracture of the patella, that flat, oval bone which works up and down when our knees are in motion, commonly called the kneepan. Owing to the fear of opening the knee joint, great precautions had been taken to get the region absolutely sterile. We had begun three days before in the ward by shaving and cleaning the region of operation. This was repeated on the second and third days. Then the patient was brought to the operating-room. The wet bichloride dressing was removed. With a sterile razor the skin was shaved and then abundantly lathered. This was washed off with sterile water, and ether followed by alcohol was applied to get every remnant of the soap and grease away. Then the limb was carefully stroked with a sponge red with a saturated solution of potassium permanganate. This in turn was dissolved with the oxalic acid. Abundant libations of 1:1,000 bichloride of mercury were then applied and sterile towels placed around the knee, leaving only a slit through which Dr. Halsted was to operate.

The occasion was considered so important that rubber gloves had been sterilized for Dr. Halsted and his entire operating team. A few feet away from the table stood a bearded old practitioner, Dr. Crim. With his knife poised, Dr. Halsted turned to Dr. Crim, who had referred the patient, and said, "When you first saw this girl, how far apart were the two fragments of this fractured patella?" "The upper fragment was right here," said Dr. Crim, as he placed his large, dirty hand on the limb we had spent three days in cleaning for operation. With a cry of anguish, Dr. Halsted stepped back, nurses rushed in, pulled off the draping, and the ritual of cleaning up the field of operation was begun again—soap, ether, alcohol, permanganate, oxalic acid, and bichloride. After a few incisions the fractured ends of the bone were brought to view, the ragged edges cut off with a saw, and the two halves approximated with heavy silver wire, which was left buried in the wound as the skin was drawn together.

With the use of sterile rubber gloves a new era in surgery dawned. With the safety furnished by them the surgeon went forth to invade one region after another that had been sacrosanct. Instead of many wounds broken down by suppuration and gangrene, and patients dying of blood poisoning, the surgery of clean wounds became so safe that even a stitch abscess was extremely rare and called for investigation.

Dr. Halsted became bolder and bolder. He brought out new methods in abdominal surgery. He perfected his great operation for cancer of the breast. By removing far more tissue than had been cut out before and following the line of invasion into the armpit— and even above the collarbone—by his block dissection and excision en masse of great areas of tissue, Dr. Halsted obtained far more cures than ever before. He removed so much of the patient that a wag composed a ditty in which the orderly said to Dr. Halsted, "Which half goes back to the ward?"

There was not one slightest detail that he overlooked. It was because of his close attention to every item that he was able to revolutionize the surgery of that day. Whereas previously wounds had been allowed to bleed, the vessels being stopped either by pressure, by application of heat, or by the simple process of eventually clotting, Dr. Halsted employed hundreds of clamps, delicate pincers that he specially designed with fine points, so that very little tissue would be crushed. In his breast operations he used hundreds of these clamps. I have seen a large case in which almost a thousand were applied, although most of them were removed. Many of the bleeding-points were "tied off" with delicate silk so fine that the greatest care was necessary to prevent its breaking.

It was beautiful to watch Dr. Halsted in his great finesse. It was only on account of his meticulous attention to sterilization of the

DR. HALSTED 63

patient, the wound, and the operator that he dared leave silk buried in his wounds. Other surgeons used absorbable ligatures of catgut, as they feared the stitch abscess, or sinuses that ran down to an infected ligature of buried silk. Such had been the practice all over the world up to now. It has only been within the last two or three years that those trained by Dr. Halsted have shown by their superior results—the perfection of wound healing and almost invisible scars—the great advantage of silk, that there is a movement to adopt the Halsted principles of fine buried silk ligatures and stitches. By care in stopping all bleeding when he came to close his wounds, he made them absolutely dry. He frequently used silver not only for buried stitches, but also for closing his wounds with a beautiful stitch like a snake immediately beneath the skin, drawing the edges together and leaving no stitch holes. The silver was pulled out about a week later.

The use of silver came as a result of an interesting experiment in the laboratory. Into a flat plate of sterile gelatin inoculated with the bacteria of suppuration small bits of silver foil were dropped, the cover was replaced, and the dish was put in an incubator. A day later there was a clear space around each piece, which showed that no bacteria grew within almost half an inch of the silver. This demonstrated the antiseptic character of metallic silver. Dr. Halsted carried the silver technique a step further by applying sterile leaves of silver foil upon the closed wounds and adjacent skin. This not only formed an antiseptic covering but hermetically sealed the wound, and gave brilliant results.

Like all geniuses, Dr. Halsted was often absent-minded. One day the staff was cleaned up and ready for him to commence operating at ten o'clock. He failed to appear. Eleven o'clock and no Dr. Halsted. At half-past twelve he arrived and said, apologetically, in his high voice, "I'm sorry to keep you, but Mrs. Halsted and I have been busy killing rats in our cellar."

One time Mr. Ernest Gittings and I had been duck-shooting. We got a few canvasbacks and many other ducks not of such fine quality. I wanted to send some to Dr. Halsted, Dr. Finney, Dr. Osler, and Dr. Welch, and I hardly knew how to apportion them. "Well," said Mr. Gittings, "Dr. Halsted won't know one duck from another. Give him some of the mallards." But Dr. Halsted was my chief, and I sent him canvasbacks. A few days later Dr. Halsted said: "Young, those were beautiful canvasbacks you sent me. I arrived just as they were being served at dinner. Mrs. Halsted could not tell me what kind of ducks they were, so I sent for the cook, but he didn't know either. I told him to bring me the heads, but they had been thrown away. After dinner I took a lantern out to the garbage can in the alley and went through all the trash until I found the heads. They were canvasbacks, just as I suspected."

Dr. Halsted was quite a gourmet. He kept his own stock of terrapin in the cellar. Everything for his table had to be of first quality and came from dealers in various parts of the country who had a reputation for selling the best. His house was filled with lovely antique furniture and fine old silver. A dinner at Dr. Halsted's was an event to be remembered.

He delighted in practical jokes. We had all assembled to banquet Dr. William S. Thayer in celebration of his refusal to leave the Hopkins and go to Harvard. Many eulogistic speeches had been delivered, and then Dr. Halsted was called upon. Reaching beneath the table, he drew out a large morocco case and placed it before him. "I've just returned," he said, "from the German Surgical Congress in Berlin. While there I received a summons from the Emperor, who said, 'You have in Baltimore a man whose discoveries in malaria have been of inestimable value to my subjects in East Africa. Please take back and present to him, in recognition of his wonderful work, this greatest decoration of the Reich—the *Schwartze Adel Erste Klasse*.' " With that Dr. Halsted opened the box, withdrew a flaming broad ribbon to which was suspended a great black eagle, and presented it to Dr. Thayer, placing the ribbon around his neck. The applause was deafening. Dr. Thayer was overwhelmed, and the party broke up in great excitement. It leaked out later that Dr. Halsted had bought the decoration in a pawnshop.

Dr. Welch got even with him. He and Dr. Halsted were dining at the Maryland Club and Dr. Welch asked him what were the symptoms of aneurysm of the aorta. Dr. Halsted explained that this saccular enlargement of the great artery above the heart produced a pulsation in the upper left chest. Nothing more was said. Two or three nights later Dr. Welch said: "I believe I have an aneurysm of the aorta. I have those symptoms you described the other night, right now." Dr. Halsted looked him and said, "It's ridiculous, with your fine color." Dr. Welch insisted that he felt the characteristic pulsation very strongly. "Put your hand under my vest and see for yourself." Dr. Halsted said that, sure enough, there was a pronounced, regular pulsation, about eighty to the minute, corresponding to the heartbeats. Terrified at the thought of losing his friend from this fearful malady, Dr. Halsted continued to feel the rhythmic pulsation that went on beneath his fingers, wondering all the time how much longer his dear friend would be here, when suddenly there was a violent pulsation, which he found was produced by a flat rubber bulb, inflated by another bulb secreted in Dr. Welch's pocket.

Dr. William H. Welch was famous the world over as one of the greatest pathologists. He lived alone and usually got his meals at the Maryland Club, where a coterie of bons vivants constantly awaited him. His closest friend was Major Venable, a Confederate veteran who had risen to distinction in law.

As father of the Hopkins Medical School, Dr. Welch was affectionately called Popsy by everyone. He frequently left town over the week end without saying where he was going. One of the students composed this ditty:

> Nobody knows where Popsy eats,
> Nobody knows where Popsy sleeps,
> Nobody knows whom Popsy keeps,
> But Popsy.

Dr. Welch founded the *Journal of Experimental Medicine* in 1896 and became its first editor. He never had a secretary, and was completely swamped by his correspondence. He often failed to acknowledge the receipt of manuscripts. When many months had passed and their articles were not published, contributors began to request that the editor return their manuscripts. Still no reply. Dr. Henry M. Hurd, the punctilious editor of the *Johns Hopkins Hospital Bulletin*, told me that he had received letters from some of the most prominent medical men in the country begging him to rescue their manuscripts from Dr. Welch's study. As soon as Dr. Welch went off on one of his week ends, Dr. Hurd would go to his library, hunt among the many papers until he found the manuscripts he was looking for, and return them to the anxious authors.

One day I called on Dr. Welch and was admitted to his library. There was no place to sit down. Every one of the eight chairs was piled high with mail, most of it unopened, and so was the desk. Dr. Welch apologized for the appearance of the room. He explained that while I might think his study was in a state of disorder, he really had an excellent system. "On that armchair there I have the letters that have come during the past week; I hope to read these in the near future. On that chair I have the letters that have come within the past month. On the other chairs are letters and magazines anywhere from six months to a year old which I hope to get to sometime." As to the desk, he said that when it got too cluttered up he would open a newspaper, and spread it over the letters and manuscripts, and start afresh. I counted four such layers. There was one little corner of his desk pad which was vacant —just room enough to place a small sheet of note paper on which he wrote in his cramped handwriting.

I begged Dr. Welch to allow me to send him a dictaphone. I explained that any time, night or day, whenever he had a spare moment, he would be able to dictate his letters, that my stenographer would call the next morning for the cylinders and bring his typewritten letters back in the afternoon. He seemed greatly taken with the idea. I had my stenographer take the dictaphone to Dr. Welch and show him how to use it. The next day he returned and got a cylinder. I was anxiously waiting to see what had been recorded. There was only one letter, which began: "Dear Mr. Robinson. I wish to apologize for not writing sooner. I couldn't find time to- to- to—Young, I can't use this machine. Send your boy around to get it."

But Dr. Welch was never too busy to discuss interesting problems at length with even the youngest members of the staff, and occasionally he would write long letters in his own hand to them, commending one of their papers that had appeared in a medical journal. His knowledge of medical literature was encyclopedic, and he was brilliant in discussing papers at medical meetings.

Dr. Osler also kept closely in touch with the publications of the hospital staff. As a rule he would merely write something like this on a post card: "That was a fine article in the *Journal of the American Medical Association.* Keep up the good work and you'll get to the top."

Dr. Osler had a group of students and house officers come to his home almost every Saturday evening. There would be an informal discussion of interesting cases at the hospital. Then they would sit down to beer and pretzels in his library. Dr. Osler would get out his favorites among the old masters and talk in a fascinating way about them. He inspired many to delve into the history of medicine and pursue its literary side.

Dr. Osler was responsible for the Johns Hopkins Hospital Historical Society and also for a similar one that was organized in connection with the library of the State Medical Society, where Osler's active interest and popularity soon banished the hard feelings widespread in the city because no Baltimore physicians were chosen to head the departments of the Johns Hopkins Medical School and Hospital. To form his staff, Dr. Welch had picked young men from all over America and abroad who he thought showed great promise.

The fourth member of the four doctors who have been immortalized in Sargent's great portrait was Dr. Howard A. Kelly.

He was only thirty-seven when Dr. Welch placed him at the head of the Department of Gynecology. He was the most brilliant operator in America, and by his researches and inventions in genito-urinary surgery in women opened up an important new field.

When the work of the resident surgical staff was over in the operating-room, we assembled in the pathological laboratory, which was on the second floor immediately adjacent to Dr. Welch's office. He frequently came to discuss the specimens from the operating-room. Each one of us had to describe and cut sections for microscopic study from the specimens removed from patients on our individual wards.

In addition to pathology, we did our own bacteriology. We had to wash our test tubes and make all the media. The inoculation of cultures, the transfer of the bacteria from one tube to another, and the final diagnosis from the manner of growth on agar and gelatin, in bouillon, milk, and other complicated media, were most exciting. These were the early days of bacteriology. New germs were being discovered, and it was thrilling to see what organism would show up.

It seemed to me that a more scientific method than the cone could be devised for producing ether anesthesia, and I began experiments. I wanted to avoid the spasm and coughing produced in the early stages of anesthesia that occurred so frequently with the use of the old cone. Dr. Halsted became interested in the apparatus that I had constructed and allowed me to use it on his patients. It was the forerunner of some of the devices now in use.

In the early days, people were afraid of hospitals and averse to going there, even for an operation. This was particularly true of those not in affluent circumstances. Dr. Finney's practice was increasing rapidly, and it was the privilege of some of us to go out frequently to assist him. The patients could rarely afford nurses or orderlies, and there were so few on the surgical staff that often only one of us could be spared to go with Dr. Finney. Before starting it was necessary to pack the required dressings, instruments, and so on into two large baskets, and as automobiles did not exist and hacks were prohibitive in cost, we had to go by streetcar. Often several transfers were necessary, and then a walk of several blocks to the house, with a heavy basket on each arm.

One day Dr. Finney asked me to help him with a rectal case. I went an hour or two ahead of time to make the preparations. It was a tiny house with a small parlor below and a bedroom above. The only table available for the operation was an oval, marble-topped affair with bandy legs that curved down to a small base; it was long enough for the patient's body and would do. When Dr. Finney arrived, I had the instruments boiled and laid out on a chair; on another chair were the sponges and a basin of bichloride. I etherized the patient in her bed, and with the assistance of her husband got her down the narrow stairway and placed her on the table. It was necessary to get the husband to hold her legs up in the proper position. Dr. Finney seated himself on a chair between the instruments and the sponges. The operation was begun, but I was busy with the anesthesia and paid no attention to anything else until the swaying of the husband caused me to look up just as he fell forward, dropping his wife's legs upon Dr. Finney's shoulders. Finney was carried back to the floor by the woman's body. The table toppled over and I lost my balance. Struggling to my feet, I proceded to rescue Dr. Finney, first pulling off the husband, who had fainted completely, and then the patient. The husband soon came to, but was of no further use. Somehow, Dr. Finney and I managed to get things going again and the operation was completed.

I went back home to spend my vacation, and there met Mrs. Fannie Long Taylor. She asked me what interested me most at the hospital and I told her anesthesia. She surprised me by saying, "My father, Dr. Crawford W. Long, was the discoverer of ether anesthesia." Having been brought up on the idea, so vigorously promulgated from Boston, that ether anesthesia was the result of Morton's work at the Massachusetts General Hospital, I was greatly surprised, and said, "Have you any proofs of your father's claims?" She told me she had a trunk full of letters and documents. I was at her house the next morning and read with greedy eyes her father's notes on his first cases, the letters and affidavits of others who had been present at the operation, and Dr. Long's first account in the *Southern Medical Journal*. When I asked Mrs. Taylor if she would allow me to take her documents to the Johns Hopkins Hospital and present them to the medical society, she gladly consented.

I informed Dr. Halsted of my discovery and he advised me to present a paper on the subject. This was in the fall of 1896, and a great celebration of the fiftieth anniversary of the discovery of anesthesia by Morton at the Massachusetts General Hospital was about to be held. Delegates from the Hopkins as well as from all over the world assembled in Boston, and several days were given in laudation of the work of Morton, and the surgeon Warren who operated upon the first case.

Immediately after this celebration I presented my paper, with Dr. Long's original documents, before the Medical Society of the Johns Hopkins Hospital. Coming on top of the Boston celebration, this demonstration of Dr. Long's original documents, which proved conclusively that he had operated upon patients in the obscure country town of Jefferson, Jackson County, Georgia, over four and a half years before Morton, aroused much interest.

In later years the fact that I had presented complete proof of Long's claims to be the first to produce anesthesia using ether led to my being asked on numerous occasions to present papers or addresses on Crawford W. Long. The most important of these was the occasion for the dedication of a statue to him in the rotunda of the Capitol at Washington. Crawford W. Long and Alexander H. Stephens had been selected to represent Georgia in this hall of fame. The Long monument was a lovely full-length statue that was presented in a charming address by Governor Hardman of Georgia, himself a distinguished physician. Among the other addresses on the program was one that I had been asked to give as representing the medical profession, when I took occasion to comment on the tremendous advance made in surgery after anesthesia had been established.

Before anesthesia only thirty-four patients a year were operated upon at the Massachusetts General Hospital. In five years the number had tripled, and in fifty years, when the ether celebration was held in Boston, the increase had been a hundredfold. In the surgical textbooks before 1842 I found described only minor procedures and emergency operations. Within ten years the changes wrought were enormous. Splendid new conquests over disease by surgery were reported, but not until Pasteur's great work in 1862 that laid the foundations of bacteriology, and Lister's announcement of his discovery of antisepsis in 1867, was the capstone placed on Long's work of fifteen years before. Surgery was delivered of the horrors of pain and infection and, like an animal freed from a black dungeon of despair, bounded forth into the pure light of science. Disease, now explained by the germ theory, rapidly fell before one masterful research after another, while surgeons boldly went forth to conquer the hidden terrors of the abdomen, the chest, and the brain, and every corner of the human organism was finally brought under the searching rays of scientific medicine. My address closed with these words:

"Without the gift of anesthesia, where would surgery be today? Accustomed as people are to behold with complacency the wonderful accomplishments of modern medicine and surgery, what a tumult would ensue were surgeons to revert again to the days before the advent of the great discoverer whose memory we celebrate in the unveiling of this splendid replica of Crawford W. Long."

Later I was invited to participate in the celebration of the anniversary of Long's graduation from Franklin College. In an address at the chapel I was introduced by Dr. Frank K. Boland, Jr., of Atlanta. He made an introductory speech in which he, wishing to inject an amusing note, told the story of a Confederate soldier who bragged that he had captured six Yankees all by himself at the Battle of Manassas and seven Yankees at Cold Harbor. A friend stopped him and said, "How many did you capture at Appomatox?" Whereupon the bragger said: "I was away at that time and when I returned to General Lee's headquarters I found him with head bowed. He looked up and said, 'Jones, if I had known you were here I never would have surrendered.' " Then the Doctor introduced me. Thanking the president of the university for the honor they had done me, I paused to say that I did not quite understand why Dr. Boland had told that story of the bragging Confederate. If it had been intended to reflect on my father, who was a Confederate officer, I wished to say that I had never heard him assert that he had killed a single Yankee, but if it would give the Doctor any comfort, I was glad to admit that I myself had killed a lot of Yankees. In my address I pointed out that Dr. Long was the youngest member of his class and had come out second when he graduated as Master of Arts at the age of nineteen, and that he had roomed with Alexander Stephens. I paid a tribute to Dr. Long's wonderful daughter, Mrs. Fanny Long Taylor, who for many years fought a lone fight to have her father recognized in this country and abroad as the discoverer of anesthesia, her work culminating in her masterful biography of her father.

One of Dr. Long's daughters, a woman far advanced in years, was present, and afterward took me to the house in which her father had died. It was the home of a woman who was in labor. Dr. Long personally administered ether, turned the mask over to a member of the family, and himself delivered the child. As he arose to hand the baby to a nurse, he was stricken, and died at the foot of his patient.

From the university the celebrants moved to Danielsville, the birthplace of Dr. Long. As we came down the street that led to the courthouse in front of which was the statue to be unveiled, I saw two truckloads of convicts in their striped clothes parked near by. Turning to former Governor Hardman, I asked whether it had been so difficult to get an audience for me that they had to empty the penitentiary. An assemblage of patriotic Georgians crowded the space and even occupied adjacent trees. It was a warmhearted audience that I addressed.

From Danielsville the Governor and other members of the committee moved to Jefferson, where we visited the house in which

Dr. Long had held the ether parties in which he made the discovery that ether would prevent pain, and in which he applied it in the extraction of a small tumor from the neck of J. W. Venable in 1842. In front of this old building is a large bronze plaque recording this momentous event.

Harvey Cushing had come on the staff. He and I were both greatly interested in bacteriology and frequently worked late into the night on our cultures. He made some interesting discoveries. I obtained an unusual growth in one case that no one could identify. At first it grew long branching filaments, then broke up into rods, and finally into little balls so that, in the stained smear, one could find every type of organism: bacilli, staphylococci, streptococci, streptothrices. Cushing declared that I had found the father of all bacteria, and named it Adam.

While Cushing was assistant resident surgeon in charge of a female ward, a patient came in who had been shot in the neck. With an X-ray, one of the early taken in America, Dr. Cushing showed that the bullet was still present and lodged against the spinal cord. The case was accompanied by remarkable neurological symptoms and changes in reflexes. Cushing made an exhaustive study of the case and drew up beautiful charts that showed its remarkable features. This he presented to the Hopkins Medical Society, along with splendid anatomical and pathological drawings, some of which showed the operation Cushing had performed to remove the bullet. This presentation made a great impression upon the faculty and hospital staff, and turned Cushing's interest to neurological surgery, in which he subsequently specialized, becoming one of the world's greatest operators in that field.

At an operation on a patient with liver abscess, I encountered peculiar pus. It was different from any I had seen before, so I asked a fourth-year student, who was assisting me, to prepare cultures and stained slides for microscopic examination. Richard P. Strong, to whom the assignment was given, found amoebae and a strange worm, one that had never been described in America. He made an exhaustive study of the subject, mastered the whole of helminthology (the study of parasitic worms), and prepared a brilliant paper on the case, with his extensive investigations and the literature. Shortly after this a medical commission was appointed to go to the Philippines to study the diseases of those islands, and Strong was one of them. As a result of the splendid report he made he was soon called to Harvard as professor of tropical medicine.

In the fall of 1896 I was transferred to the ward devoted to urological cases (those of the genital and urinary organs). A patient had complained of frequency of urination for years. His bladder held only a tablespoonful (15 cubic centimeters) and he had to void every fifteen minutes. It occurred to me that it might be possible by hydraulic pressure to increase gradually the size of the bladder. I rigged up a fifteen-foot pole on which a fountain syringe was suspended. By holding the nozzle tightly into the end of the urinary tract (penile urethra), by hydraulic pressure I was able to force the fluid through the urethra (the canal carrying urine from the bladder) and into the bladder. At first it was possible to introduce only 15 cubic centimeters, but by repeated dilatations several times a day the bladder became more tolerant, and it slowly commenced to get larger. In a week the bladder held two ounces of fluid; in two weeks, three ounces. Simultaneously the intervals between voidings increased to forty minutes. At the end of a month the patient was voiding about every three hours. In six weeks his bladder was half the normal size, and he was voiding at intervals of four hours, and eventually he was quite normal. This discovery was applied to other cases that appeared about the same time, and with equally good results.

The question arose whether hydraulic pressure might not cause fluid to pass up the ureters (ducts through which urine passes from kidneys to bladder) into the kidneys and carry infections with it. To determine this it was necessary to conduct a series of experiments on animals and on cadavers, and to search the world's literature on the subject. One day Dr. Welch was doing an autopsy. He had removed all the abdominal organs except the urinary tract, and I begged him to allow me to introduce a deep-blue solution by hy-draulic pressure through the urethra, as I had done in patients, to see whether any of the dye would pass up to the kidneys. The bladder became larger and larger, and the deep-blue liquid could be distinctly seen within. A pint was introduced, and then a quart, and still the bladder continued to expand. It looked as if might burst any minute. Dr. Welch and his staff beat a hasty retreat. When we opened the bladder, we found that none of the fluid had gone beyond it. Hydraulic pressure could be employed without danger of the fluid's reaching the kidneys and setting up inflammation. These studies furnished material for a paper that I presented to the Johns Hopkins Medical Society, with many charts and anatomical and pathological illustrations.

While attending the genitourinary cases in Ward E, I became greatly interested in their bacteriology. One of these patients was a milkman who for eight years had carried the typhoid bacillus in his urinary tract, and probably had transmitted the infection to many of the homes where he carried milk. This case furnished the material for my first foreign publication, which I presented to the Tenth International Congress in Paris on August 9, 1900. This case and additional ones afforded material for an extensive paper in Volume 8 of the *Johns Hopkins Hospital Reports*, which, under the editorship of Dr. Osler, was devoted entirely to typhoid fever and its complications. I subsequently found the typhoid bacillus in the center of a stone taken from a kidney in a patient who had had typhoid fever many years before.

In my bacteriological studies I ran across some remarkable gono-coccal infections and published several papers on them. I had the good fortune to be the first to demonstrate that chronic inflammation of the bladder and also of the kidney could be due solely to the gonococcus (the bacterium causing gonorrhea), and that the same organism could be responsible for a general peritonitis. These cases were published in extenso in an article contributed to a memorial volume to Dr. Welch by his students in 1900.

But all this time my interest was in general surgery. I almost never visited the genitourinary outpatient clinic conducted by Dr. James Brown, and what urological work I had done was while I was an intern on Ward E. I had looked forward to being transferred to wards devoted to other forms of surgery.

One day in October, 1897, I was walking rapidly down the long corridor of the hospital. As I turned a corner, I ran into Dr. Halsted with great force and almost knocked him down. I caught him just before he hit the floor and began to apologize profusely. Dr. Halsted, still out of breath, said: "Don't apologize, Young. I was looking for you, to tell you we want you to take charge of the Department of Genito-Urinary Surgery." I thanked him and said: "This is a great surprise. I know nothing about genitourinary surgery." Whereupon Dr. Halsted replied, "Welch and I said you didn't know anything about it, but we believe you could learn."

Shortly after this I was taken down with jaundice. At the suggestion of my friend Dr. James F. Mitchell, I decided to recuperate at the farm of his uncle, Mr. James Farnandis, at Belair, Maryland. I took with me books on genitourinary surgery, which I procured at the library. One of these was the *System* of Prince Morrow. During the next two weeks I read and reread this splendid book. I owe much to that attack of jaundice!

I took over the Dispensary of Genito-Urinary Diseases at the Johns Hopkins Hospital on November 29, 1897. My predecessor was Dr. James Brown, a brilliant man. He was the first to catheterize the ureters in the male on June 9, 1893. He modified Brenner's cystoscope by the addition of a curved spring stylet which, when it was introduced within the ureter catheter (a flexible tube), gave it the curve necessary to make it possible to introduce it into the ureter in the male. He made a diagnosis of pus kidney, and Dr. Halsted removed it—the first recorded case of operation after ureter catheterization in the male.

Dr. Brown died suddenly on a steamer en route for Boston, on June 16, 1895. He had become infected from an accidental wound received in performing a surgical operation. While convalescing, pulmonary disease developed, leading him to seek a change of climate, and he died on the journey. Urology suffered a great loss in his death. The post was held temporarily by Dr. Gaither, until the appointment came to me so unexpectedly. I continued to live in the hospital, worked hard on the literature of urinary and genital diseases, and had charge of the patients in this branch of surgery.

CHAPTER 5. STARTING IN PRACTICE

IN BALTIMORE

IN THE summer of 1898 I began to look around for an office in Baltimore. Believing that it was wise to have an attractive place, I secured two splendid rooms and a bath on the first floor of the Colonial Apartments, 1005 North Charles Street, near the Maryland Club. Dr. Osler suggested that it would be a good plan for me to have a tunnel from the Maryland Club to my office so that the old sports at the club could come there unseen. But despite my beautiful office and its central location, patients were slow to arrive. The first was a heavily bearded man from the mountainous district of Tennessee. Rough and unkempt, he came in demanding to see Dr. Young. When I asked him to take a seat, he said, "I want to see Dr. Young." I assured him that I was Dr. Young, when he promptly burst out, "By Gawd, I want to see your daddy."

Among my first patients was a charming judge, Thomas Curtin of Bristol, Tennessee, and in a few days one of his good friends, Mr. R. J. Reynolds, head of the Reynolds Tobacco Company, appeared. These two patients provided me with a great deal of occupation and, incidentally, paid my first year's office rent at the end of the month. My worries for the present were at an end.

In the summer of 1898 I assisted Dr. Halsted in an acute abdominal case, and this ultimately had a marked effect on my practice in Baltimore. The patient, a boy of fifteen, was a member of a very prominent family, who had gone to the Blue Ridge Mountains for the summer. He developed acute appendicitis, and before Dr. Halsted arrived a huge abscess had formed. This was opened by Dr. Halsted and a gangrenous appendix was removed. For a time the patient improved, and Dr. Halsted left, leaving me in charge. On the following day the boy's pulse grew rapid and his temperature rose to 104°. He was vomiting frequently, and I gave him a pint and a half of salt solution (which I had prepared on the cookstove), beneath the breast to make up for the fluid lost. In the evening his temperature was almost 106°, his pulse 156, and it was evident that he had blood poisoning. Through an incision in the arm I opened a vein, removed several ounces of the infected blood, and introduced a quart and a half of salt solution. The pulse, which had reached 160, fell to 130 and the temperature from 105.8° to 104°. It was evident that the transfusion had been very beneficial, but not sufficient to combat the blood-stream infection. The next morning the temperature was 103.8°, the pulse 146, and he was very weak. I opened a vein in the opposite arm and introduced two and a half quarts of salt solution. The temperature and pulse fell rapidly to normal, and thereafter the patient steadily improved and, eventually, recovered completely.

The adult man has about four quarts of blood in his body. This patient, a delicate boy of fifteen, probably had very much less; yet he had received four and a half quarts of salt solution into his vascular system without any bad effect. In a paper that I published in the *Maryland Medical Journal* I said I thought the curative effect was due to bloodletting and removal of some of the infected blood, the dilution of the poison in the remaining blood, and the stimulation of rapid elimination through the kidneys induced by the marked increase in blood pressure that the large amount of fluid introduced had caused. I concluded that all toxic conditions would seem to come within the province of bloodletting and saline transfusion, not alone in cases of septicemia (blood poisoning) but in the toxic states of infectious diseases. I saw no reason why this procedure should not be repeated as many times as necessary to combat blood-stream infections. I reported another case, one of severe malarial fever, in which the physician, at my suggestion, had removed thirty ounces of blood and followed this by a transfusion of two quarts of salt solution, with excellent results. My case was, as far as I know, the first in which bloodletting to get rid of the poison and large amounts of salt solution to dilute that remaining in the blood and to cause its rapid elimination had been carried out. It opened up a new field of intravenous therapy. I am told that the amazing results obtained in this case became the "talk of Baltimore society." Soon after I opened my offices a reception was given me by the grateful family, and my start in practice was made distinctly easier. During the next four months work increased and I was greatly pleased with the returns.

I slept on a settee, which during the daytime served as a sofa for my patients and at night was dragged back into the consulting-room. As the mosquitoes were then very abundant and screens unheard-of, it was necessary to hang a mosquito bar to the ceiling. In order to do this I had to go out into the back building on the first floor, get a stepladder, mount to the ceiling, hang up the mosquito bar, and then arrange my bedding before retiring. Occasionally I would oversleep and some patient would get into the waiting-room before my settee had been returned to its proper place.

The poor sleeping-quarters, inadequate ventilation, and sedentary life had their effect. One day, while busily at work, my old friend Dr. William M. Dabney called. When he shook hands with me, he said that he thought I must have some fever. On his taking my temperature the thermometer registered 104°. I admitted having a pain in my chest. I was sent to the Union Protestant Infirmary, where Dr. Osler confirmed Dr. Dabney's diagnosis of pleurisy, possibly tuberculous. At the end of two weeks, as I still had a nightly fever, it was decided to send me South. I went to the home of my old friends the Hugers, at Charleston, where I remained a month. The daily fever continued, so I decided to go to my old home in

San Antonio. After six weeks there I went to a ranch with an intimate friend, Julia Johnston, where we spent delightful days on horseback.

But the miserable fever continued, and I decided to go to the mountains of western Texas. I spent the next two months at Fort Davis, which has an elevation of several thousand feet and a dry climate. Here I rode with the cowboys, hunted, and eventually got rid of my fever. While I was off on a hunting trip one day, some cowboys came from a side road and said they had heard there was a doctor in our party. A physician in a neighboring canyon wanted help with a woman in labor. I followed them to the cottage of a woman who had been in labor for two days. The history of the case disclosed that the patient had had three previous attempts at labor, each a month apart, and that she had carried the child fully twelve months.

The baby was so large that it was impossible to deliver it even when I inserted my hand and pulled the legs out (version). There the child hung. The doctor was busy administering ether. Operation was immediately necessary to save the mother. Going to my saddlebags, I got out the few instruments I always carried and hastily boiled them on the cookstove on which her sister was nonchalantly preparing dinner, with the patient only a few feet away. A Caesarian operation was impossible. The only thing left to do was to make an incision low down in the abdomen, divide the ligament that holds the two halves of the bony pelvis together (symphysiotomy), prize the two pubic bones apart, and thus increase the size of the outlet so that the greatly enlarged head could be drawn out below. Although I was without assistance, this was carried out without much difficulty. The two bones were drawn together again and held there by heavy stitches, after which the incision in the skin was closed. The child had probably been dead some time, but the mother's life was saved.

Realizing that this was an unusual case, I made careful measurements of the child's head, which showed that the diameters in all directions were an inch longer than normal and that the bones of the head had become firmly knit together (the sutures ossified), so that they could not be squeezed together as often happens during delivery, thus facilitating passage of the head.

Quizzing the doctor, I discovered that when the patient first went into labor three months before, the pain was so severe that he had given morphia in a dose so large that labor was interrupted and the woman went another month before she went into labor a second time. Again, on account of severe pain, the timid physician had given an overdose of morphia, with identical results. A month later the same thing happened, and when I was called to see the patient she was in labor for the fourth time.

When I returned to Baltimore I found that Dr. Williams, professor of obstetrics at the Johns Hopkins Hospital, was presenting a paper on symphysiotomy before the Baltimore City Medical Society. In the discussion that followed I reported my case of symphysiotomy, to the astonishment of the obstetricians, who, in their extensive practices, had never encountered a similar case.

I had been away from Baltimore about eight months. I was heavily in debt, but I felt that I should not return to my practice until I had been free from fever for a month. It was imperative that I find some way to make money. I had heard a lot about the rich little mining city of Chihuahua in northern Mexico from Dr. Frank Pascal of San Antonio, who had once lived there while chief physician to the Mexican Central Railroad. He had mentioned the fact that there were no qualified surgeons in this town. I wrote to Dr. Pascal and proposed that he and I go to Chihuahua and divide equally the money we made. He replied that he needed a vacation and would be glad to accompany me.

We put up at the Hotel Palacio and sent out cards to all the physicians, on which we frankly stated we were there on a professional visit and were prepared to do surgical work. Dr. Pascal was an expert in removing cataracts from the eyes. He operated upon a prominent woman who had a large hacienda several miles from the city. Under cocaine, cataracts were removed from both eyes successfully. Every afternoon we went out to change the dressings. We traveled in a stylish victoria with two men on the box, who were gaily dressed in the height of Spanish livery with sombreros bedecked with colors, flaring trousers with silver ornaments, and gorgeous jackets.

But we also operated in many a lowly home. In one I removed a large tumor of the breast. As the afternoon light began to fade, a brother was called in to hold the lamp. He fainted, and almost dropped the lamp in the wound. On another occasion I operated in a hovel in the midst of a corral of donkeys who got greatly excited over something and began to bray so loudly that the doctors could not hear each other. For twelve days we were kept busy operating upon rich and poor, having established delightful relations with the medical profession of Chihuahua.

Dr. Pascal at once called upon his old friends, many of whom were men of prominence. They were delighted to see him again, and one arranged a big dinner for us, at which I met many of the physicians of the city and some lovely ladies. Next to me sat pretty Señorita Carmen Gonzalez. As she could not speak English, I was forced to try out on her the meager phrases that remained with me after a short course in Spanish at the University of Virginia seven years before. Most of my conversation with her referred to feminine pulchritude, and I got along fairly well. A night or two later I found myself again seated by the side of Señorita Carmen at a dinner. The same phrases were used, with a few additions I had learned in the meantime. A third, a fourth, and a fifth dinner were given, each time Señorita Carmen being placed next to me. My Spanish was improving considerably.

Carmen and I had got to know each other very much better, and she proved to be "*muy simpatica.*" Our "affair" had not gone beyond a few complimentary remarks, and I had never seen her except at dinner. Imagine my surprise when an American girl who had been present at several of the dinners said: "Dr. Young, I want to have a serious talk with you. These Mexicans have all noticed your marked attention to Señorita Carmen Gonzalez. The family has thought it wise to have a conference concerning the matter, and at this conference, which was attended by the father, mother, uncles, aunts, and the other children, it was decided to ask you what your intentions are. Her uncle, Tio Pablo, has been deputed to interrogate you." I assured her that I had no intentions whatever. I had merely been carrying on a mild flirtation such as any fellow would with a pretty girl he found constantly sitting next to him at the table. She replied: "Yes, I understand, but these Spaniards do not look at these affairs the way we do. Their courtships are always clandestine and through bars which cover the window openings of their low houses, but owing to your presence here with the much older Dr. Pascal you have been admitted into their homes in a way that no other single young man here has, and you have met this girl on terms of greater intimacy. Your evident interest in her has aroused them to take this action, so you may expect a call from Tio Pablo at any moment." I asked, "Is Tio Pablo a huge man who carries a pistol—a man over six feet tall, with a large black mustache and eyes that penetrate one like gimlets?" "Yes, that's the man." "I don't care for that pistol he wears," said I.

I thanked her fervently and hurried back to the hotel. Dr. Pascal was having his siesta. Rousing him rather rudely, I said: "I want to talk to you a moment. It seems to me we have done about all the operating there is to be done in this town, and I think I'll be moving on to Mexico City, which I have been crazy to see for years." Dr. Pascal, rubbing his eyes, remarked: "This is very strange, Young. It is true we have not operated for two days, but surely some other cases will come. Why this sudden desire to leave?" I pretended that I was extremely anxious to see the old Aztec ruins and the volcano of Popocatepetl, and after that wanted to get back soon to Baltimore, where my practice sadly needed my attention. I took the next train for Mexico City, wondering what Tio Pablo would do when he heard of my sudden departure.

Dr. Pascal and I had collected $5,000 in two weeks. With my share I paid off my most pressing debts when I returned to Baltimore and resumed my practice. During my absence my devoted friend Dr. William E. Huger had done my work at the hospital and in my office. He had gone deeply into his own pocket to keep things going. No one ever had a more devoted or self-sacrificing friend than he.

UROLOGISTS may with perfect right be proud of the fact that their branch of medicine is the only one mentioned in the Hippocratic oath. This document, which was promulgated by the school of the father of medicine over three hundred years before Christ, may be rated next to the Scriptures as the greatest of moral commandments. That portion which is particularly interesting to us states:

> With purity and with holiness I will pass my life and practice my art. I will not cut a person who is suffering with a stone, but will leave this to be done by practitioners of this work. Into whatever houses I enter I will go into them for the benefit of the sick, and will abstain from every voluntary act of mischief and corruption; and further from the seduction of females or males, bond or free.

The Development of the Cystoscope

In 1876 Dr. Max Nitze, a urologist of great ingenuity, with the assistance of clever mechanics and lens-makers constructed the first practical "cystoscope" to view the interior of the bladder. A platinum loop in its beak furnished a bright light when heated with galvanic current. To prevent burning the bladder it was necessary to circulate a stream of ice water within the sheath of the instrument, which also carried a lens system through which the operator viewed the interior of the bladder. This was indeed a remarkable instrument to have been constructed sixty-four years ago; it was sufficiently perfect to illuminate and permit inspection of the bladder and to disclose the presence of stones or tumors and blood emerging from the ureteral orifices. Two years later Edison brought out his incandescent light. The Austrians within a short time made a minute electric bulb and placed it in Nitze's cystoscope long before house-lighting by electricity became general in America.

The first cystoscopes were merely for observation. Before long an instrument was made with tubes that would carry small catheters up the ureters to obtain urine from the kidneys; another had a photographic attachment with a plate on which ten successive pictures could be obtained—a veritable bladder Kodak. Another had insulated wires with which tumors could be snared, burned off, and their bases cauterized—all without any external incision and by means of an instrument introduced through the natural urinary passage. These procedures were done under visual control by the operator, who looked into the interior of the bladder by means of a system of lenses that the instrument carried.

Not satisfied with these instruments for the study and treatment of the urinary tract, Nitze extended his inventions to include other external cavities, and even produced instruments with which he could look into the stomach and into the bronchial tubes.

When I took charge of the Department of Genito-Urinary Diseases at the Hopkins, the only cystoscopes there were two crude instruments. Considerable progress had been made in cystoscopy abroad, and I decided to go to Berlin for study and experience. I spent two months at the clinic of Dr. Leopold Casper, who had devised the most practical cystoscope for ureter catheterization. It was not difficult to learn to use his instrument, and I profited greatly by his lectures and the large number of cases I saw at his clinic.

Nitze had devised a retrograde cystoscope with a complicated system of lenses and a mirror to look backward and view the neck of the bladder. It had never been successful, because the mirror became clouded. Working with a lens-maker, I constructed a four-sided prism with which we could replace Nitze's mirror. A cysto-scope constructed with the prism in place gave an excellent retro-grade view of the bladder. Casper was delighted that I had been able to improve an instrument made by Nitze. When I proposed to take it to the father of cystoscopy, Casper said: "Don't do it. He will insult you." Nitze had broken with almost everyone with whom he worked. He brought lawsuits against Leiter, who constructed his first cystoscope, Hartwig, who made several others for him, and Heinemann who had also worked with him. When Casper brought out his catheterizing cystoscope, Nitze had sued him for a large sum. I thought it was my duty to show my instrument to Nitze before returning home and, disregarding Casper's advice, I went to see him.

When I showed the instrument to Nitze, he almost exploded. "This is an old idea and very bad construction. Johann, come here and be a witness to what I tell this American." A rough-looking servant with a black apron appeared and the Professor poured into his ear in vitriolic German what he thought of me and my invention. Finally my temper got the best of me. In very bad German I told him what I thought of him, and there came near being a knock-down and drag-out fight.

Before long the American Surgical Society met at the Johns Hopkins Hospital. I was invited to appear before the meeting in the amphitheater and to catheterize the ureters of a male patient. Dr. Howard A. Kelly was to do the same in a female. Kelly's patient, under deep ether anesthesia, was brought in; she was in the knee-chest position. He introduced his cystoscope, which was an open tube with external illumination from a head mirror, but without lens system. The bladder was distended with air; Dr. Kelly quickly inserted a catheter first up one ureter and then up the other amid the applause of the audience. I was nervous when I brought in my patient, who was not anesthetized. Introducing Casper's cystoscope, I too had little difficulty finding the ureters and promptly catheterized them. The audience had their watches out. The contest was close, and each of us required only two or three minutes.

Improvements in catheterizing cystoscopes were soon made by Albarran in Paris, and then by Nitze, who modified Albarran's ingenious elevator by which the catheter was manipulated. Before

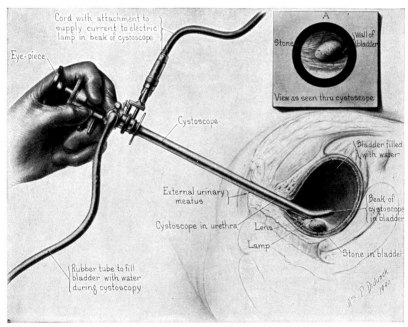

Fig. 1. A cystoscope in the bladder disclosing a stone. The instrument has an outer sheath or tube with a curved beak (inner end) that carries a small electric light with which the field is illuminated. The operator looks through the eyepiece of the telescope and is able to study the interior of the bladder, to watch urine coming down from the ureters, and to pull the instrument out into the urethra to inspect it. Fluid may be introduced into or evacuated from the bladder during the inspection (cystoscopy).

long excellent cystoscopes were being produced by Reinhold Wappler in the United States. He made many instruments for me. One of my design is shown in Fig. 1. It consists of a sheath that carries an electrical wire by means of which the tiny lamp in the beak is illuminated by current that comes through a cord connected with either a battery or a transformer. The telescope contains a series of lenses through which the operator can see the field illuminated by the small lamp in the beak. With the simple telescope, study of the interior of the bladder and urethra can be made. At the same time fluid can be introduced or withdrawn through the stopcocks, which rotate upon the outer portion of our instrument as it is turned around. When one wishes to obtain urine from the kidneys sepa-

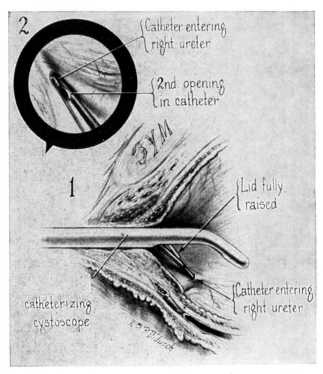

Fig. 2. The catheterizing cystoscope has been introduced into the bladder, and is being used to insert a tube (catheter) into the right ureter to obtain urine from the kidney.

rately, the telescope shown in Fig. 2 is introduced. This provides a space in which tubes or catheters can be introduced, and with the deflector giving them the proper direction, no difficulty is experienced in inserting these catheters up the ureters and obtaining urine separately from the two kidneys. The same instrument can be used to take a bougie (a tapering instrument) of large size through the central tube in the external portion (Fig. 3). With this it is possible to dilate strictures of the ureter and relieve obstructions. In the same

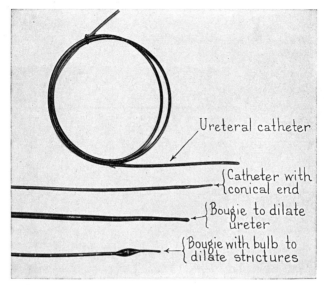

Fig. 3. Flexible instruments (catheters and bougies) that can be passed through a cystoscope into the bladder, and up the ureters

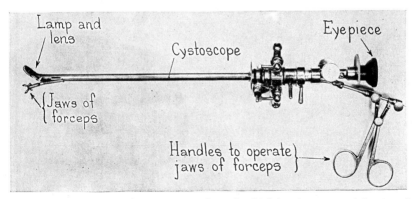

Fig. 4. A photograph of a cystoscope through which has been passed forceps, the jaws of which within the bladder may be opened and closed by handles externally.

way a small forceps (Fig. 4) with a flexible shaft may be introduced to remove pieces of tumor from the bladder for microscopic study.

The Phthalein Test

The phthalein (pronounced thăl'ēn) test is valuable in showing early impairment of the kidney (or loss of function), and the most important test to put the surgeon on his guard in cases in which operations on the prostate gland and certain other operations are contemplated.

In 1884 Dr. Ira Remsen, professor of chemistry at the Johns Hopkins University, discovered a new chemical compound, a purple dye that he called by the formidable name "phenol-sulphone-phthalein." He published an account of it as an interesting chemical product, and then put it away on the shelves of his laboratory. Many years later Dr. John J. Abel, professor of pharmacology, in experimenting with this drug discovered that it was eliminated almost entirely by the kidneys, but he attributed no importance to that fact. In 1909 his assistant, Dr. Leonard Rowntree, at a meeting of the Interurban Surgical Society, asserted that the drug was eliminated more rapidly by a diseased than by a healthy kidney. He demonstrated this on a dog in which, under anesthesia, he had exposed one kidney and injected the renal artery with uranium nitrate, with which he thought he had produced a chemical nephritis (Bright's disease), and then divided the ureter and brought it out upon the skin, where he could collect the urine from it. The phenol-sulphonephthalein was then injected intravenously, and urine from the right kidney collected through the ureter, which had been brought out upon the skin, and that from the left kidney through a catheter in the bladder. It was soon evident that a much larger amount of the purple dye was excreted through the kidney in which the artery had been injected with uranium nitrate than through the other (normal) kidney. After the lecture was over I told Dr. Rowntree that I had a patient with the same conditions presented by the dog upon which he had operated—the right ureter blocked by a stone and all the urine escaping through a sinus in the side—and said it would be a good case in which to repeat upon a human being the experiment just carried out upon the dog.

The following day an intravenous injection of the dye was made into my patient, and a study of the urine from each kidney showed exactly the same result as in the dog. Most of the drug was eliminated with the urine coming through the operative fistula leading to the right kidney and very little through the bladder, which drained only the left kidney. The correctness of Dr. Rowntree's test on dogs seemed to be confirmed. A few days later my patient came down with a fever and a large mass appeared on the left side. It was evident that an abscess was present. At operation the left kidney was found to be greatly diseased, a great sac of pus (pyonephrosis). This discovery showed that Dr. Rowntree's interpretation of the action of the drug was erroneous and that, as a matter of fact, diseased kidneys eliminated the drug in much less quantity than did healthy kidneys. Subsequent use of the drug in other cases proved undoubtedly that such was the case. Another member of my staff discovered a method by which the exact percentage of the drug excreted could be read off on a scale. This made it possible to determine accurately the degree of impairment that kidneys had suffered from disease or back pressure from prostatic obstruction to urination. In an extensive study that was carried out upon my patients by Dr. Geraghty, associate in urology, and Dr. Rowntree, the great value of the phthalein test was demonstrated conclusively. A new method of examining kidneys to determine their functional value or efficiency, of great importance in both surgery and medicine, was thus introduced. With this test it was possible now to detect conditions such as had resulted fatally in my hundred and twenty-ninth case of prostatectomy, elsewhere referred to.

The use of the thalein (we shall spell it thus phonetically hereafter) test proved a lifesaver in the case of the great chemist who had discovered the drug and who had put it aside as valueless. Dr. Remsen had been elevated to the presidency of the Johns Hopkins University, but for a year his health had rapidly declined. His mind became clouded, and it seemed that his days of usefulness to the university had ended. A successor was elected. Soon after this Dr. Remsen came to us complaining of frequency of urination. He had only slight difficulty in voiding, but when a catheter was passed almost a quart of residual urine was obtained, and the thalein test showed that the kidneys had been greatly impaired as a result of back pressure. It was only by the most carefully controlled drainage and the use of large amounts of water to keep the kidneys functioning that death from uremia (poisoning from the urine) was averted. Under this treatment the kidneys steadily improved until the thalein test showed almost normal kidney function. As his kidneys improved, the cloud (uremia) that had obscured Dr. Remsen's brain gradually rolled away and he became mentally alert and physically vigorous. Finally a prostatectomy was carried out successfully. Three very large lobes were removed, and he left the hospital entirely restored in health. He laconically remarked that had he known before what was the cause of his infirmity he would not have resigned the presidency.

Medical history, I believe, furnishes no more remarkable case of personal benefit from a great discovery than the use of phenol-sulphonephthalein in the case of Dr. Ira Remsen. The employment of this test has now spread all over the world, and countless lives have been saved as a result of this remarkable method of determining in exact percentages the impairment of kidneys, and their functional value compared with the normal or with each other.

Dr. John J. Abel also came down with prostatic disease, and the thalein test was very helpful in his case. I was the third of those who participated in the promulgation of the drug to benefit by its use when years ago I had acute nephritis (from which I soon recovered). We have not got Dr. Rowntree yet; Dr. Geraghty is dead.

Enlargement of the Prostate Gland

While still a resident in the hospital, I had become greatly interested in cases of enlarged prostate. By some strange freak of nature, when men pass middle life the prostate is apt to enlarge; indeed, one man in five past the age of fifty has what is known as

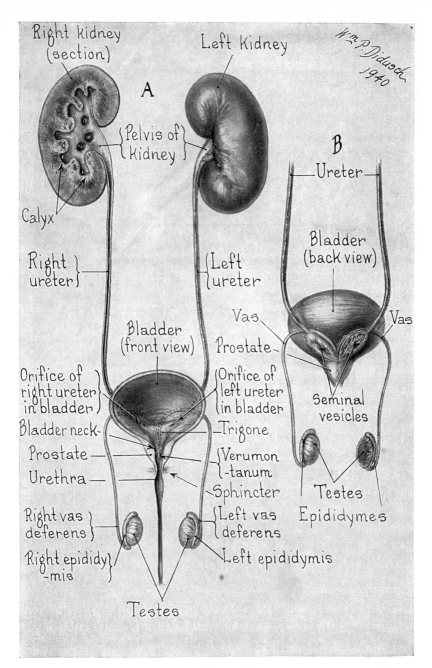

Right kidney (section)

Left Kidney

Wm. P. Didusch 1940

A

B

{Pelvis of} {Kidney}

Ureter

Calyx

Bladder (back view)

Right } ureter}

{Left {ureter

Vas

Vas

Bladder (front view)

Prostate

Orifice of right ureter} in bladder}

{Orifice of {left ureter {in bladder

Seminal vesicles

Bladder neck

Trigone

Prostate

{Verumon {-tanum

Urethra

Sphincter

Testes

Right vas } deferens }

{Left vas {deferens

Epididymes

Right epididy} -mis }

Left epididymis

Testes

Fig. 5. Urinary and genital tracts of the male. Urine is secreted by the kidney substance, from which it passes into each calyx (note that there are six calices) and from there into the pelvis, ureter and bladder. From the bladder the urine passes out through the urethra. The outflow of urine is controlled by contracture of the sphincter muscle below the prostate. Semen is conducted from the testes through the verumontanum to the prostate, where it is ejaculated. In *B* the posterior view of the bladder, the prostate, and the seminal vesicles and vas from each testicle are shown.

95

prostatic enlargement (hypertrophy), which causes obstruction and difficulty in urination.

The prostate is a sexual gland about 1 by $1\frac{1}{4}$ by $1\frac{1}{2}$ inches in size that lies just below the bladder (Fig. 5). Above lie the seminal vesicles, at the inner side of which are the vasa deferentia, the tubes that come down from the testicles, bringing the sperm cells (spermatozoa). The seminal vesicles and the vasa join to form the ejaculatory ducts—two tiny tubes—which lead the secretion that collects in these two structures down into the prostatic urethra through the verumontanum, a highly sensitive, elevated structure that plays an important part in the orgasm at the height of sexual intercourse. The glands of the prostate, which are also stored with secretion, are also emptied into the urethra during orgasm and supply part of the fluid that is poured out (ejaculated).

Fig. 5 shows the entire urinary tract—the secreting kidneys above, the calices (cups), and the pelvis of the kidney, which collect the urine and conduct it to the ureters, small tubes which lead the urine to the bladder, where it collects until it is emptied by the opening of the bladder neck. The urine flows through the urethra to the outside. In Fig. 5 will be seen the relationship between the ureter and the seminal vesicles, and between the prostate and the bladder. This is also depicted in Fig. 6, in which the bladder is shown cut in half.[1]

When the prostate becomes enlarged, there form within it two or three round masses (lobes), which gradually increase in size and flatten the urethra between them (Fig. 7). They often grow back into the bladder in the form of a middle lobe that raises up and obstructs the opening from the bladder into the prostatic urethra (Fig. 8). The bladder becomes thickened from overwork necessitated in forcing the urine through the obstructed orifice, and the interior of the bladder becomes irregular, with small pouches

---

[1] In the text and the legends under the figures the reader will find described and illustrated the important item or items under discussion. Additional details have been added to the drawings for the benefit of those who wish to study all the details.

(cellules). The ridges around the ureters become enlarged (hypertrophy of the trigone). It is impossible for the bladder to empty itself completely, and there is always "residual urine" left at the end of urination.

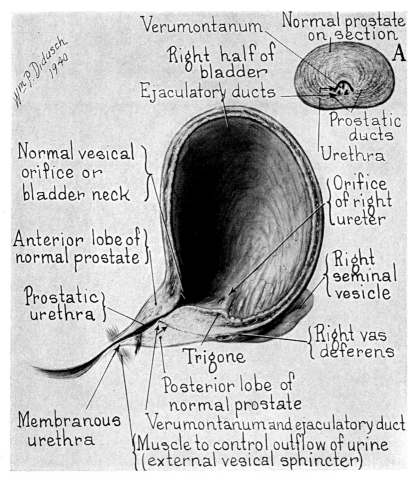

Fig. 6. A section through the median line of the body showing the right half of the bladder, ureter, prostate, and urethra

In Fig. 9 is shown a case of prostatic enlargement that has gone on to the formation of a very large middle lobe that projects far into the bladder and, on account of its great obstruction, has led to the formation of deep pouches (diverticula) that project outside

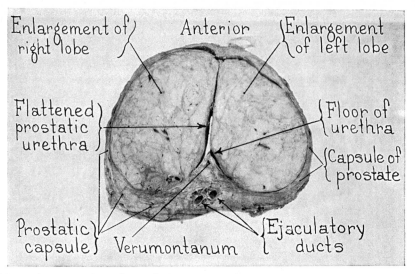

Fig. 7. A cross-section of an enlarged prostate showing the capsule, lobes, flattened urethra, verumontanum, and ejaculatory ducts behind

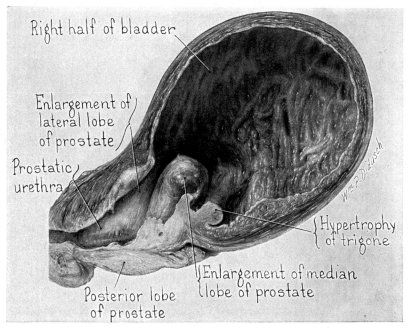

Fig. 8. A section showing the right half of the bladder; the prostate much enlarged, with a middle lobe projecting into the bladder; and the urethra flattened by large lateral lobes (benign growths). The bladder is thickened and the trigone is enlarged (hypertrophy).

the bladder wall. Marked changes also occur in the upper urinary passages. In Fig. 10 is shown a normal kidney split in half. The secreting substance surrounds the pelvis, and its calices collect the urine and lead it to the ureters, through which the urine passes down into the bladder (Fig. 10). In Fig. 11 the changes are shown

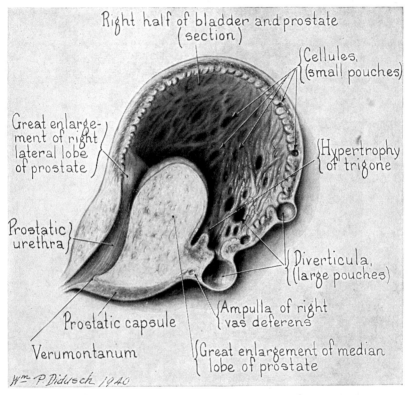

Fig. 9. A median-line section showing the right half of the bladder with a huge middle lobe of the prostate projecting into the bladder, which contains small and large pouches (diverticula) produced by the obstruction to the outflow of the urine through the urethra.

that may occur as a result of long-standing back pressure from an enlarged prostate. The ureter has become greatly dilated, the pelvis and the calices likewise much enlarged, and the secreting substance (the cortex of the kidney) has become thinned and impaired by the obstruction to the outflow from the small tubules that secrete urine.

Enlarged prostate has afflicted elderly men since before the dawn

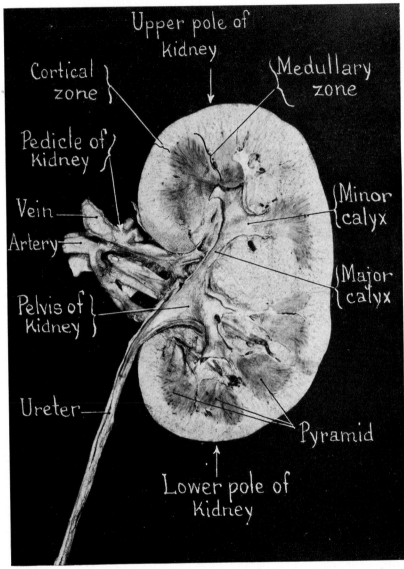

Fig. 10. A section of a normal kidney split open to show the secreting substance (cortical zone) from which the urine passes through tiny tubes (tubules) to each calyx, and from these calices into the pelvis of the kidney and the ureter. The blood vessels that form the pedicle of the kidney are shown.

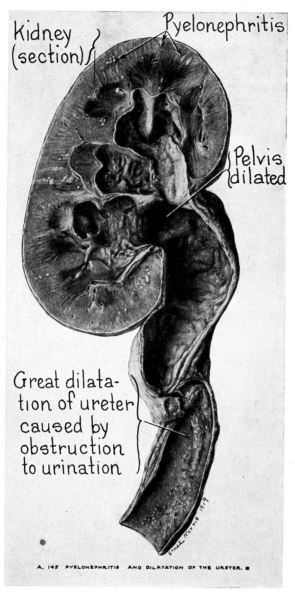

Fig. 11. An abnormal kidney with marked dilatation of each calyx, the pelvis, and the ureter, and thinning of the kidney substance from back pressure due to an enlarged prostate.

of history. One of the greatest difficulties that beset Hippocrates and others among the ancients was the problem of relieving men of these dangerous obstructions to urination. Through the ages medical literature has been filled with expedients to combat this malady. It has long been known that eunuchs do not develop enlargement of the prostate, and in 1893 this was seized upon by Dr. J. William White, professor of surgery at the University of Pennsylvania, as an excuse to remove the testes of men with enlarged prostate to see if this would not restore normal urination. The obstruction was relieved in the first cases in which castration was used. Immediately the fact was broadcast that at last a simple means to combat this ancient infirmity had been found.

However, the beneficial results of castration were only temporary, and in a short time the operation fell into disuse, but not before thousands of testes had been sacrificed.

Removal of the Prostate (Prostatectomy)

About this time a Negro was brought to the hospital in deep uremia, unconscious from the poisoning associated with a severe case of prostatic obstruction. It was impossible to pass a catheter of any type through the urethra into the bladder to draw off the urine, so we made an opening into the bladder by an incision in the lower abdomen and thus provided drainage above the bones of the pelvis with a rubber tube to provide exit for the urine. The result of this drainage was indeed remarkable. In a few days the uremia disappeared, the patient became conscious, and I saw for the first time the amazing good that would come from free drainage of the bladder, allowing free passage of urine from the kidneys that had become impaired by the long-standing back pressure produced by an enlarged prostate.

In a month the patient was so greatly improved that one could consider operative removal of the enlarged prostate that was causing the obstruction to urination. At operation a finger was inserted through the opening into the bladder and found a large rounded mass projecting about three inches into the bladder cavity (Fig. 12).

With the assistance of a gloved finger in the rectum (Fig. 12), it was not difficult to shell out this great mass (Fig. 13) from within the prostatic capsule, thereby removing the obstruction—my first prostatectomy.

The technique employed differed from that of Belfield, McGill, and Fuller, whose operations were often incomplete merely because

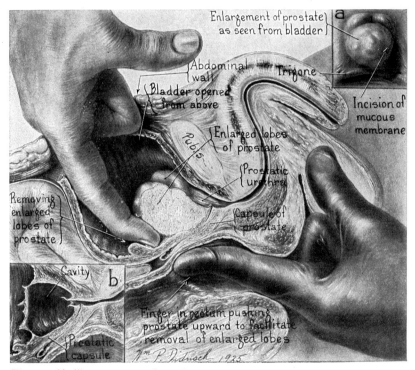

Fig. 12. Shelling out an enlarged prostate through a mid-line incision above the pubis (suprapubic prostatectomy) with the assistance of a finger in the rectum (Young's method).

they had not thought to provide counter pressure against the prostate from below, as I had done with my gloved finger in the rectum, which pushed the prostate up so that it could be shelled out with the other index finger inserted into the bladder above.

The success obtained in this case stimulated me to use the same technique in other cases, and in 1900, at the International Medical Congress in Paris, I was able to give to Ramón Guiteras, of New

York, who was presenting a paper on this subject, a description of my methods and results, which we incorporated in a paper he gave the next day.

Although a rapid and efficient way had been found to remove completely the enlarged prostatic lobes that produce obstruction

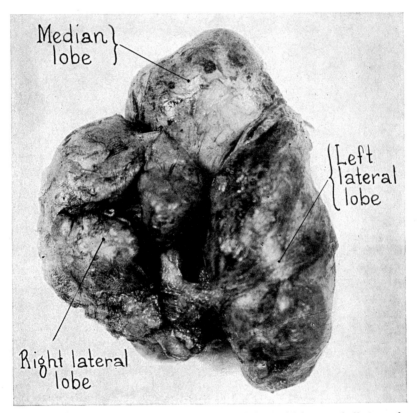

Fig. 13. A photograph of a specimen of enlarged lobes, which were shelled out from within the prostate. The normal prostate still remains

to urination, the mortality was high. In a few cases the bleeding was profuse, and in some the postoperative infection so severe that the patient died.

Improvements in Perineal Prostatectomy

Just at this time Mr. Samuel Alexander came from Hawaii with his daughter, doctor, and nurse. "Doctor, I've read everything I could get hold of on the prostate. I like what you have written and I've come to you for relief, but I honestly think you have not yet got the perfect method. Could you give me something better?" I knew he was right. For some time I had been thinking of trying a new method of attack. I told Mr. Alexander that if he would be willing to wait I would make instruments with which the operation could be done more effectively and safely than ever before. He was

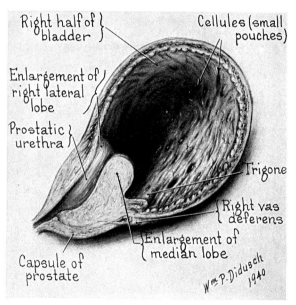

Fig. 14. A section showing the right half of the bladder, and the prostate with moderately enlarged lobes

glad to wait. I went at once to an instrument company and, working at the bench with a machinist, made what I needed.

After showing these instruments to Mr. Alexander I sketched the condition present (Fig. 14). The enlarged middle prostatic lobe projecting up into the bladder and the enlarged left lateral lobe below it. These lobes I proposed to shell out through the perineum, that portion of the body immediately in front of the anus (Fig. 15). I explained to Mr. Alexander by drawings how the enlarged prostate was to be removed, and he agreed to let me carry out the operation.

The operation was carried out as designed on October 8, 1902. Through a curved incision (Fig. 15) in front of the anus, the perineum was opened, the rectum pushed back, the prostate brought into view (Fig. 16), the urethra opened, and the new instrument (Fig. 16 *b*) I had made was inserted, through the opening in the urethra, into the bladder. Turning the curved inner end or beak, which was in the form of a loop, downward (Fig. 17), traction was made upon it by pulling on it with the hand externally. In this way

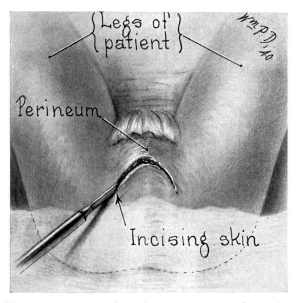

Fig. 15. The curved incision through the perineum in front of the rectum

the enlarged prostate was drawn right down into the wound. It was almost as big as a fist, and beneath the capsule lay the enlarged lobes that I wanted to shell out.

To remove these lobes an incision was made across the capsule (Fig. 16). After passing through normal tissue to a depth of about a quarter of an inch, the rounded enlargements on each side of the urethra were encountered. By inserting the finger, these lobes were easily shelled out from within the capsule of normal prostatic tissue that surrounded them (Fig. 18) and also Fig. 7. Then, with the finger

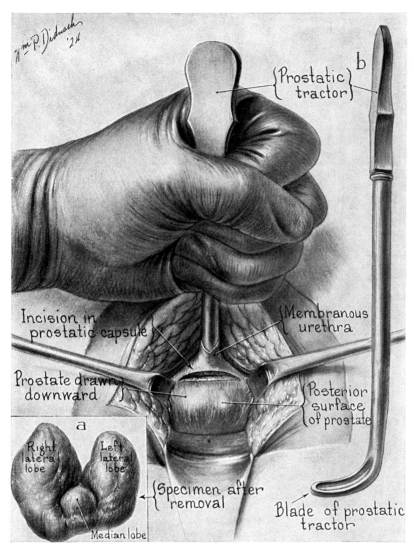

{Prostatic} tractor} b

Incision in prostatic capsule

{Membranous urethra

Prostate drawn downward

{Posterior surface of prostate

a

Right lateral lobe

Left lateral lobe

{Specimen after removal

Median lobe

Blade of prostatic tractor

Fig. 16. An incision has been made just below the apex of the prostate through which the tractor, *b*, has been introduced and used to draw the prostate down (Fig. 17) An incision was made through the capsule, through which a finger was inserted to shell out the enlarged lobes (Fig. 18).

working beneath the middle lobe that projected into the bladder, this was finally shelled out from the mucous membrane of the bladder which covered it, and the whole hypertrophied mass, con-

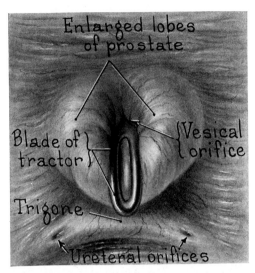

Fig. 17. Interior of the bladder, showing the prostatic enlargement and the blade of the tractor turned down to draw the enlarged lobes to the field of operation (Figs. 16 and 18).

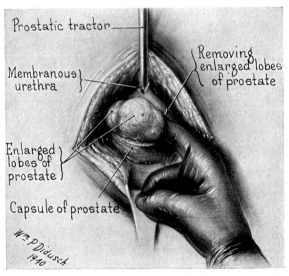

Fig. 18. Shelling out the enlarged lobes from within the prostate (Figs. 16 and 17)

sisting of three lobes (Fig. 19), was drawn out and removed. I had not removed the *prostate*, simply these enlargements which had grown within it, the extraction of which left a cavity within the prostate. This cavity soon contracted, and new mucous membrane eventually covered the defect. With a rubber tube to drain the bladder and gauze packed in to stop bleeding, after a few stitches were inserted the operation was over. It seemed to me that the ideal method had been found to remove enlarged lobes from within the

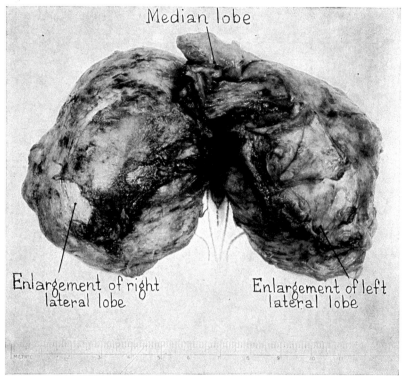

Fig. 19. Lateral and median lobes shelled out of an enlarged prostate

prostate. It was Mr. Alexander's insistence that brought action, and my indebtedness to him is great.

Mr. Alexander met a tragic death. With his daughter and a distinguished preacher as companions he went to Africa. On the bank of Lake Nyanza Victoria he fell, broke his leg, and died of infection. The clergyman died of jungle fever, and Miss Alexander, with supreme courage, brought back their bodies through hundreds of jungle miles.

My new technique was successfully used in other cases, but before long it became evident that the tractor with its single curved open beak was not ideal. It occasionally slipped out at a crucial moment. I then devised a double-bladed tractor, the working of which is shown in Fig. 20. After being introduced and opened out, the two fenestrated blades (open loops) were drawn against the lateral lobes of the prostate (Fig. 21, which is a view from within the bladder). Behind the two rounded lateral lobes is the middle lobe. Farther down the orifices of the two ureters are seen.

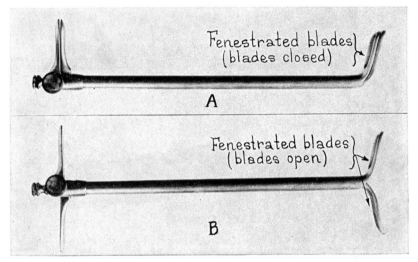

Fenestrated blades
(blades closed)

A

Fenestrated blades
(blades open)

B

Fig. 20. The prostatic tractor closed for introduction (*A*) and opened for traction (*B*) after passing through the urethra into the bladder

During the next fourteen months I had fifty cases without a death, this at a time when Whiteside in a study of the literature reported that the mortality of suprapubic prostatectomy was 20 per cent; and Belfield, the discoverer of suprapubic prostatectomy, was sending out warnings against prostatectomy as a routine procedure and advising a "return to conservative methods—non-operative treatment, the catheter life"—with all its horrors.

In 1908 I presented a paper entitled "Remarks on a Fatal Case after One Hundred and Twenty-eight Consecutive Cases of Prosta-

tectomy without a Death." This paper was on the program of a
select society consisting of about fifty of my intimate friends. I
showed the autopsy specimen and discussed at length the death,
which was due to an unrecognized disease of the kidneys. I pointed
out how, with more careful examination and proper preparatory
treatment, the death could have been avoided. When I sat down,
Dr. E. L. Keyes of New York said, "I too have had a death from
prostatectomy," and sat down. Dr. J. Bentley Squier of New York
arose and said, "I too have had a death from prostatectomy," and

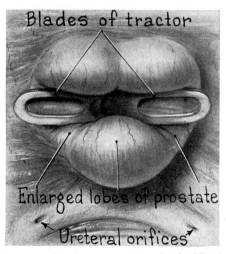

Fig. 21. The prostatic tractor has been opened out in the bladder and is being used
to draw down the prostate

took his seat. Dr. Francis R. Hagner of Washington did the same,
and so did Dr. John H. Cunningham of Boston, Dr. Hugh Cabot of
Boston, and six or seven others. White with rage, I was getting up
to vent my anger when Frank Watson, a dear friend, pulled me
down and said: "Hugh, don't be foolish enough to reply to those
rascals. They got together and concocted that scheme last night on
the train just to torment you. Forget it."

After this death I had another successful period, with one
hundred and ninety-eight consecutive perineal prostatectomies
without a death. The one hundred and ninety-ninth patient, when

almost ready to go home, developed an inflammation of the femoral vein just below the groin on the left side. We kept him quiet, applied ice, and watched him with the greatest care. The entire staff was wrought up over the complications of Case No. 199, and the assistant resident urologist, Dr. E. Clay Shaw, stayed with him night and day. But after six weeks the clot suddenly broke loose and was carried to the heart and lung, resulting in almost immediate death.

Fig. 22. The author's urological operating table. The patient is in the position for a perineal prostatectomy

Minor variations in technique, particularly in the opening of the prostate, the introduction of the double-bladed tractor, and the shelling out of the enlarged lobes, have been tried out from time to time. The method that I now employ is shown in Figs. 22 to 25. The patient is placed on a table that we designed and made in the shops of the Brady Institute (Fig. 22). Through a perineal skin incision (Fig. 15) the muscles are divided, the prostate is incised, and the tractor introduced and opened out. The prostate, which has been drawn down, is then opened widely by an inverted V incision (Fig. 23). This exposes the rounded lateral enlargements within the

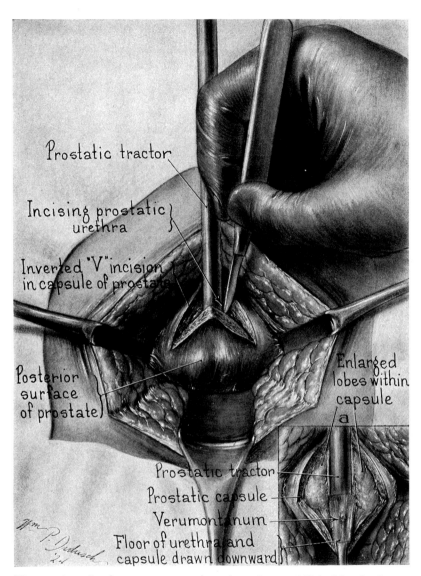

Prostatic tractor

Incising prostatic
urethra

Inverted "V" incision
in capsule of prostate

Posterior
surface
of prostate

Enlarged
lobes within
capsule

a

Prostatic tractor

Prostatic capsule

Verumontanum

Floor of urethra and
capsule drawn downward

Fig. 23. A perineal prostatectomy through an inverted V incision in the prostate. In *a* are shown the enlarged lobes on each side of the urethra in which lies the
tractor. The posterior flap is drawn backward, exposing the floor of the urethra,
and the verumontanum.

prostate (Fig. 23 *a*). By introducing the finger, these lobes are shelled out (enucleated) from within the prostate (Fig. 24). The completion of the enucleation is shown in Fig. 25. The cavity that

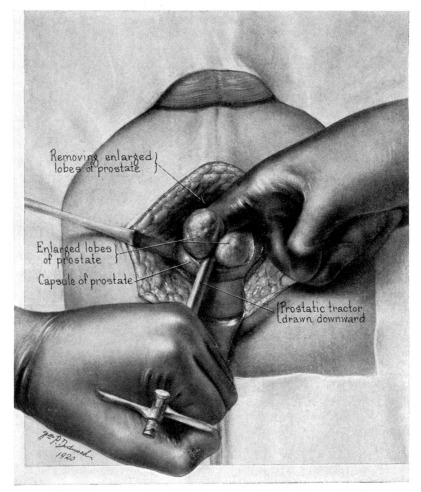

Fig. 24. With the tractor drawing the enlarged lobes down, the finger shells them out

remains is obliterated by passing stitches (sutures) from the capsule through the neck of the bladder. In a short time the prostate is practically normal on palpation and inspection.

One of my perineal prostatectomies was done on Admiral ————, who had suffered so much that he retired from the United States Navy after a splendid record. He was a big, bluff, outspoken, amusing fellow. He carried a large shillelagh, and when I asked him why he used such a bludgeon, he replied: "Because it saved my life one night in Rio. I had been calling on a lovely señorita and was on my way back to the city. A pale moon shone, but there was sufficient light for me to see, as I came to a turn in the road, the gleam of a

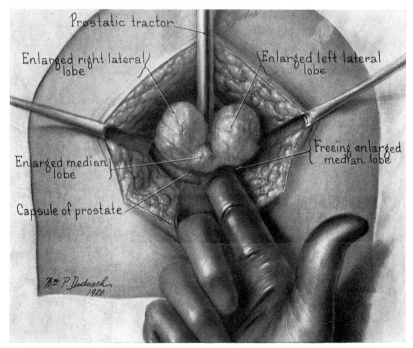

Prostatic tractor
Enlarged right lateral lobe
Enlarged left lateral lobe
Enlarged median lobe
Freeing enlarged median lobe
Capsule of prostate

Fig. 25. The deeper portions of the lateral and median lobes are being freed from the bladder and shelled out

stiletto as her jealous lover lunged forward at me. As usual, I was carrying my cane by the small end, and felled him with a blow on the head. Since then I have always carried this cane, night or day."

One week after his operation I went over to the ward to see a new patient before he was put on a stretcher to be brought to the operating-room. The Admiral was in the corridor. The patient whom I went to get was a member of the United States Senate, and as chairman of the Naval Committee had done much to anger the officers in the service. They accused him of putting a coaling-station on his own property in New England and preventing the imposition of penalties upon an ironworks that had built some cruisers which were not up to standard. As a result he was very unpopular. I saw the Senator put on the stretcher and followed him as he was wheeled out into the hall, past the Admiral in his chair. The Admiral recognized him at once and, calling me to his side, asked if I would like to do a great service for the United States Navy. I asked how in the world I could do anything for the great American Navy, whereupon he said, "You can do a great thing for the United States Navy by killing that old blankety-blank when you get him on the operating-table." The Admiral left before long to spend a few days at the White House as guest of his old friend President Theodore Roosevelt. As he was leaving he said to me: "Doctor, I am going to propose your name for an important commission. I am going to tell Teddy, who is reorganizing the Panama Canal Commission, to put you on it because of the wonderful things you have done for my canal and many other waterways."

Patients with prostatic enlargement are usually elderly or old men. The average age is between sixty-five and seventy. By this time their hearts have often become impaired, and many have chronic disease of the arteries characterized by hardening and often high blood pressure—a combination of cardiovascular-renal disease, as it is technically called. If these conditions are detected and the patient is put under appropriate preparatory treatment, the great majority eventually can be operated upon with fair safety. The following is a case in point.

A patient of seventy-eight came to me in 1928. He had an obstruction due to prostatic enlargement that had gradually increased for four years. Recently the urine had to be drawn intermittently with a catheter because he had almost a pint of residual urine remaining after he had voided as much as possible. For some time the patient had suffered with severe attacks of pain in the region of the heart, and which ran down the left arm. Examination by Dr. Warfield T. Longcope showed enlargement and dilatation of the heart. A diagnosis of angina pectoris was also made, and the patient had high blood pressure. During some of his heart attacks his condition was critical. An operation to relieve the obstruction to urination was imperative, but to prepare him for it he was confined to bed for two weeks, during which he received digitalis as a heart tonic. His cardiac condition improved greatly and the blood pressure decreased, so that finally Dr. Longcope and Dr. E. Cowles Andrus decided that he was improved sufficiently for operation. On December 24, 1928, under ether anesthesia the prostate was exposed through the perineum and the enlarged lobes were shelled out. Convalescence was rapid, and in two weeks the wound was healed. He could have been discharged but for the fact that we realized that his cardiac condition was bad and he needed several weeks' rest. In another week, however, the patient insisted on leaving the hospital to attend a dinner. Following this he had a violent heart attack, fell to the floor, and came near dying. After this he consented to remain in bed for several weeks longer, during which time he received cardiac tonics and supportive treatment. At the end of that time he had improved greatly, and he was discharged cured of his prostatic and bladder trouble and with his heart functioning much better than for years. He led an active life until his death at the age of eighty-five. His heart and blood pressure were greatly improved as a result of removing the prostatic obstruction with its deleterious effect upon the kidneys, heart, and arteries.

In my studies on the prostate I have carefully followed my patients in order to determine the effectiveness of the methods. In a questionnaire I asked the intimate question, "Has the sexual act been different since the operation?" The replies indicated that by our conservative technique there was little or no impairment, even when huge prostatic masses were removed. One patient from West Virginia wrote, "The only difference between now and before operation is that the sexual act takes about five minutes longer, but I don't begrudge a minute of the time."

The "Punch" Operation (Transurethral Resection of the Prostate)

I have already described obstruction to urination produced by prostatic hypertrophy (enlarged lobes), and have shown illustrations depicting the elevation of the bladder neck behind which residual urine remains after voiding.

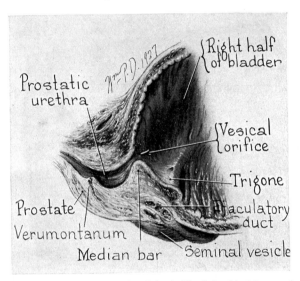

Fig. 26. A median section showing the right half of the bladder, and the prostate with a median bar that obstructs the orifice at the neck of the bladder

In some cases, on examination of the prostate by rectum with the gloved finger, it feels no larger than normal, but when a cystoscope is passed, a bar is seen. Such a bar is shown in Fig. 26, which is a sectional view.

Until 1909 conditions such as these usually were operated upon through an incision into the bladder from above (suprapubic cystotomy), the bar grasped with forceps, and cut away with scissors. Little tissue was excised. It seemed to me that this was a big operation for the removal of so little tissue, and that it ought to be possible to devise an instrument with which the bar could be

removed through the natural urinary passage (urethra) without
an external cut. Some years before I had devised an instrument for
viewing the bladder and the prostatic urethra. It consisted of a tube
with a curved inner end (beak), shown in Fig. 27. Externally was a peg

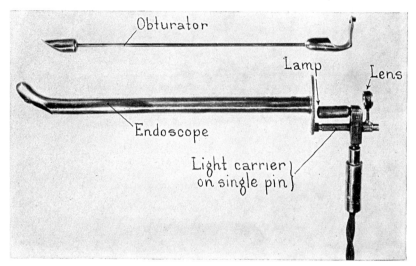

Fig. 27. A urethroscope (endoscope) which is introduced to inspect the urethra

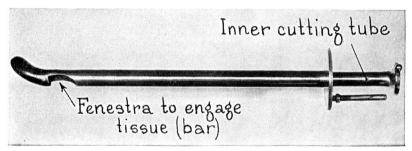

Fig. 28. The author's first prostatic excisor (punch instrument) made by cutting
a window (fenestra) in the urethroscope

on which hung a movable electric light that illuminated the urethra
for inspection. I took one of these instruments to a mechanic, and
had him make a window (fenestra) about half an inch from the end
(Fig. 28) and provide the instrument with an inner cutting tube of
steel that fitted the outer tube snugly.

The first case on which this instrument was used was a man of forty-eight. He had had difficulty on urination for twenty years. After examination I wrote the following note:

"We have here a small median prostatic bar. The symptoms are obstruction to urination and pain. The prostate is not enlarged, and prostatectomy does not seem indicated. I believe it is a suitable case for the new urethroscopic bar excisor that we have just made."

The operation was carried out on April 1, 1909, after an injection of a local anesthetic into the bladder and the urethra. The new instrument was introduced, and a good view of the urethra, illuminated by the external lamp, was obtained. The instrument was gradually pushed inward, the inner end rising up over the bar, which suddenly bulged into the window (fenestra), completely filling the interior. An attempt to withdraw the instrument showed that it was caught by the bar (Fig. 29). The excising tube was pushed home (Fig. 29), and the instrument removed. Within it was a piece of prostatic tissue over half an inch in length, and about three-eighths of an inch in diameter. The patient suffered little pain, and voided urine freely. At the end of six days his condition was excellent, and he left for home. Four years later he reported that the operation had been successful, and he was well.

Two months after this operation was done, I was able to report seven cases in which the same procedure had been used. In some of the cases three cuts were made, each removing a small piece of the obstruction at the neck of the bladder (Fig. 30). I said: "I have a simple and, I hope, a radical method of curing these troublesome cases characterized by median bars that urgently need relief, but for which prostatectomy seems an unnecessarily large operation."

The instrument was also used in cases with enlarged prostatic lobes. In these cases, in addition to three cuts made to remove the bar posteriorly, cuts were made on each side to remove portions of the lateral lobes. In this way several pieces of prostatic tissue were excised. In some of these cases the hemorrhage was more pronounced, and to arrest it I would introduce a cystoscope carrying

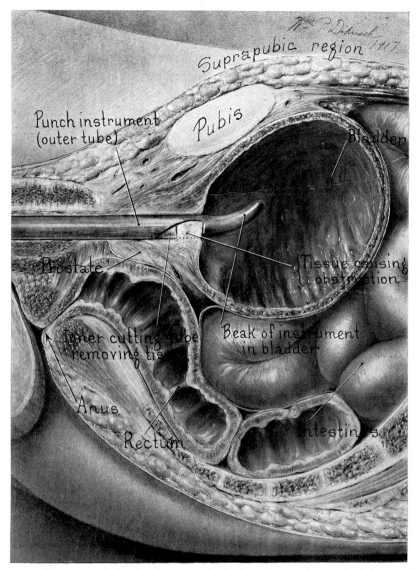

Fig. 29. The prostatic bar has been caught in the window (fenestra) of the punch
instrument. The inner tube is being pushed in to cut out the bar

an insulated wire with which an electric spark was applied to the
bleeding-point. A little later, in conjunction with Dr. Howard L.
Cecil, I reported one hundred and fifty-six cases in which the

"punch" operation had been carried out with the patient under local anesthesia without a single death. The "punch" operation was a forerunner of "transurethral resection of the prostate," the term now usually applied to removal of obstructions at the neck of the bladder by instruments inserted through the urethra.

I shall not attempt to describe the various modifications of my instrument. Transurethral resection of the prostate has been applied to prostatic obstructions and enlargements of all degrees. There are some who are so enthusiastic over prostatic resection with the punch as to use nothing else; they consider the procedure sufficiently

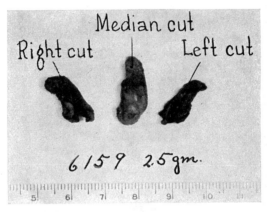

Fig. 30. The prostatic bar that was removed by three cuts with the punch instrument

successful for even the greatest enlargements. It has been argued that transurethral resection of the prostate should supplant prostatectomy, on the ground that it is a simpler and safer operation and the patient is more quickly cured. That such usually is the case, I do not agree.

The wide use of transurethral resection of the prostate is relatively recent, but already many cases have been encountered in various clinics that testify to the incompleteness of the operation, the frequency of infection, prostatitis, painful urination, recurrent hemorrhage, development of more and more obstruction, bladder stones, and other complications. A case in point:

J. H. A., a man of seventy-seven, had had difficulty and frequency of urination ten years before.   Two years later a transurethral resection was carried out without improvement. Two years after the operation a second transurethral resection was done, but the patient continued to have diffi-

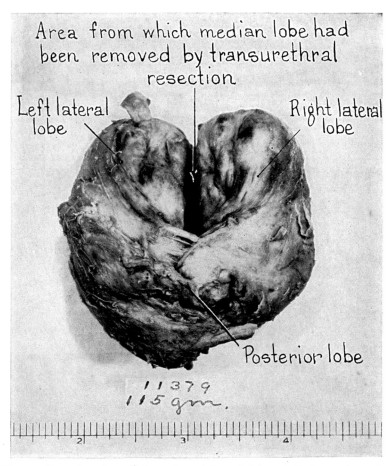

Fig. 31. Posterior view of the enlarged lateral lobes shelled out through the perineum. These great lobes remained after two transurethral resections that succeeded in removing only the median lobe, as indicated.

culty and frequency of urination for seven years, and then suddenly he had a severe hemorrhage. For six weeks before he entered the Brady Institute he had lost so much blood that he was very weak. He had only about two ounces of residual urine, but he had to void every hour or two during the day, and several times at night. He suffered much pain.

Examination showed a prostate greatly enlarged. With the cystoscope it was seen that the middle lobe had been removed by the transurethral resection but the enlarged lateral lobes remained. A perineal prostatectomy was carried out, and a globular enlargement over two and a half inches in diameter was shelled out (Fig. 31). As seen in this posterior view of the specimen, the middle lobe had been removed, but the lateral lobes formed a large round mass about the size of an orange. After shelling out these lobes, the neck of the bladder was stitched with catgut to the remaining capsule of the prostate, thus completely covering the great hole from which the lobes had been removed. In about ten days the wound was healed, the patient was up and about, and completely cured.

As one largely responsible for the development of transurethral operation on the prostate, I would be the last to comdemn this procedure that I have employed so effectively in hundreds of cases, but I am forced to state that such technique is not the ideal in many prostate cases, and shelling out enlargements is the better operation.

Cancer of the Prostate

While I was an intern, a patient came to the Johns Hopkins Hospital, examination of whom showed a swelling involving the large bone (tibia) of the right leg. It was recognized as a malignant tumor, and amputation of the leg was carried out. On microscopic examination it was discovered that the disease was cancer, and as cancer (carcinoma) never develops primarily in a bone, it was realized that it came from some distant primary growth. On examination of the prostate I found that it was very hard and irregular, undoubtedly cancerous, evidently the source of the metastasis (secondary growth of a malignant tumor) that had located in the bone of the right leg.

Several years later, in 1903, after developing the operation of perineal prostatectomy, I encountered in the tissues of two prostates removed a small area of cancer, and I was struck by the fact that had the entire prostate gland been removed with its capsule, it would have been possible to cure both these patients.

On April 1, 1904, an elderly preacher arrived complaining of pain in the prostate, which had not been relieved by a long course of osteopathic treatment. Four months before an electrocautery operation had been performed to remove the obstruction to urina-

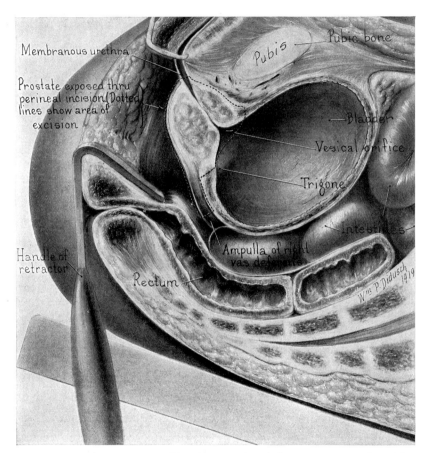

Fig. 32. Cancer confined within the capsule of the prostate, as shown by a median section of the body. The perineum has been opened and is held back by a retractor, exposing the prostate preparatory to its removal. The dotted lines show the extent of the operation to be performed. The membranous urethra is cut across thus freeing the prostate from its connections below.

tion that had developed. On examination with a gloved finger in the rectum, the prostate was found considerably enlarged, irregular, nodular, hard. It was evident that cancer was present, and as the disease had not progressed beyond the capsule, I felt convinced that if an operation were done in which a wide berth was given to the cancer as shown by the dotted lines in Fig. 32, the patient might be cured. Figure 32 is a median section showing the bladder above and the cancerous prostate around the urethra below and projecting only a short distance into the bladder.

The First Radical Operation for Cancer of the Prostate

As a study of the literature revealed that no such radical operation had ever been attempted, I made careful sketches of what I thought would be necessary and showed them to my chief, Dr. William S. Halsted, whose reputation was world-wide because of a very radical operation for cancer of the breast with which he had cured a large percentage of the cases brought to him. After examining the patient, Dr. Halsted carefully reviewed my sketches. He appeared greatly impressed, strongly advised me to carry out the operation, and said he would like to assist.

The operation was done on April 7, 1904. No difficulty was experienced in carrying out the plan of radical removal as designed. Through a curved perineal incision in front of the anus such as was used in our perineal prostatectomy (Fig. 15) the space between the rectum and the prostate was opened up by blunt dissection, and the prostate, surrounded by the capsule, was exposed. An incision was made into the urethra, the prostatic tractor introduced and opened out, and the prostate drawn down into the wound. An incision was then made across the urethra transversely thereby cutting off the prostate from the urethra below. By blunt dissection with the finger and the handle of the knife, tissues all around the prostate were pushed back, and the anterior wall of the bladder was drawn down so that its junction with the prostate was visible and easily opened into. The bladder wound was enlarged on each side, thus exposing the base of the bladder (trigone; Fig. 33) at the upper end of which lay the orifices of the two ureters. The incision was continued across the trigone, the bladder then pushed upward, exposing the seminal vesicles and the right and left vasa, which were picked up with clamps, divided, and tied (Fig. 34). The other vas and vesicle were similarly divided, and the prostate and its capsule, urethra, neck of the bladder, seminal vesicles, and vasa were removed in one piece (Fig. 35). This left a wide-open bladder to be

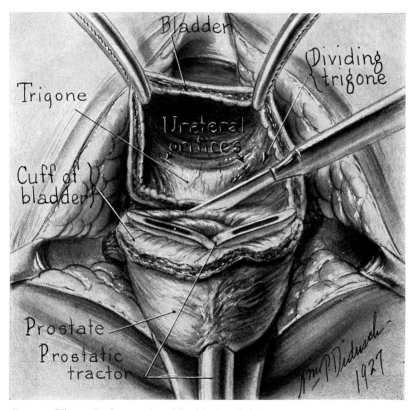

Fig. 33. The radical operation. The bladder has been opened above its junction with the prostate. The trigone is being divided at a point about half an inch below the ureteral orifice.

drawn down and stitched to the stump of the urethra three or four inches below. Owing to the mobility of the tissues, no difficulty was experienced in carrying out this junction (anastamosis; Fig. 36). The remainder of the opening was closed by additional stitches. The defect resulting from the extensive removal of the prostate and the structures above it had been completely closed. With a rubber tube in the urethra drainage was provided, and the skin wound was then closed with drainage. The hemorrhage had been well controlled; there was no shock. The patient had a smooth conva-

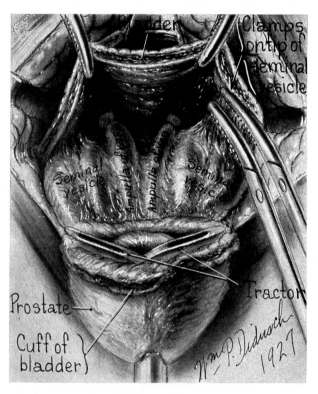

Fig. 34. The radical operation. The ampulla (lower end of each vas) has been divided and tied (ligated), and clamps have been placed above the left seminal vesicle before freeing it by an incision between them. The bladder is held up by clamps to show the field of operation.

lescence, and left the hospital with the wound healed, and voiding naturally, in three weeks.

Within the next year I had done three other cases. The fourth patient had written me about his case, giving the name of John Smith of Los Angeles. When he arrived, I beheld a big, bluff Irishman who had been told he had a cancer of the prostate. He had read everything that had been written on the subject, and catechized me for an hour. He then said he wished to make a correction—that he was not John Smith of California, but John E. Dooley of Salt Lake City, that he had expected after seeing me to go on to see other surgeons in Philadelphia, New York, and Boston, but after our talk he had decided to stay here and was willing to let me carry out my radical operation. He stood the procedure well and left the hospital in excellent condition. He lived in comfort for six and a

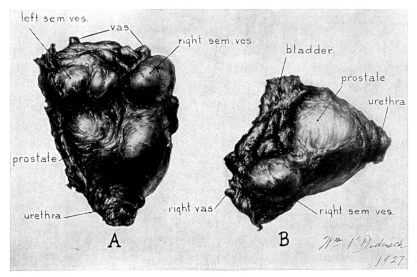

Fig. 35. A. Posterior view of a specimen removed by the radical operation for cancer of the prostate. B. Side view of the same specimen, which includes the urethra, the prostate, and the neck of the bladder removed in one piece with the seminal vesicles and each vas.

half years, then died suddenly of heart disease. Autopsy showed no recurrence of the cancer.

In 1905 I reported in detail the four cases in which I had carried out this radical operation, and the next year published in the *Johns Hopkins Hospital Reports*, Volume 14, a monograph of one hundred and forty-three pages. Here was assembled everything that had been written on cancer of the prostate in this country and abroad, and a complete transcript of sixty-two cases of cancer of the prostate

that had come to our clinic. I cited in detail the cases in which
I had failed to recognize the presence of cancer in patients who

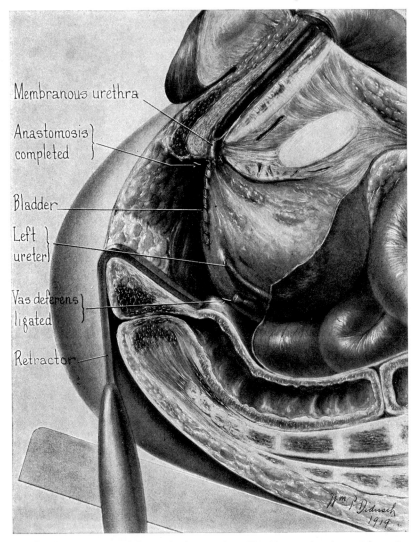

Fig. 36. The last stage of the radical operation. The bladder has been drawn down
and stitched (sutured) to the urethra (anastomosis)

might have been cured. It was shown that a small, hard nodule in a
prostate otherwise normal or the seat of a benign enlargement

(hypertrophy) usually meant cancer; that if one were not sure of the diagnosis, it was his duty to expose the prostate through an incision and inspect, palpate, and, if necessary, cut out a portion for microscopic examination, and then carry out a radical operation if it were cancer; if not, a simple shelling out (enucleation) of the enlarged lobes to remove the obstruction could be carried out.

In December, 1939, a careful analysis of the results obtained by my radical operation for cancer of the prostate was made. With patients in anything like good condition, the operation itself is practically free from danger. Most of the patients are able to void normally even though a great mass of tissue, four inches in length and comprising the entire prostate, the neck and floor of the bladder, and the seminal vesicles, has been removed. Over 50 per cent of the patients followed for five years or more after leaving the hospital were apparently cured of the cancer. Some patients were alive for periods of from twelve to twenty-five years.

These results compare favorably with those of any other operation for cancer of deep-seated organs. If patients could be examined early and if doctors would be suspicious of even small areas or nodules that are hard, many cases of cancer of the prostate would be brought to radical operation and cured. It behooves all elderly men to undergo occasional examinations in which the prostate is carefully palpated.

Some twenty years ago I startled the medical profession by announcing that 20 per cent of the patients who came to me with obstruction to urination had cancer of the prostate. But not until five years ago did anyone realize the very great frequency of such cancer. Arnold Rich, of the Department of Pathology, Johns Hopkins Hospital, announced that in two hundred and ninety-two consecutive autopsies on men over forty years of age, cancer had been found in the prostate gland in forty-one cases (14 per cent). Often the cancer was small, even invisible to the eye, or "occult." Robert A. Moore simultaneously made studies in Vienna, and discovered cancer of the prostate in 18 per cent of two hundred and forty-two consecutive autopsies in all men past forty. These investigators confirmed the pronouncement that I had made many years before—that cancer of the prostate starts usually as a nodule in the posterior portion of the prostate, where it is readily palpable by a gloved finger in the rectum.

Operations for Cancer of the Prostate Too Advanced for Radical Cure

Unfortunately, in many cases the disease is too advanced for radical cure. These patients often have great difficulty, frequency of urination, bleeding, and pain. These cases were often treated by drainage of the bladder with a rubber tube (catheter) inserted through an incision in the lower part of the abdomen. This the patient had to wear as long as he lived, a truly miserable existence.

In 1904 one of the early cases on which I had done my conservative perineal prostatectomy and removed the lateral and median lobes of the prostate turned out to be cancer; but regardless of this, the wound had healed, the patient voided naturally, and lived three and a half years in comparative comfort. He died finally of emaciation from the general spread of the cancer through his system, but without any recurrence of the urinary trouble. The remarkably good result obtained in this and two similar cases showed that this conservative operation could be employed with great benefit in these extensive cases of cancer.

Subsequently, with the introduction of my punch operation by means of which obstructions at the neck of the bladder could be removed from the prostate, many cases of cancer were treated by this transurethral method. Where the disease was not extensive, a simple excision around the prostatic orifice with this simple instrument was sufficient to cure the patients of obstruction. A remarkable fact that was demonstrated in these cases, and in those in which prostatectomy had been performed, was that the mucous membrane of the bladder and the urethra was able to grow over cancer and form an intact new mucous membrane.

With the cautery modifications of my punch instrument and the introduction of the electric resectoscope, in some clinics almost all cases of cancer of the prostate were subjected to this form of transurethral resection. The obstructing masses of cancer of the prostate around the neck of the bladder were cut away with an electrically heated loop while being observed with a telescope that the instrument carried. For a time this was hailed as the operation of choice and a great advance in the treatment of these extensive cases of cancer of the prostate, but I now consider prostatectomy preferable.

Spread of Cancer through the Body from the Prostate

An admiral had been in the Brady Urological Institute just one year while his body and spirit battled with the inexorable invasion of cancer throughout his body. What a brave fight he made! Only two days before his death he said to his wife: "Day after tomorrow will be the anniversary of my arrival here. I wonder where I'll be a year from now?" Strange to say, he never suspected that he had cancer, and his hope of being restored to health was always strong. He had retired three years before, after a brilliant record in the United States Navy, the hero of numerous exploits for which he received decorations and citations. Suffering then with discomfort in the region of his prostate, he was told by his medical examiners that he had simply a little chronic inflammation and needed no operation. He received local treatment for a year, but as the obstruction became great the enlarged lobes, which were interfering with urination, were shelled out through an incision in the lower abdomen (suprapubic prostatectomy). Microscopic examination of portions of the prostate removed showed no evidence of cancer, and the family was told that the case was benign.

Another year passed by, and he came to me with recurrence of the obstruction and pain. Digital examination showed that he was suffering from a cancer of the remaining portions of the prostate, which had already extended so widely that the disease had got into the circulation and localized in the bones of his pelvis and spine.

Radical operation was out of the question, but it was necessary to relieve the obstruction to urination. I carried out a transurethral resection and, by means of an electrified wire loop, obstructing masses were removed from around the bladder neck, restoring normal urination. The mucous membrane healed over the cancerous area and the patient had no more trouble with his bladder during the ensuing year, in which we battled against the spread of cancer throughout his body and tried to keep him comfortable with X-rays. Frequently nausea and vomiting occurred, until emaciation became so great that it was necessary to feed him through intravenous injections of various nutritive substances. He looked with positive pleasure on his venous breakfasts, as he called them. Although he fell away to skin and bones, he was kept fairly comfortable and never lost his courage and spirit. A brilliant raconteur, with the frequent use of droll poetry, he made my daily rounds delightful with such gaiety that it was hard to realize that the end was near. His quips often bordered on the risqué. One day when we were talking of our experiences and discussing the relative virtues of regulars and volunteers, he recited:

> As I was walking down Broadway as happy as could be,
> A lovely girl in a picture hat came up and spoke to me.
> She threw her arms around my neck and whispered in my ear,
> "I don't belong to the regulars; I'm only a volunteer."

And so he passed his days, apparently never suspecting they were numbered. The breakup came suddenly. His body seemed to be overwhelmed by the poison of the disease. He suddenly lost consciousness. His cheeks fell away, his splendid upturned mustachios drooped over his saffron chin, he passed into a deep coma, and died.

My interminable interest in the prostate, and my propaganda for the early radical operations in cases of cancer, finally led Dr. Edward L. Keyes to compose some amusing verses on me entitled "The Surgeon and the Senator," and to remark, "The prostate makes most men old, but it made Hugh Young."

Traumatic Rupture of the Prostatic Urethra

Soon after I started to practice in Baltimore I had an emergency call to see a patient who had been caught between two freight cars, fracturing the bones of his pelvis. He was in a cabin at the yards of

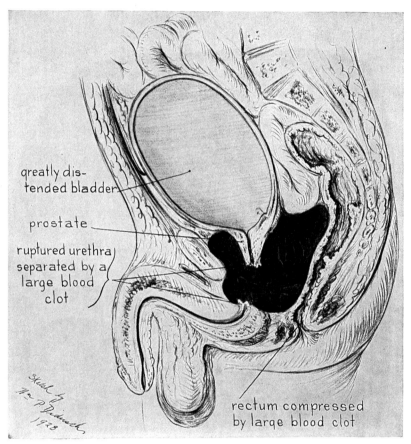

greatly dis-
tended bladder

prostate

ruptured urethra
separated by a
large blood
clot

rectum compressed
by large blood clot

Fig. 37. A median section showing the prostate torn away from the urethra

the Baltimore & Ohio Railroad outside the city. The accident had happened twenty-four hours before, and the patient had not passed urine since. A distended bladder the size of a large cantaloupe was palpable in the middle of the abdomen. Examination showed that the prostate had been torn off from the urethra (Fig. 37). A catheter that was passed through the urethra evacuated blood. With a gloved finger in the rectum the prostate could not be felt, but the fractured bones of the pelvis were palpable on each side and, above them, a great accumulation of blood (Fig. 37). An operation to repair the ruptured urethra was necessary. He could not be moved, and the operation was done in the cabin. An intern I had brought with me gave the anesthetic and, working alone, I cut through the perineum and evacuated a pint or two of blood. I could see the ruptured end of the prostatic urethra at least four inches above its normal position. By grasping it with toothed forceps it was easy to draw it down to its normal position (Fig. 38). A catheter was introduced, and evacuated about a quart of urine (Fig. 38 *a*). This catheter was then withdrawn, and another one was passed through the urethra and continued on up through the rupture at the apex of the prostate into the bladder. Urine began to flow at once and another quart was evacuated. Without much difficulty stitches were placed around the catheter to hold the prostate in its normal position (Fig. 38 *b–c*). The approximation of the two ends of the ruptured urethra was satisfactorily obtained. In ten days it was possible to withdraw the catheter that had been left in place to drain the bladder, and the patient voided naturally. He was confined to bed for several weeks on account of the fractured pelvis, but eventually was able to walk normally, and urination was perfect.

A few months later he appeared at my office with his pretty young wife and a lawyer. He was suing the railroad company for $10,000 because the accident had deprived them of their marital relations. I was asked to testify. I got an artist to prepare large colored charts showing the anatomy and physiology of the urinary and genital tracts. These charts showed the blood vessels and nerves that had been ruptured when the bones were fractured and the urethra torn across. The wife gave a frank recital of the changed conditions. I was called to the stand and explained in detail my charts, which were hung around on the walls of the courtroom, and pointed out how the lack of nerve and blood supply to the organs below was responsible for the plaintiff's sad condition. Apparently such anatomical exhibits were rare, and the courtroom rapidly filled to overflowing. The jury evinced great interest and one juror, while

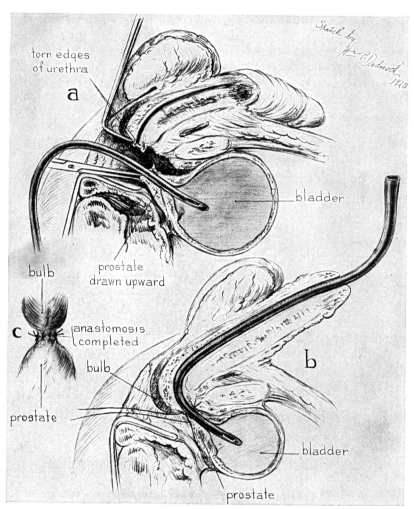

Fig. 38. The details of the operation to draw down the prostate and bring together the two ends of the ruptured urethra. *a.* A catheter has been introduced through an incision in the perineum to empty the bladder. *b.* A catheter has been introduced into the urethra and on into the bladder. Around the catheter the ruptured ends of the urethra are sewn together. This approximation (anastomosis) is shown completed in *c.*

craning his neck to see one of my charts, fell out of the box. On being questioned, I said I thought that $10,000 was too little for the loss of one's sexual power. Had the decision been left to the jury, I have no doubt that the case would have been decided in the plaintiff's favor. Unfortunately, the judge took it from the jury on the ground that the accident was due to "contributory negligence."

Congenital Valves of the Prostate

On November 11, 1912, a youth of seventeen came complaining of difficulty of urination since birth. He was thin, pale, and sallow. Palpation of his lower abdomen showed the bladder distended, and when a catheter (rubber tube) was passed, a pint of residual urine was obtained. A cystoscope was introduced with difficulty, and disclosed two thin valvelike membranes in the prostatic urethra which had caused so much obstruction that the bladder could not empty itself, and the ureters were greatly dilated. The passage of a cystoscope ruptured these valves, and the patient was relieved of the obstruction.

Another patient arrived with the same condition, but the obstruction produced by the valves had so greatly impaired the kidneys that the patient died in a few days of uremia. Autopsy showed the valves (Fig. 39) springing from the verumontanum in the posterior urethra. The kidneys and the ureters were greatly dilated.

It is remarkable that before my case this condition had not been recognized in the living, and that no operation had been done to remove these valvular obstructions.

Before long another child appeared with obstructing valves. For this case I prepared a tiny prostatic punch, similar to the instrument that I had devised for removing bars and other obstructions at the neck of the bladder in adults (Fig. 28). The instrument was used as shown in Fig. 40, which is a median-line section. One valve is shown in the middle of the prostatic urethra. Above it the dilated bladder neck and the ureter are shown. In *b* the little punch has been introduced, and the inner cutting tube withdrawn, opening the fenestra (window) on the posterior aspect.

The instrument was then rotated to the right, and drawn outward, thus entrapping the valve that was caught in the fenestra (Fig.

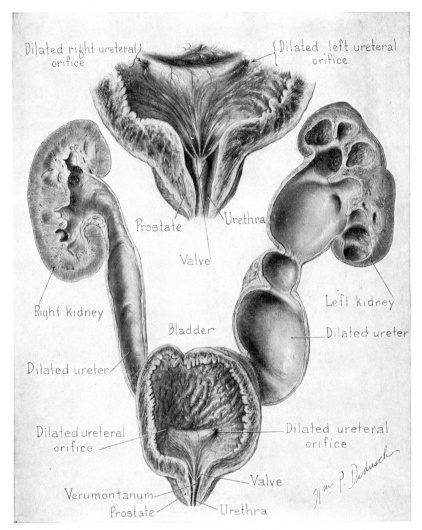

Fig. 39. An autopsy specimen from a child. This shows valves in the prostatic urethra causing obstruction that led to great dilatation of the ureters and the kidneys.

40 *c*). The valve was cut away by pushing the inner cutting tube home. In *d* the result is shown; the valve has been removed.

In November, 1913, I reported three cases cured by my instrument—the only cases in which this condition had been recognized in the living. In 1937 I reported thirty-two cases operated upon without a single death. All these had been cured either by the punch instrument or by destruction of the valves with an electric cautery wire through a urethroscope.

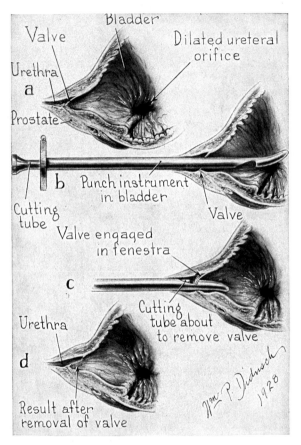

Fig. 40. A small punch instrument devised to catch valves and remove them

This important condition, unfortunately, is still rarely recognized. The babies so afflicted usually die with a diagnosis of unexplained uremia, which could be cleared up by simply trying to pass a rubber-tube catheter. This would be arrested by or caught in the membranous valves, which could then be destroyed easily in the way I have described.

Obstructive Bar within the Bladder (Hypertrophy of the Trigone)

A patient from New Brunswick, Canada, had undergone four operations on the prostate and the bladder in London by the noted Sir Peter Freyer, but without relief. Freyer had first performed a

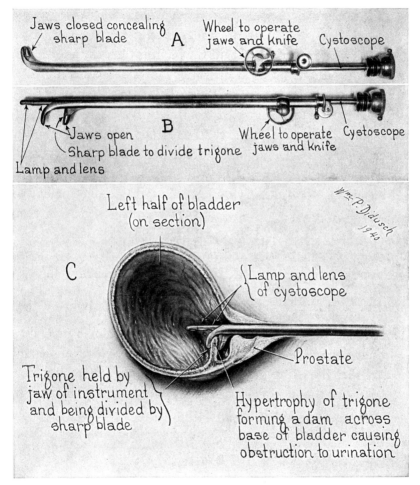

Fig. 41. C. A transverse bar in the bladder that obstructed the outflow of urine. A–B. An instrument that we devised to grasp and divide this bar

prostatectomy and shelled out enlarged lobes, but the patient still could not void. The three other operations upon bladder and urethra failed to detect the cause of the obstruction or to relieve it. He still

led a "catheter life." On cystoscopic examination I found a remarkable condition—a bridge across the base of the bladder (Fig. 41)
in the form of a hypertrophied trigone that stood up almost one
inch high behind the bladder orifice. Although no operation had at
that time been done for such a condition, I told the patient I felt
sure that if this bridge were freely divided, the obstruction would
be removed and he would be cured. He refused to submit to any
more cutting operations, and said that unless the obstruction could
be removed without an open operation he would prefer to remain
as he was.

I told the patient I believed I could design a cystoscopic instrument with a concealed knife that could be introduced into the
bladder, and with it divide the great bar without any external
operation. He said he would be willing to have such a procedure
tried on him. I worked with a mechanic, and the instrument was
soon completed (Fig. 41). No difficulty was experienced in seeing
the bar, separating the blades, and grasping and dividing the bar
completely. In a few days the patient was voiding naturally. He
has never since required the catheter and has remained well.

Tumors of the Bladder

Next to stones, tumors are among the most common maladies of
the urinary tract. Unfortunately, they are apt to develop so in-
sidiously that they may grow to considerable size before any symptom arises. The first thing noticed by the patient usually is the
presence of blood in the urine. Sometimes only a small clot is passed,
but at others frank hemorrhage occurs. Blood may appear once
and not recur for a long time, during which the tumor may grow
apace and become inoperable. It is on this account that whenever
one finds blood in the urine a careful study should be made to determine where it comes from and the character of the lesion that
produces it. Until the perfection of the cystoscope, the most remarkable of diagnostic instruments, this was mere guesswork.
The older physicians often were unable to tell whether the blood in

the urine came from the kidney, the ureter, the bladder, the prostate, or the urethra—unless definite localizing symptoms or signs arose. Operations usually were performed late, and cure was relatively infrequent.

The treatment of bladder tumors was entirely in the hands of the operating surgeon. A wide incision was made in the mid-line of the abdomen, the bladder opened, and the tumors removed with a burning cautery or scissors.

At a meeting of the German Congress of Surgery, a general discussion of the results obtained in the treatment of bladder tumors was held. One surgeon after another acknowledged failure in most cases, recurrences, and death from invasion of other organs. Nitze then presented an amazing series of cases that he had cured with his operating cystoscopes. Guesswork having been removed, the diagnosis was made early, and with his cauteries and snares he had been able to destroy tumors before they had developed into invading cancers.

Ingenious as Nitze's inventions were, their use was difficult, even in his own hands. There was no general adoption of his methods. In the meantime, a French urologist, Oudin, had developed the high-frequency current for the treatment of small tumors on the surface of the body. This invention is particularly important, because it laid the foundations for modern wireless and radio.

Working in New York was another great inventor of cystoscopic apparatus, Reinhold Wappler. In 1910 he discovered that the high-frequency current of Oudin would produce a spark under water with which tissue could be destroyed. In describing his experiments he told me how he had frequently used this upon a piece of meat immersed in a basin of water. Finding that he was able to burn it up with the electric spark, he brought this observation to the attention of Dr. Edwin Beer and Dr. E. L. Keyes, Jr., and suggested that it might be applied effectively to destroy bladder tumors by means of an insulated wire that could be passed through one of his cystoscopes. In a short time Dr. Beer and then Dr. Keyes published reports of cases of bladder tumor that had been completely cured by means of "fulguration"—sparking with the high-frequency current of Oudin. These publications were of great value and the methods were soon adopted the world over, furnishing a simple means for the cure of many bladder tumors, hitherto very intractable.

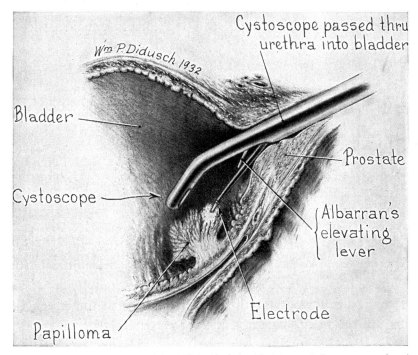

Fig. 42. A sectional view of the left half of the bladder and the prostate showing the destruction of a bladder tumor (papilloma) by an electric spark that is carried by an electrode.

Fig. 42 shows the use of this electric spark upon a tumor (of a type known as papilloma) of the bladder, and the destructive effect of the treatment. With the methods of Drs. Beer and Keyes, cystoscopists were able to destroy many tumors of large size without resorting to open surgery, but many tumors failed to respond and eventually showed evidence of cancerous invasion of the bladder.

In 1913, at an International Congress in London, Pasteau and Degrais reported that the introduction of radium into the bladder through a simple rubber tube had resulted in the arrest of cancer of the bladder and the prostate. Returning to Baltimore, I secured 100 milligrams of radium, only about one-half inch long and the thickness of pencil lead, which at that time cost $12,000. Inserting it into

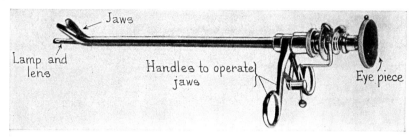

Fig. 43. The author's cystoscopic bladder forceps (rongeur) for removing foreign bodies and pieces of tumors

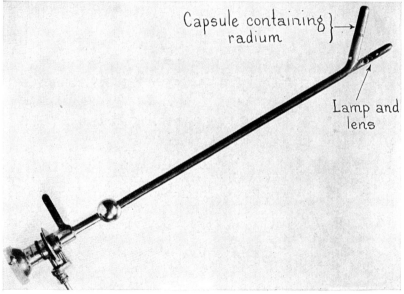

Fig. 44. The cystoscopic radium-applicator for treating tumors in the bladder

a rubber catheter, I introduced it into the bladder to treat cancerous conditions. It soon became evident that this method was very inaccurate. One could not tell just where the catheter lay. Using the same straight cystoscope with which my bladder forceps (Fig. 43) was equipped, it was easy to construct in the machine shop of the Brady Institute a radium-carrier that contained the tube of 100 milligrams in its beak (Fig. 44). After this instrument was introduced the cystoscope was pushed out so that the bladder could be inspected, the tumor located, and the radium brought against it by manipulation of the external handle (Fig. 45). An adjustable clamp fastened to the table caught the bulbous enlargement of the instrument and, gripping it tightly, held the radium close against the tumor.

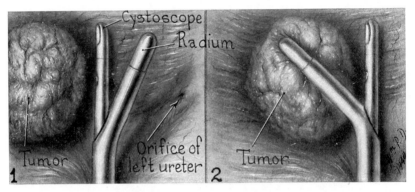

Fig. 45. While being observed through the cystoscope the beak that carries the radium is placed against the tumor in the bladder

No difficulty was experienced in making such applications over the period of an hour with only moderate discomfort to the patient. In a short time, definite results were being secured. With the high-frequency current the tumor was thoroughly sparked to destroy as much as possible, and then, with my cystoscopic instrument, a number of applications of radium were made. These hastened destruction of the tumor, and carried the treatment deep into the adjacent tissues. The advantage of radium was that while the tumor was markedly affected and disappeared, there was little effect on the normal tissues. With this combined use of electrical sparking and radium applications I was soon able to report a series of cases that had been cured by these methods.

In the meantime it was found desirable to make radium applications within the prostate and also by rectum. Here no cystoscope was necessary, and a simple applicator (Fig. 46) was designed that could be passed into either urinary or intestinal tracts, placed in the desired position, and held there by a clamp fastened to the table. The applications of radium to bladder tumors could thus be supplemented by radium therapy to the base of the tumor, applied

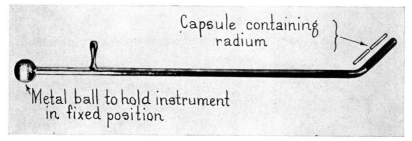

Fig. 46. An instrument that carries radium in its beak but has no cystoscopic attachment. It is used to introduce radium into the rectum or the urethra

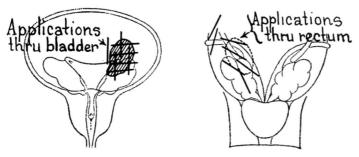

Fig. 47. The method of charting applications of radium that are made within the bladder and with the applicator that is introduced through the rectum

through the rectum. Fig. 47 shows the recording of the applications made with the cystoscopic radium applicator and the rectal applicator. This crossfire attack with radium upon tumors soon showed its efficiency in even more malignant cases.

Before long it became evident that my cystoscopic applicator was not well suited to applying radium against tumors well out on the lateral walls of the bladder. In our shops we then produced another instrument, which, operated by an external screw, opened out like a parallelogram. The use of this instrument on a tumor on the lateral wall of the bladder is shown in Fig. 48. For the posterior wall, still another type appeared desirable. I designed a model in which the radium could be brought transverse to the beak (Fig. 49). By these instruments it was possible, after locating the tumor with the cystoscope, to apply radium in any desired position. The clamp attached to the table held it in place, usually for one hour.

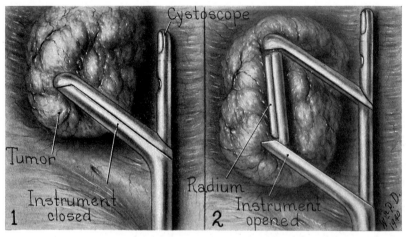

Fig. 48. Young's cystoscopic radium-applicator No. 2. The radium has been applied to a tumor on the side wall of the bladder

Generally, four to eight applications of sixty minutes each were given.

Regardless of the good results that I had obtained with my limited amount of radium, the desirability of making more intensive treatments with larger amounts was constantly before me.

In 1916 I was spending the summer with my family on a ranch in Colorado. We had frequently gone West, for roughing it was good for all of us and learning how to ride and care for their mounts was good for the children. At a polo match I met Mr. L. M. Hughes, the president of the Chemical Products Company of Denver, Colorado, who told me of their production of radium from a carnotite ore, which I believe was then to be found only in Colorado. The process of extraction was exceedingly difficult and it took many carloads of ore to produce a gram of radium, which at that time was valued at more than $100,000. One of their chemists, he said, had discovered a new process of extraction, but to make the installation to produce radium in quantity would entail an expense they could not afford. I told him of the remarkable results we had obtained with radium and of my desire to acquire more of the element. He said

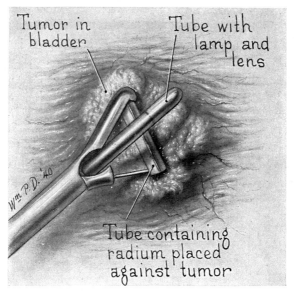

Fig. 49. The transverse cystoscopic radium-applicator

that their estimates indicated that for $35,000 they would be able to equip their plant for quantity production of radium, and if I would advance that amount, he would guarantee me the first gram of radium produced. To get this much-needed therapeutic agent at a little more than one-third of the market value was so appealing that I agreed. Numerous delays occurred, and when I went to France during the World War no radium had been produced, but the company reported that the prospects were good. Engrossed in my work in France, I thought nothing further of it until early in

1918 a cable from Mrs. Young said that a gram of radium had been produced by the Chemical Products Company of Denver, Colorado, and that the British Government was anxious to buy it, as they had great need for radium to be used for special gun sights for night firing, particularly for the big guns that were replying to the "Big Berthas" of the Germans. They offered $50,000. Although this was only one-half the market value, I was anxious to aid the British and needed the money, so I cabled my acceptance.

In certain cases, where the tumor is malignant (cancerous) and invades the bladder, surgical excision through a wound in the lower abdominal wall is often advisable. When the tumor is on the posterior part, it is often advisable to excise a large area around the tumor, with the bladder muscle and also the peritoneum that covers the bladder behind. This operation previously has been done through a large incision into the abdomen, but I have devised a method by which it can be done entirely through the bladder (Fig. 50). As seen in the illustration, clamps have been placed on the mucous membrane at a distance of almost an inch from the tumor. An incision is then made through the bladder wall opening into the peritoneal cavity (Fig. 50). This incision is continued with scissors until the entire area surrounding the tumor, with the peritoneal covering, has been removed in one piece. The opening in the peritoneum is closed by a continuous stitch (Fig. 50). The mucous membrane and the bladder muscle are closed in the same manner. With this operation it is possible to do a radically curative procedure at one séance.

With the assistance of Dr. W. W. Scott and Dr. R. W. McKay we presented a detailed study of five hundred and thirty-four cases of bladder tumor in which these modern methods were employed. A series of intricate tabulations describing the treatment and results were published in *Young's Practice of Urology*. Suffice it to say that simple mushroomlike tumors with no cancerous tendency were sometimes cured by the electrical spark alone. Others required radium.

Recently Walter L. Denny and I have published reports of cases of malignant tumor of the bladder that have been followed from five to fifteen years with no recurrence. The treatment consisted of

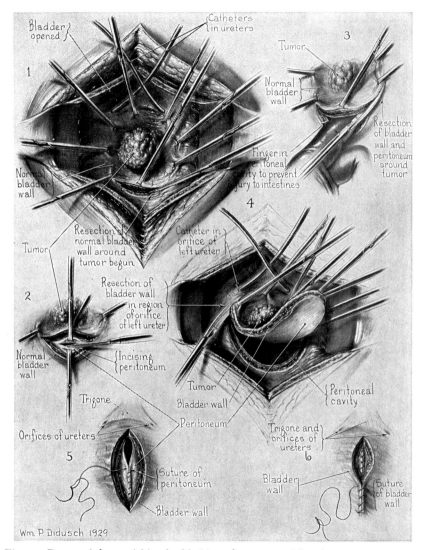

Fig. 50. Removal from within the bladder of a tumor with a large area including the entire thickness of the bladder wall and the peritoneum covering it

destruction of the tumor with the electric spark and applications of radium with our cystoscopic instruments. These cases demonstrate apparently conclusively that these cystoscopic methods give a larger percentage of cures in many types of malignant disease of the bladder than are effected by extensive surgical operations.

Pouches (Diverticula) Connecting with the Bladder

Bladder diverticula (pouches) are among the most serious complications associated with prostatic obstruction. In my early days

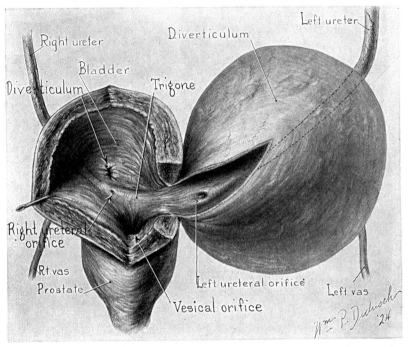

Fig. 51. An autopsy specimen. An opening has been made into the front of the bladder and into a diverticulum

at the Johns Hopkins Hospital I obtained an autopsy on a patient who had died as a result of the destruction of his kidneys by the obstruction to the ureter produced by the diverticula. The condition present in one of these cases is shown in Fig. 51. The bladder has been opened in front, and on the left side, exposing a large pouch (diverticulum) into which the left ureter opens. Behind the right ureteral orifice is the opening of another pouch.

Realizing that these patients could be saved only by operative removal of the diverticula, on February 10, 1904, I opened the

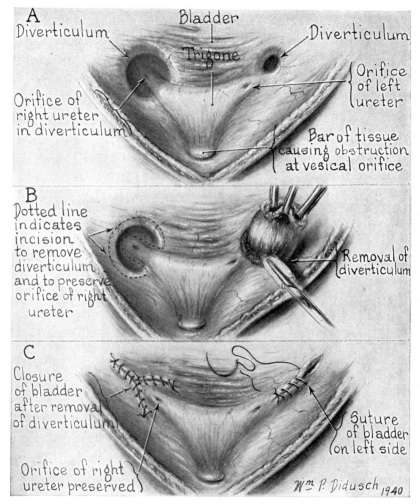

Fig. 52. The operation for bladder diverticula (pouches), showing (*B*) the removal of the diverticulum on the left side. In *C* the orifice of the right ureter has been drawn back into the bladder during the closure of the wound.

bladder in the mid-line of the abdomen to attack two pouches that had been seen with the cystoscope, and into one of which the right ureter opened (Fig. 52). The condition present is shown in Fig.

57 *A*. As seen here, back of the orifice of the left ureter is the small opening of a pouch. On the right side there is a much larger opening leading into a pouch of considerable size, in the wall of which lay the orifice of the ureter (Fig. 52 *A*). At the prostatic orifice was a bar obstructing free urination and probably responsible for the development of the pouches. An incision was made around the orifice of the left diverticulum and it was then shelled out (Fig. 52 *B*). If the same technique had been employed on the right side, I would have removed the ureter with the diverticulum. It occurred to me that this could be avoided by running the line of incision around the ureter in the diverticulum, thus preserving it when the pouch was dissected out (Fig. 52 *B*). The opening of the smaller one was closed with stitches in a straight line. The opening of the larger was closed in the form of a Y (Fig. 52 *C*) so that it drew the flap containing the orifice of the ureter back into the bladder to its normal position. The bar obstructing the prostatic orifice was then divided by the electrocautery knife in order to provide free urination. The patient made an uneventful recovery, and was cured.

A search of the literature disclosed only four reports of operations that had been done for these bladder pouches: one diverticulum had been removed in Paris nine years before through the vagina; two had been removed in Germany by dissections outside the bladder; and the fourth had also been operated upon in Germany by an incision around the rectum. One of the four died, and in one the wound never healed. In one of the cases in which the ureter opened into the pouch it was cut off and transplanted instead of being drawn back into the bladder and preserved in its entirety, as I had done. The ease with which these two pouches had been removed in my case and the success obtained led to my using the same technique in many other cases. In one of these cases in which the X-ray (Fig. 53) was taken after the bladder had been filled with a 12 per cent solution of sodium iodide (which shows a shadow with the X-ray), the bladder on the right and the pouch on the left are both connected by a narrow opening. By inserting a large glass tube and applying powerful suction the pouch was drawn into the bladder (Fig. 54), thus turning it inside out. With an incision around its neck, the sac was easily stripped off, and the opening was closed (Fig. 55).

In 1939 Dr. John E. Dees made a careful study of all the cases in which pouches had been removed—diverticulectomy—on our

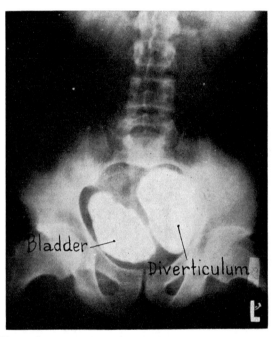

Fig. 53. An X-ray that was taken after the bladder was filled with a solution of sodium iodide. Although it is transparent, the sodium iodide throws a shadow denser than bones. The narrow opening that leads from the bladder to a large diverticulum on the left side is seen.

service. There were ninety-five cases. In a third of the cases, the diverticula had developed before the age of prostatic enlargement, and one patient was only ten years old. Two-thirds of the cases were definitely associated with obstruction due to prostatic enlargement. In some the pouches may have been congenital—present before birth—but in the majority the condition came on in later life as a result of obstruction at the bladder opening into the prostate.

In many cases the pouch had so greatly impeded the outflow of urine from the ureters into the bladder that serious kidney disease was present. This was largely responsible for the eight deaths that

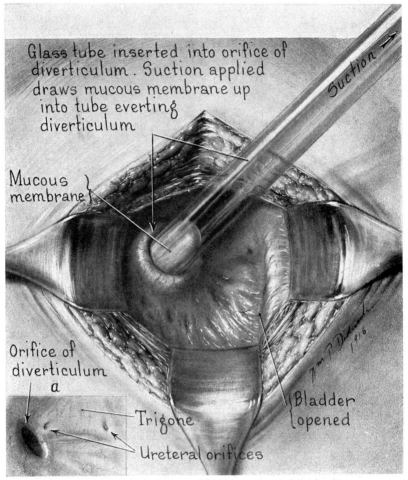

Fig. 54. Author's method of applying suction through a glass tube in a diverticulum to draw it into the bladder. In *a* is shown the orifice before the tube is introduced.

followed operation. Without operation many more would have died promptly. Seven times we were able to use my method of bringing the ureteral orifices from the pouch into the bladder after excision of the pouch, and in only one case was it necessary later to transplant

the ureters into another part of the bladder because of severe strictures in the ureters. In many of these cases the pouch was larger
than the bladder itself, and being filled with decomposed urine, was

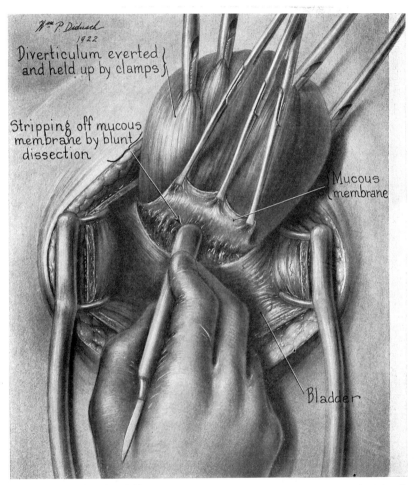

Fig. 55. The diverticulum has been drawn into the bladder, and an incision has
been made around its neck before shelling it out

a constant source of septic poisoning. Although these operations
are difficult and time-consuming, there has been a high percentage
of cures. The presence of stones makes the operation imperative in
many cases, and in one case X-rays (Fig. 56) showed two very large

calculi (stones) that had formed in the diverticulum. At operation I grasped these stones with forceps and used this as a tractor to drag the pouch into the bladder.

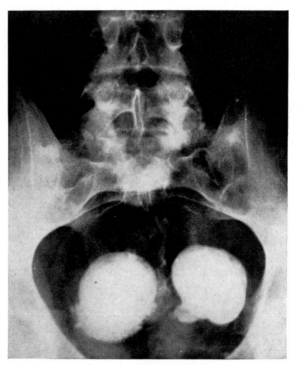

Fig. 56. An X-ray showing two large stones incarcerated in diverticula back of the bladder

Urinary Calculus (*Stone*)

The formation of stones in the urinary tract (Fig. 57) has tortured humanity since time immemorial. In ancient times it was perhaps the greatest cause of pain and horrible death. In rare instances the pain became so terrible that a knife was plunged in to remove the stone. The patient had no anesthetic. One of the early Dutch painters depicts a man holding in one hand a stone the size of a goose egg, and in the other a knife he had plunged through his abdomen to remove it (Fig. 58). In one of these early attempts the stone was the size of an infant's head and blacksmith's hammers and

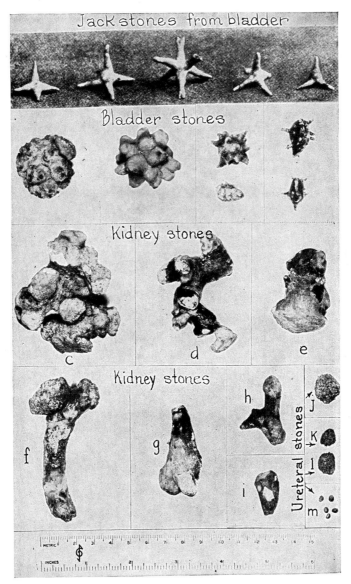

Fig. 57. Varied shapes of calculi (stones) found in the urinary tract

chisels were employed in an attempt to break it up and remove it. In the Middle Ages the Callot family for many generations held sway as about the only operators capable of removing bladder stones. Later the Jesuit priests learned the art, and one of these, Frère Jacques, traveled back and forth over Europe removing stones from hundreds of patients.

During these painful years ingenious mechanics were at work with the medical profession, and numerous instruments were invented to crush, bore into, pulverize, and extract stones either through the natural channels or through operative wounds. One of the greatest of these instruments was that brought out by Bigelow

Fig. 58. A portrait showing a large stone removed by the sufferer by plunging a shoemaker's knife into the bladder

of Harvard over fifty years ago. Casting about for a name to give his operation, he called upon Oliver Wendell Holmes who suggested "litholapaxy"—the Greek for "crushing and evacuating a stone" (*lithos*). These remarkable instruments were a godsend to humanity, particularly in tropical countries such as India, where a large percentage of the young male population was afflicted with stones. One surgeon in the British Army, Major Keegan, reported 10,000 cases upon which he had operated.

But litholapaxy was tedious because, after crushing some of the fragments, the instrument had to be removed, a tube introduced, and through it small fragments aspirated. It was necessary to repeat these alternate procedures until every fragment was removed. The operation was done blindly, and the surgeon was never certain that every particle had been removed.

To remedy this defect, I designed an instrument that would carry a cystoscope (Fig. 59 *A*). With this it was possible to grasp the stone while viewing it through the cystoscope. After crushing

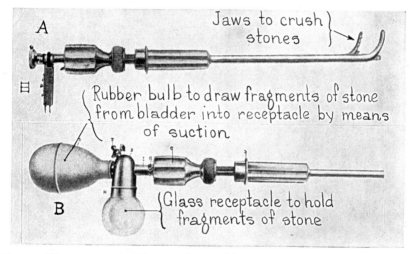

Fig. 59. The cystoscopic lithotrite for crushing and evacuating calculi (stones) from the bladder

it, the fragments could be evacuated through the inner tube (Fig. 59 *B*). This instrument was intended for stones of medium size or smaller and not for the very big or hard ones, as it was not quite so strong as the lithotrites. This shortcoming was forcibly brought out in a case that came to me a little later. The patient, who was eighty-three, had a large stone in the bladder. Introducing my instrument, I saw the stone and grasped it between the blades, which had to be separated one and a half inches to encompass the stone (Fig. 60). The clutch was locked, the handle screwed down, and, although great pressure had to be exerted, the stone was felt to break. The blades were again opened, a large fragment was caught, and the crushing process started. Suddenly there was a loud crack. When the instrument was withdrawn, I found that one of the blades had broken off and remained in the bladder. Fortunately, a short time before I had devised a cystoscopic bladder forceps (Fig. 43)

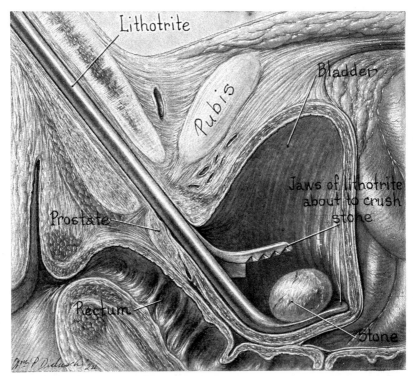

Fig. 60. The lithotrite introduced into the bladder has been opened out, and is about to crush a stone

which, when introduced into the bladder, could be opened out and, while they were observed through the cystoscope, objects could be accurately picked up and, if small enough, removed intact. This instrument I used to get out the broken lithotrite blade. With the cystoscope I saw the blade on the floor of the bladder, partly covered by three large stone fragments (Fig. 61). These were pushed

out of the way with the beak of the instrument, and the broken
blade was picked up by one end, but when I inspected it through
the cystoscope, I discovered we had it by the wrong end (Fig. 61 B).
The sharp oblique barb on this blade would have torn the urinary
passages had I pulled it out by the grasp I had upon it. Turned
loose, it fell to the bottom among the stone fragments, which were
again pushed aside and the blade grasped by the other end, in which

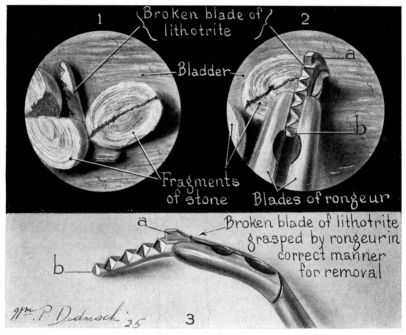

Fig. 61. The removal of a broken blade from among the stone fragments with the
cystoscopic bladder forceps (rongeur)

position the barb would not tear the urethra, and the blade was
then easily removed (Fig. 66). After that a very powerful lithotrite
was introduced and the fragments were crushed and evacuated.

Early in my career a patient came to me and X-ray showed a
small stone within the pelvis. When a cystoscope was introduced,
the stone was seen projecting into the bladder, being caught in the
orifice of the ureter (Fig. 62). A bougie (a gum-coated silken rod,

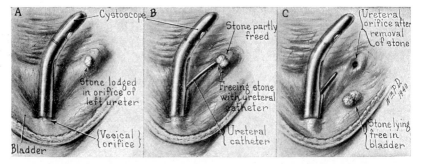

Fig. 62. The first case in which a stone that was caught in the lower end of the ureter was removed by means of a cystoscope in the bladder

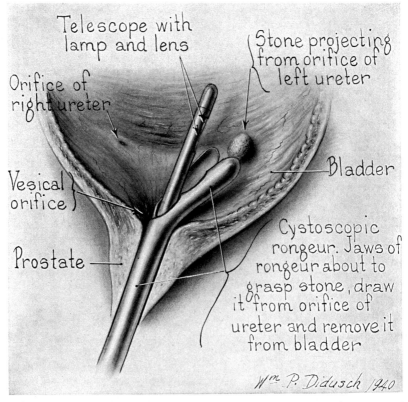

Fig. 63. The cystoscopic forceps (rongeur) grasping a stone that projected into the bladder through the ureteral orifice

Fig. 3) was introduced, and under the observation of the eye the stone was loosened from the ureter in which it was caught, and dropped into the bladder. This case, reported in 1902, was the first in which a stone had been removed by means of the cystoscope. Since then I have designed a cystoscopic bladder forceps with which such stones are easily grasped and removed (Fig. 63).

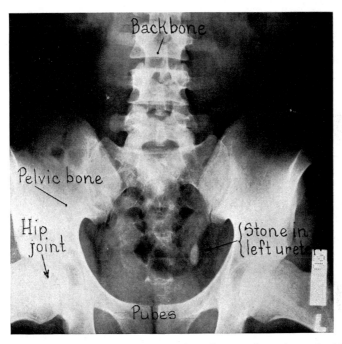

Fig. 64. An X-ray that shows a stone in the left ureter just above the bladder

During the same year a patient came with symptoms of colicky pain in the region of the left kidney that extended down to the groin and bladder. X-ray showed a stone almost as large as a small olive (Fig. 64). By use of a cystoscope, a swelling in the bladder wall showed that the stone was lodged just above in the ureter (Fig. 65). A bougie introduced through the cystoscope traveled only a short distance before it met an impassable obstruction (stricture). Through an operation in the lower left side of the abdomen (Fig.

66 *A*) the ureter was exposed without going through the peritoneum into the abdominal cavity. The ureter was about the size of the thumb, and following it down to the bladder, I discovered the stone, loosened it, and drew it up the dilated ureter until it was close to the external wound, where it was easily removed through an incision (Fig. 66 *B*). Instruments were then passed down to see if a

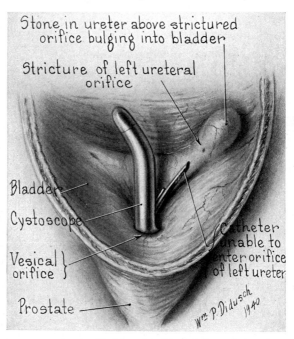

Fig. 65. A cystoscope in the bladder showing bulging of the mucous membrane that is produced by a stone in the ureter above the greatly narrowed orifice into which a catheter is about to be inserted.

narrowing (stricture) was present below the site of the stone. Not even the smallest instrument would pass. Unless I could cure this stricture, another stone would develop in the ureter. Although I knew of no such case that had been operated on, I decided to expose the bladder through the same incision. After it was opened, no difficulty was experienced in dividing this strictured area (Fig. 66 *C*), thus making it possible to pass large instruments from above into the bladder. The wounds in the bladder and ureter were then closed (Fig. 66 D).

This case was reported in an address to the Philadelphia County

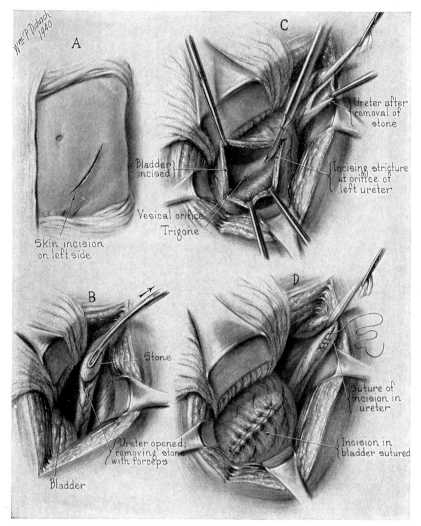

Fig. 66. The operation to remove a stone that was lodged in the ureter just above the bladder. The skin incision is shown in A. In B the stone has been pushed up the greatly dilated ureter, and is being removed through an incision. In C, through the same incision the bladder has been opened and the knife inserted to cut the strictured end of the ureter. In D the bladder wound has been closed, and the ureteral wound is being closed with sutures.

Medical Society in 1902 in which a review of the literature was given. No such case operated on in America had been published. I found, subsequently, that six cases had been operated on in Europe, but at the time of my operation I did not know of them. Dr. Christian Fenger of Chicago, in a classical work on the ureter, said the year before: "There is no difficulty in gaining access to the upper three-fourths of the ureter. . . . It is different with the lower fourth of the ureter which is located deep in the pelvis and is even held by Le Dentu to be inaccessible."

Nowadays, when the entire ureter is easily exposed and stones are removed with great facility from all portions, it seems incomprehensible that surgeons once considered the lower portion to be beyond operative reach.

A few years ago, during a voyage through the West Indies, a passenger told me that he had recently been suffering with attacks of colicky pain in his left side that had been diagnosed as kidney stone. On being questioned, he stated that whereas at the beginning of his trouble the pain was severe in the back and beneath the ribs, recently the symptoms had changed completely, and he now had pains of a complex nature that extended not only upward to the region of the kidney, but downward into the bladder, into the rectum when at stool, and also to the penis during sexual intercourse. On considering this strange symptom complex it seemed to me that to produce these varied types of pain the stone must be caught in the lower end of the ureter. After we landed in New York, he came to Baltimore with me, and we hurried to the hospital. I introduced a cystoscope, and saw a stone about the thickness of a lead pencil projecting from the left ureteral orifice, just as I had suspected. The cystoscopic bladder forceps was introduced, and the stone was grasped and removed with ease (Fig. 63).

Study of the literature showed that this symptom complex had not been described. Since then I have had a number of cases that have presented the same symptomatology. A glance at Fig. 5 will show the close proximity of the vas deferens, the seminal vesicles, and the rectum to the lower end of the ureter, and explains how a stone located in that region will produce pain on defecation and intercourse and present a definite symptom complex diagnostic of its position as I described it above.

With continued improvement of cystoscopes and instruments to bring down stones from a ureter into the bladder, the operative removal of stones from the ureter and the kidneys has become less common. Many stones of fair size, some as large as a lead pencil in diameter, are now passed without operation as a result of ureteral dilatations and other instrumentation.

In some cases the stone is so irregular that it becomes caught in the mucous membrane of the ureter, fails to descend, gradually increases in size, and causes progressive dilatation of the ureter and the renal pelvis above. As long as there is no infection, little impairment of the kidney may result, but long-continued lodgment in a ureter ultimately causes progressively greater damage to the kidney. To emphasize these points, here is the case of a patient who came from the Philippines, and which was described in the *Philippine Herald:*

The inside story of why President Quezon was operated at the Johns Hopkins Hospital and not in Paris where he went first for an operation was revealed by Dr. Estrada, private physician of President Quezon. Professor Marion of the Broca Hospital in Paris declared after his examination that the stone could not be made to come down by means of the cystoscope and that operation was necessary. Professor Gosset declared that operation upon the ureter would be dangerous and the stone could be made to pass. With these experts differing in their views, President Quezon decided to go to America and take up his case with experts there.

He gave a history of intermittent attacks of sharp pain in the left back and side and occasional passage of blood in small amount. Examination of the urine showed no infection. X-ray showed the shadow of a stone (in the form of an L) lodged in the ureter about halfway between the kidney and the bladder (Fig. 67). At cystoscopy a catheter was passed into the left ureter, but it would not go by the stone. Urine collected through this catheter showed definite impairment of the kidney function. A urogram (X-ray) obtained after injecting one ounce of neoiopax into a vein in the arm gave a dense shadow in the upper urinary passages, which

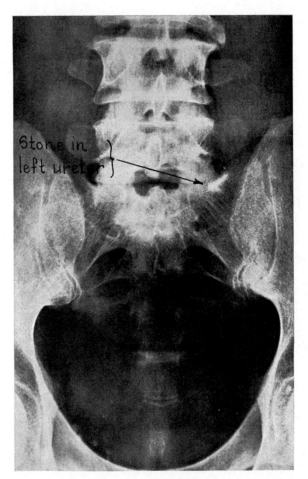

Fig. 67. An X-ray showing a stone in the left ureter alongside the spine

showed definite enlargement of the kidney pelvis and ureter. The patient was told that the stone would not pass, and he readily consented to operation.

The technique employed is graphically shown in Fig. 68. In the operation, the muscles were separated but not divided, and the ureter exposed. An incision was made through the ureter upon the stone, which was removed by forceps without difficulty. The opening in the ureter was closed with a fine continuous stitch of catgut.

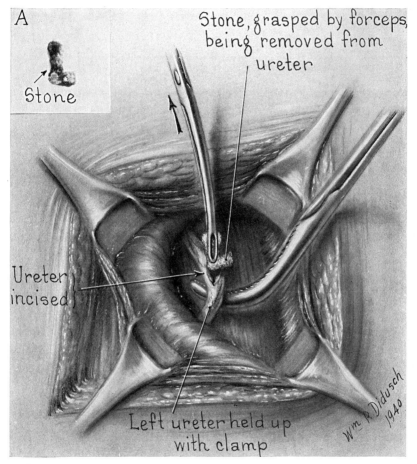

Fig. 68. The removal of the stone (shown in *A*) through an incision in the ureter

The skin wound was closed, and a tube was left in place to provide drainage in case there was urinary leakage through the line of closure. This did not occur, and in two weeks the patient was able to leave the hospital. The function of the kidney had already improved. There was no infection, and his general condition was excellent.

When President Quezon arrived at the hospital, he was accompanied by a large staff and required a suite of rooms. When his numerous bags were opened, an orderly assisting was struck dumb when he saw a machine gun in one of them. The day of the operation his physician asked me if two of Mr. Quezon's staff might be present at the operation. He assured me that, although they were not doctors, they would not faint at the sight of blood. During the operation I saw these small, dark-eyed men watching me intently. They left the operating-room when the patient was taken back to the ward. Some physicians who had witnessed the operation reported to me that as they came down the steps to the operating-room these men had stopped them, quizzed them, and searched them for arms. I wonder what would have happened to me had the patient died on the table.

President Quezon's fear of foul play was entirely justified. During his absence dynamite was placed around his home in Manila, but fortunately was discovered before he returned home.

Operations upon the kidney are generally not very difficult or dangerous, but not infrequently complications are present that may end fatally before surgical operations can be carried out. Among the most serious complications are those associated with the gastro-intestinal tract, and before anything can be done in a surgical way it is often necessary to combat serious stomachic conditions.

The case of Hernando Vasquez, President of the Dominican Republic, is interesting from many standpoints. Sixty-nine years of age, he was the absolute military dictator of his country and leading a very active life when one day, while mounting a fiery horse, he was thrown to the pavement. Although greatly stunned, he conquered the animal and rode him for half an hour afterwards. Four days later he took to his bed with a shaking chill and a high fever. Soon blood and pus appeared in his urine, and vomiting became so continuous that his life was despaired of. His physicians proposed bringing him to me by ship, but when he found that no ship would leave for a week and that it would be twelve days before he could reach Baltimore, he chartered a large plane in which he left, accompanied by members of his family and staff, his physician, two pilots, and a radio operator—nine persons in all. The plane started from Santo Domingo at five o'clock in the morning, crossed over the Dominican Republic, Haiti, and Cuba and the intervening sea, making three landings before crossing the Straits of Florida and coming down at Miami eleven hours later. The distance traversed was thirteen hundred miles. After a short stay in Miami he came by train to the hospital.

Soon after admission he had another severe chill and a temperature of 103°, vomited continually, and was unable to take water or food. X-ray showed a great number of large stones (calculi) in the right kidney (Fig. 69). Cystoscopic examination, at which tubes were passed up into each kidney and urine obtained, showed a large amount of pus and no output of thalein from the right kidney, which was filled with stones. There was a marked reduction in the function of the opposite kidney. I had to combat uremia, intermittent septicemia, poor kidney function, high blood pressure, nausea, and vomiting so great that he could neither eat nor drink. To make up for this the patient was fed through his veins with solutions of sugar and given blood transfusions, but as the terrible vomiting continued, it looked as if we would lose him. Finally I decided to introduce a tube through the stomach into the intestines (duodenum) below. Weighted at the end, this "duodenal" tube was readily passed through the nostril into the quiet intestine below the spasmodic stomach, which was constantly retching with vomiting. We first gave him large quantities of water to replace the great depletion caused by many days of vomiting, and then liquid foods were introduced in increasing amount. At his suggestion tropical fruits were added, his favorite being mashed-up bananas mixed with milk and eggs. Dr. Charles R. Austrian was the medical consultant.

Within three weeks a great transformation had occurred. The chills and fever disappeared, the blood and urine more nearly approached normal, and the patient's strength improved so greatly that he was able to undergo an operation, under spinal anesthesia, in which we removed the right kidney, which was found to contain great quantities of very soft stones (Fig. 70). There was some shock following operation, the nausea returned, and the duodenal tube

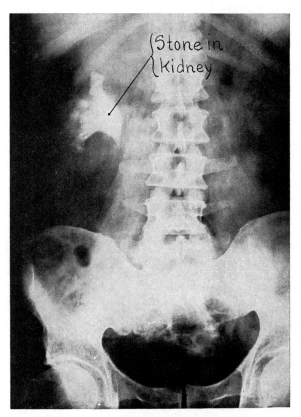

Fig. 69. An X-ray of a large stone in the pelvis of the right kidney

had to be reinserted, and through it large amounts of water and liquid foods passed for nine days before his strength had so improved that the tube could be removed. After this he was able to eat and drink normally, and he made a rapid convalescence. Within three weeks he was able to leave the hospital.

But, sad to relate, during the six weeks he had been away from his country an insurgent had organized a revolution against him, and although President Vasquez hurried back by plane, he arrived too late. General Trujillo, whom he had trusted and left in command of his army, had meanwhile risen against him, and when Vasquez

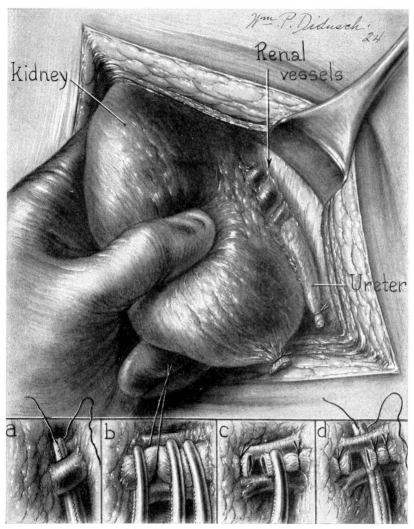

Fig. 70. The removal of the kidney (nephrectomy) containing many stones through an incision on the right side. The ureter has been ligated (tied) and divided. The blood vessels supplying the kidney (renal vessels) are shown. In *a* the large vein has been isolated with a clamp, and a ligature is being drawn around it. In *b* three clamps have been placed upon it. In *c* it has been divided and ligated. In *d* other vessels are being tied.

arrived in the Dominican Republic it was only to be imprisoned. Subsequently he was allowed to depart peacefully to Puerto Rico, but he never regained his throne, which is still occupied by Trujillo, who even changed the name of the ancient city of Santo Domingo, a name sacred to the memory of Columbus, whose bones were once preserved in its cathedral, to Ciudad Trujillo.

Genitourinary Tuberculosis

By modern methods, tuberculosis of the lungs is arrested in more than 70 per cent of the patients, but when the genitourinary tract is involved, the number of cases cured or arrested is small. In a study of eight thousand cases in several sanatoria in Colorado I found that few operations had been done in these cases with tuberculosis of the genitourinary tract. The great surgeon Kocher, of Switzerland, had written fifty years ago advising the removal of tuberculous testes and adjacent structures, even in the presence of tuberculosis of the lungs. He, indeed, had urged that if tuberculosis of the lungs were to be arrested in these cases, it was essential to operate upon and remove the tuberculous genitals. He reported a number of cases in which tuberculous processes in the lungs were greatly improved by the removal of foci of tuberculosis in or adjacent to the testes or in the kidneys. That excellent results were obtainable by removal of a tuberculous kidney was admitted everywhere. With the development of cystoscopy and ureter catheterization, the ability to obtain urine from each kidney separately and to find the red-staining bacilli of tuberculosis on slide smears or in cultures had increased greatly the possibility of early diagnosis. A further great advance came when a drug was found that, when injected intravenously, was excreted in a few minutes through the kidney and cast upon an X-ray film a dense shadow (pyelogram, Fig. 71) that would show an ulcer or abscess in the kidney produced by early tuberculosis. The thalein test, which in these cases showed less excretion by the tuberculous kidney than the healthy one, also aided greatly in the precision of diagnosis. With these great advances, cases of kidney tuberculosis were being recognized much earlier than before, and cured by an operation to remove them

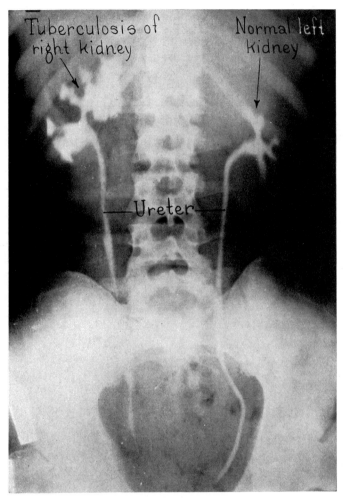

Fig. 71. An X-ray that was taken fifteen minutes after an intravenous injection of neo-iopax. It shows a normal kidney pelvis and ureter on the left side, a very abnormal pelvis greatly enlarged by tuberculous excavation of the kidney, and a dilatation of the ureter on the right side.

(nephrectomy; Fig. 72), in which both kidney and ureter were removed.

Unfortunately, in certain cases the genital tract was also involved.

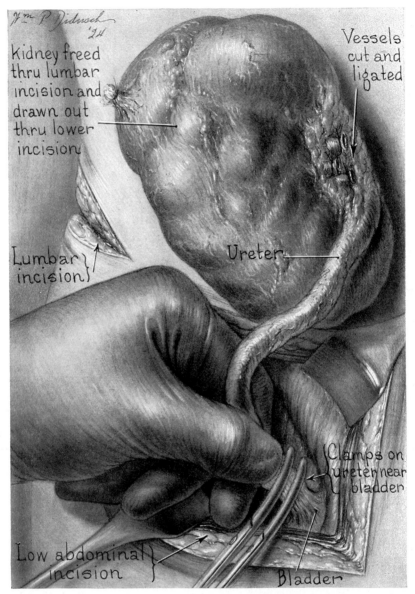

Fig. 72. An operation to remove the entire ureter after the kidney has been freed through an incision higher up and brought down into the lower wound

Tubercle bacilli had settled in either the seminal vesicles or the prostate or had traveled farther down and invaded the structures

next to the testes epididymes. A chart showing such involvement
is given in Fig. 73. The tuberculous areas are shaded, the degree
marked + or + +.

In 1900 a patient appeared at our clinic with genital tuberculosis,
the testes, vasa, seminal vesicles, prostate, and a portion of the
bladder being involved. A careful study of the literature showed
only eight cases in which a radical operation had been done for

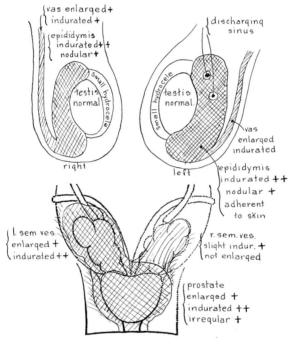

Fig. 73. A diagram of the normal prostate and seminal vesicles upon which has
been drawn the great enlargement produced by tuberculosis of the prostate, and
the left seminal vesicle. The areas involved are indicated by crossed lines. Above,
a great enlargement of each epididymis caused by tuberculosis is similarly shown.

such deep-seated tuberculous processes. As the results in these
cases had not been good, I determined to attempt the removal of
these deep-seated structures by a new route, but this also did not
prove successful, and in a paper two years later I frankly stated that
such radical methods were inadvisable.

By careful surgery it was possible to separate and remove the epididymis (epididymectomy) from the testis without injuring the nerve, artery, and veins upon which the testis was dependent for its vitality. Although the testis was very seldom involved, the

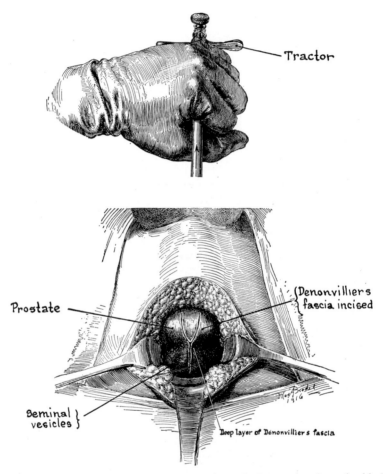

Fig. 74. A long tractor has been passed through the urethra into the bladder. An incision has been made in the perineum. The tractor has drawn the prostate and seminal vesicles down into the opening.

seminal vesicles often were, and epididymectomy did nothing for the deep-seated involvement in them or in the prostate.

Finally I prepared an exhaustive study of every case of tuberculosis of the seminal tract (which extends from the testes to the prostatic urethra). The statistics obtained were presented in a lengthy document entitled "The Radical Cure of Tuberculosis of the Seminal Tract" in the *Archives of Surgery*, 1922. I showed that operations upon testicles and adjacent structures in many cases were purely palliative; that these procedures removed the external, easily visible tuberculous involvement, but failed to attack the process in the vesicles and the prostate, which was present in most cases. Study of the ultimate results of these operations showed that most of the patients had died. My methods had been inadequate, and it

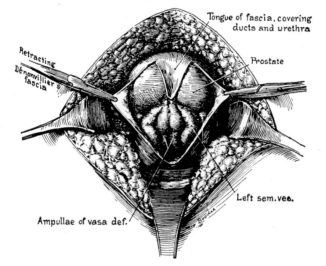

Fig. 75. The capsule has been incised, exposing the prostate, the seminal vesicles, and the vasa (ampullae)

was apparent that much more radical surgery was indicated. A review of the literature showed that no satisfactory method had yet been brought out to remove these deep-seated tuberculous processes.

I set to work to develop new instruments and technique. A tractor was made, similar to the one I had employed in operations upon the enlarged prostate, but three times as long, and so delicate that it could be introduced through the normal urinary tract into the bladder without making an incision. With this instrument an entirely new operation was developed. The prostate was exposed through an incision in the perineum, but without opening the urethra (Fig. 74). By traction and leverage upon this long tractor, the prostate (Fig. 74) was drawn down so that the prostate and the

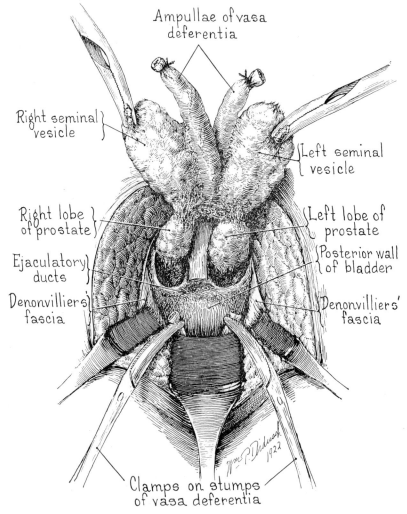

Fig. 76. The seminal vesicles and vasa have been freed, and are being removed with the lobes of the prostate without opening the urinary tract

seminal vesicles could be brought into view. By making an incision through the fibrous covering, the lobes of the prostate and the seminal vesicles could be exposed (Fig. 75), isolated, and removed without opening either bladder or urethra (Fig. 76). If an epididymis were involved, this was then removed by epididymectomy (Fig. 77) without injuring the testis. The specimen removed at one of these operations is shown in Fig. 78.

For the first time an effective radical procedure was at hand with which the entire tuberculous involvement from the testes to the urethra could be removed. Two years later I reported fifteen cases in which this radical operation had been done. In five of these the

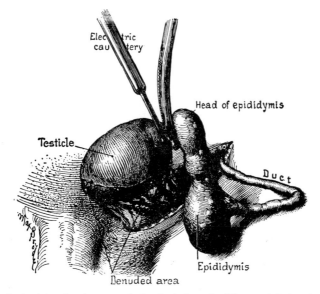

Fig. 77. An incision has been made in the left groin. The testicle has been drawn out, and the tuberculous epididymis is being cut off from the testicle. It is then removed with the duct (vas).

kidney also was removed because it was tuberculous. Although in seven of the patients the lungs were involved, only one patient had died. Others showed amazing improvement, so that it was possible to present a strong argument for the application of radical surgery to tuberculosis of the seminal tract.

Immediately great opposition arose on all sides. Many opponents were the same men who had opposed my radical operations for cancer of the prostate, and others took a stand against my procedure simply because they were by nature conservatives. Thus was started a bitter fight in the local, national, and international societies between the radicals and the conservatives on the treatment of tuberculosis of the genitourinary tract.

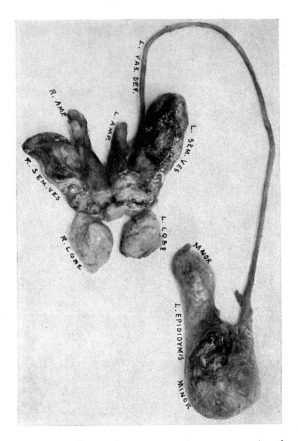

Fig. 78. A photograph of a specimen removed at an operation for tuberculosis of the seminal tract. It consists of right and left lobes of the prostate, right and left seminal vesicles, right and left ampullae (of the vasa), and the entire vas deferens and epididymis, thus removing the entire tuberculous involvement of the tract from the testicle to the prostate.

Movable (Floating) Kidney

A painful condition to which women are particularly prone is movable kidney, often called floating kidney. The kidneys are surrounded by a layer of fat that lies within a hammocklike membrane in which they move up and down with the diaphragm during respiration. Occasionally the kidney becomes abnormally movable, and travels to a considerable distance from its normal position, particularly when the person is standing. In these excursions the kidney sometimes revolves on its pedicle, which consists of blood vessels, arteries, and veins and also the ureter. Not infrequently when the kidney descends far below its normal position, the ureter becomes bent or kinked and the down flow of urine is arrested. The kidney pelvis becomes overdistended, and severe pain results. It usually is necessary for these patients to go to bed or to change their position so that the kidney can resume a more normal position in which the kinking of the ureter is relieved and the obstruction to urine is removed.

Years ago this condition was treated by operation in scores of cases, but in many of them in the course of time the mobility of the kidney returned. The kidney often "floated" just as much as before and the painful attacks or crises recurred. There arose a strong protest against operations for floating kidney unless severe pathological conditions absolutely required intervention. I too had had poor results from the customary operation before a better technique was devised.

After studying the anatomy of the kidney for an explanation of the failure of operations in these cases, I concluded it was because the kidney is surrounded by a firm, smooth capsule that failed to become adherent to the muscles of the back when the kidney was placed in the proper position and held there by stitches that went through the kidney capsule and the muscles of the back. When these stitches dissolved or worked loose, the kidney began to move again. It seemed to me that by stripping off this capsule on the posterior surface of the kidney it would be possible to get the kidney to adhere and remain in the proper position.

After sketching out a plan of operation, I carried it out successfully in March, 1926. Subsequently the technique was improved, and the operation was employed with excellent results in a difficult case. A woman of forty-seven for a long time had suffered from fearful seizures of pain on the right side. X-ray showed that when she was on her back the right kidney remained in normal position high up beneath the ribs, but when she sat erect, the kidney dropped several inches and the ureter was twisted or kinked in two places.

Operation was indicated to fasten the kidney in its proper position, and prevent its slipping down and producing these kinks and

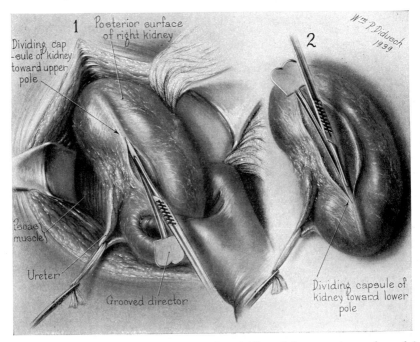

Fig. 79. *1.* Division of the capsule along the mid-line of the posterior surface of the kidney. *2.* Completion of the capsular incision

obstruction to the ureter that were gradually destroying the kidney. Fig. 79 shows the kidney exposed and the capsule being divided along the posterior surface with the knife (Fig. 79). The capsule was then stripped back on each side (Fig. 79 *2* and 80 *1*) and rolled up, exposing the raw surface of the kidney freed of its slick capsule (Fig. 80 *2*). The rolled-up edges were used as strong cords around which to place the stitches (Fig. 80 *2*) with which to fasten the

kidney in proper position to the muscles of the back (Fig. 81).
When these stitches, which were of heavy catgut, were tied, the
kidney was drawn up into its normal position with the raw surfaces
of the kidney in close apposition to the muscles (Fig. 81). In the
healing process scar tissue (Fig. 81 *2*) formed between the kidney
and the muscles, and held the kidney permanently in place. An

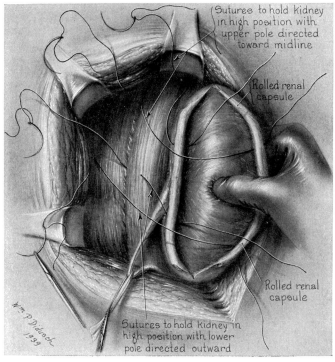

Fig. 80. Stitches have been placed through the rolled-up capsule of the kidney
on each side, and through the muscles of the back. When tied these draw the raw
surfaces of the kidney to the muscles.

X-ray taken after operation showed the kidney in normal position,
when the patient was both lying down and erect.

This operation is simple, because the substance of the kidney
and the urinary channels below it have not been opened. It has been
employed successfully in many cases.

The pain that accompanies floating kidney may sometimes be

mistaken for tuberculosis if one does not exclude, by careful cleansing, a red-staining bacillus almost identical with the tubercle bacillus that is found in the lower urinary tract. A case in point:

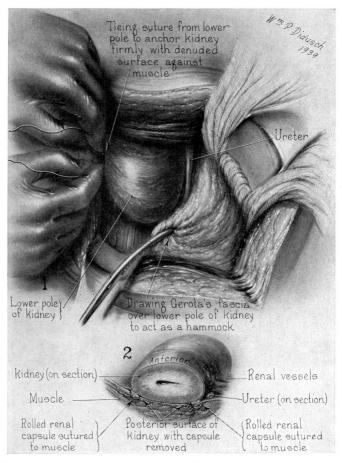

Fig. 81. *1.* Tying the last (lower, external) suture. *2.* Schematic cross-section showing the kidney, from which the capsule has been removed, drawn to the muscles of the back.

Physicians connected with one of the service hospitals in Washington telephoned me that a very important woman had tuberculosis of the right kidney, and asked me to come over, study the case, and remove the kidney. I went over the clinical and laboratory reports that had been made. Smears from the end of the urethra and also from the voided urine had shown on staining a bacillus corresponding to the tubercle bacillus. The right kidney was lower than normal and, the doctors thought, enlarged.

The case was of such great importance that I proceeded to study it anew from every standpoint. With great care the external region was cleansed, the urethra irrigated, and cultures obtained with a sterile catheter. The urine obtained was clear, containing no pus cells, and a study for bacteria showed none of the red organisms that had been found and thought to be the tubercle bacillus. A cystoscope was introduced. The urethra, the bladder, and the ureteral orifices were normal. Catheters were inserted into both ureters, and urine obtained from each kidney was normal in appearance; it contained no cells, and bacteriological studies were negative. A solution of 12 per cent sodium iodide was then injected through each catheter into the kidneys. When about 15 cubic centimeters (half an ounce) had been injected, an X-ray was taken with the patient in a horizontal position. Both kidneys were in normal position and there was no evidence of tuberculosis. An X-ray taken with the patient upright showed that the right kidney dropped about two inches and produced a kink in the ureter. This apparently produced the obstruction which brought on the attacks of pain. The condition was one of floating kidney, not tuberculosis.

The attending physicians were delighted at this demonstration that their patient would not have to lose her kidney. They suggested that I go with them to report to her husband. At a big white house we were conducted to an upstairs office and awaited the husband. He soon came. The officers stood at attention. I was introduced. He simply said, "How do you do," and sat at his desk. I expected to be invited to take a seat near him, but not a word. Finally I drew up a chair. Without looking at me, out of the side of his mouth he said, "What did you find?" I said I could explain the conditions better if I had a pad and a pencil. He made no effort to get one for me. One of the officers got a piece of paper for me. I rapidly sketched the outline of the body and drew in the urinary tract. I showed where the smegma bacillus, which was so frequently confused with the tubercle bacillus, was often present in normal individuals, and told him that by great care in external cleansing and catheterization this bacillus had been excluded. The bacilli that had been supposed to indicate tuberculosis were not present. I said, "Your wife has not got tuberculosis," and waited for some comment. Silence. Going on with my demonstration, I drew the position of the kidneys when the patient was recumbent and showed the marked drop of the kidney on the right side when she sat upright. "This," I said, "explains the pain. She has a floating and not a tuberculous kidney, and it will not have to be removed." Another wait for some commendation. Not a word was forthcoming. I started again and said: "No surgical operation will be necessary. The case isn't serious. We shall only have to give her a pad to wear beneath an abdominal band, and before long she will be well." A short wait. Still not a word. Starting again, I said, "I think, however, it would be advisable for her to remain quiet in bed most of the morning and to avoid tedious receptions or long official dinners." Again a pause and not a word. Finally I said, "I believe, sir, I've told you everything about the case." Whereupon he opened his mouth and said, "Good day, sir."

Resection or Removal of One Half of a Double Kidney

A patient came to me in 1916 with symptoms of pain on the right side and blood in the urine. X-ray showed a large stone in the region of the kidney, but unusually high. The ureters were catheterized, sodium iodide solution injected, and an X-ray taken. This showed on the left side the ureter and the pelvis of a normal kidney. On the right side the X-ray showed that the ureter branched, the inner half traveling upward to the position of the stone and the lower half traveling to a lower half of the kidney that contained no stone. It was evident that only the upper half of the kidney was diseased and that its stone should be removed without injuring the lower (healthy) half. This is graphically shown in the illustrations (Figs.

82–83). In Fig. 82 the kidney has been drawn out of the wound. The upper half, which contains the stone and its own ureter, is shown. The lower half, which is not enlarged, has a separate ureter.

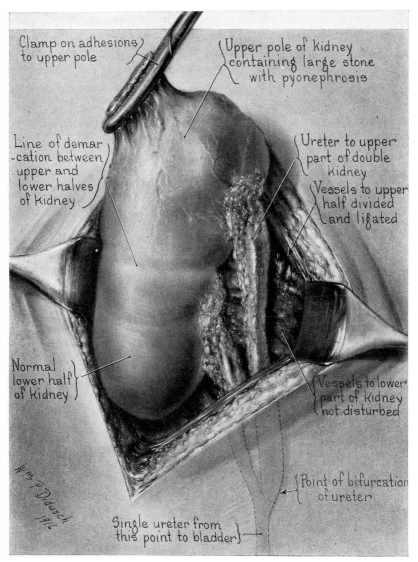

Fig. 82. The first stage of an operation to remove one half of a kidney (hemi-nephrectomy). The upper larger portion containing the stone is demarcated from the lower normal portion by a furrow. The point of division (bifurcation) of the ureter is indicated by dotted lines.

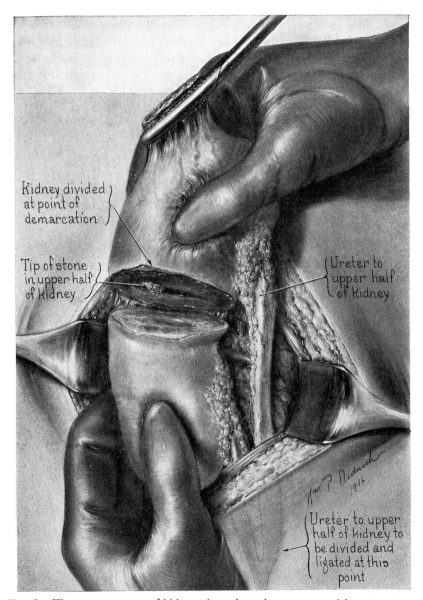

Fig. 83. The two segments of kidney tissue have been separated by a transverse incision just above the level of the furrow

The point of juncture is indicated beneath the skin. Fig. 83 shows the operation in which the two halves of the kidney were cut apart. The lower, undiseased half was returned to the body after stitches were placed through the upper end to close it. The upper stone-bearing half of the kidney and its ureter (about six inches long) were then removed in one piece.

Operations to Cure High Blood Pressure

High blood pressure (hypertension) is a common and very puzzling disease, often ending fatally. Years ago we discovered that it was not infrequently associated with prostatic obstruction, when back pressure from the bladder up the ureters to the kidneys greatly impaired the function of the kidneys. Relieving this by catheter drainage, or by prostatectomy, was often followed by a prompt decrease in the blood pressure, and in some cases complete cure of hypertension. The onset of high blood pressure, especially in young persons who have no prostatic disease, is a most distressing condition.

Several years ago Dr. H. Goldblatt showed that the placing of a clip upon an artery leading to the kidney so as to reduce its lumen, and cut off part of its blood supply, was followed by a great increase in blood pressure. Experimental studies seemed to indicate that reduction of the blood supply to the kidney caused "pressor substances" to be eliminated by the kidney, and absorbed into the circulation. These substances are thought to be a cause of some types of hypertension in man.

These remarkable experiments excited great interest, but the first demonstration and cure of the condition produced by Goldblatt was in a case at the Brady Institute four years ago. A white man of thirty-one entered the medical service under the care of Dr. C. Holmes Boyd. He complained of severe headaches, and of marked impairment of his eyesight of several months' duration. An attack of severe abdominal pain was thought to be due to an inflamed appendix that had been removed seven weeks before he came to the Johns Hopkins Hospital. His blood pressure had rapidly increased to 200, nearly double what it should be normally. Examination of his eyes showed swelling and inflammation of the retina, and the kidneys showed impairment of their function.

Dr. Lloyd G. Lewis of our department injected air within the capsule surrounding the kidney and adrenal on each side. An X-ray taken a short time afterwards was thought to show enlargement of the left adrenal. As adrenal disease was occasionally the cause of hypertension, it was decided to carry out an operation upon the two adrenals, as shown in Fig. 96, Dr. Lewis working on the left side and I on the right. When the adrenals were exposed, they were found to be practically normal, and there was no reason to remove either one. I discovered evidence of considerable disease in the upper portion of the kidney on my side. When the adhesions had been separated, and a satisfactory view was obtained, I found that the upper third of the anterior surface of the kidney was bright yellow. This was subsequently found to be due to the fact that the artery which supplied that portion of the kidney had been obstructed by a clot within it, cutting off the blood supply, and had caused that region of the kidney to undergo fatty degeneration. It was evident that this kidney should be removed, and this was done by Dr. Lewis.

The operation was followed by an amazing result. The blood pressure that had been so high promptly fell to less than normal. In a few days the eyesight began to improve. Before the patient left the hospital he was able to read again. After returning home his eyesight continued to improve, and now, two years later, he has practically normal eyesight, and has been completely relieved of the hypertension, his blood pressure being 140. The terrific headaches disappeared very soon after the operation, and have not recurred.

In this case the conditions found in the kidney were practically identical with those produced by Goldblatt with clips upon a renal artery. For the first time it was shown that by the removal of one kidney that was found to be the subject of arterial disease hypertension that had baffled medical science for generations could be cured.

About the same time another patient came to our department with somewhat similar conditions. This patient was only eleven years old, but since he was three studies in other departments in the hospital had shown a marked increase in the blood pressure, and enlargement of the heart. In the Brady Institute examinations had disclosed that one of his kidneys was misplaced, being down in the bony pelvis close to the bladder, and abnormal in shape. The blood pressure varied from 164 to 220.

The kidney was removed by the resident urologist, Dr. Wyland F. Leadbetter. The conditions present are shown in Fig. 84. The kidney had descended far below its normal position, and was twisted and rotated. The vessels supplying blood to the kidney were on such tension that they had formed a deep groove in the surface of the

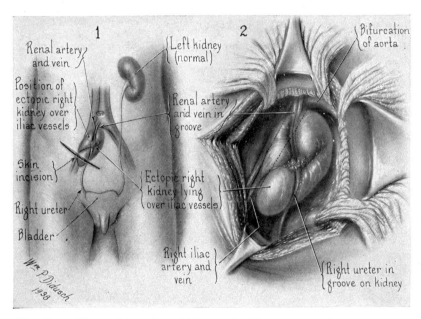

Fig. 84. 1. The position of the kidneys, the blood supply of the right kidney, and the skin incision used for the right nephrectomy is shown schematically. *2.* The right kidney has been exposed at operation. The vessels running to this kidney have produced a deep groove in the upper portion of the kidney. The ureter appears to be normal.

kidney. The blood supply was much impaired. After the kidney was removed, examination showed that its main artery was partially closed (occluded). The result of the operation was an immediate drop in the blood pressure from over 200 to 125. In a few months the blood pressure had dropped to 100, and the child was apparently well.

These two cases were published simultaneously in the *Journal of*

Urology for May, 1938, and excited great interest. Since then the work has been taken up in many other clinics, and numerous cases have been reported in which hypertension has been relieved by removal of a single kidney with disease of its blood vessels. In some instances the results obtained have been just as striking, and the cures as remarkable, as in the two cases from the Brady Institute. A great field for research, experimental and clinical, has been opened up. Hope is strong for the ultimate cure of many of these distressing and often fatal cases of high blood pressure.

Epispadias

Incontinence of urine associated with epispadias (deformity of the urethra) is a distressing abnormality. The normal urethra is absent and the urine escapes through an opening in the lowest part of the abdomen, next to the genitalia. It rarely affects girls, but occasionally affects boy babies. The patient is constantly wet from the outflow of urine, and to relieve the horrible condition in which these young patients live surgeons have often cut off the ureters and transplanted them into the rectum so that the urine escaped into that cavity. By this procedure the patient was kept dry, but he was left with a great deformity and led an abnormal life. No successful procedure to cure this condition had been published, as far as I could find in 1920. It occurred to me to try by new plastic methods to cure the defect. After succeeding in a few cases in which epispadias was present not accompanied by incontinence, I carried out the new procedure in 1920 on a boy who had led a distressing life on account of the continued outflow of urine and the great genital abnormality due to the absence of the urethra. The operation is shown in the drawings (Figs. 85 and 86). A finger could be introduced from below into the bladder. As seen here, through a low median line incision the bladder was opened. This exposed the wide bladder neck through which the urine constantly escaped. A large part of the anterior and lateral walls of the greatly dilated urethra were excised (Fig. 85, 2). The mucous membrane was then drawn together to form a narrow outlet for the bladder, and the muscles around it were then approximated so as to produce a muscular neck that would give urinary control. The same excision of redundant canal and tightening with stitches was done below in the region of the external sphincter (cut-off muscle). By continuing the incision downward a urethra was made out of the trough of skin on the superior surface of the penis. When the edges of this were drawn together

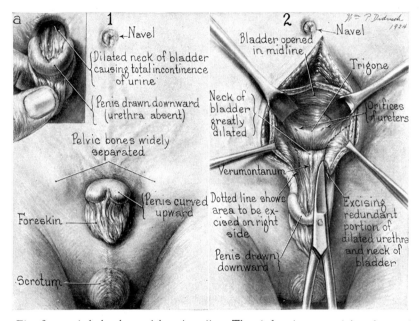

Fig. 85. 1. A baby boy with epispadias. The defect is covered by the penis. In *a* the defect is exposed. *2.* The author's operation. The bladder has been opened, and the redundant mucous membrane is being excised.

with a continuous stitch and the tube had been buried between the lateral masses in its proper position, the patient was practically restored to normal, and complete bladder control was accomplished. The patient voided urine at normal intervals and ultimately lived a happy married life, both of which would have been impossible without this operation. By this comparatively simple procedure, mutilating operations to divert the urine to the intestinal tract have been avoided. Although rare, I have had two cases of epispadias with incontinence in girls. A procedure similar to, but not so as extensive as, that described has restored them to normal urination, doing away with the continued escape of urine.

Imperforate Anus with Connection between Rectum and Urethra

One of the most distressing abnormalities is when the intestine opens into the urinary tract. Some of these cases are not detected

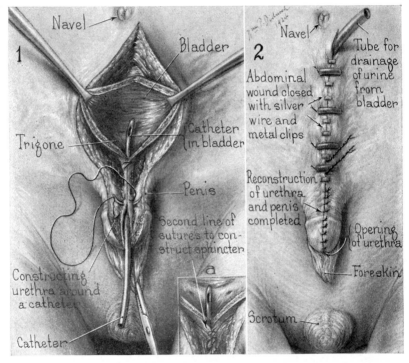

Fig. 86. 1. A urethra and a tight bladder neck are being constructed with stitches around a rubber catheter. *2.* The author's operation to cure epispadias with incontinence of urine has been completed. The bladder neck has been tightened, a urethra has been constructed, and the penile deformity has been closed.

immediately at birth and are rapidly fatal. In others the child grows up with bowel movements escaping with the urine. This condition is due to an embryological fault. In early fetal life the urinary and intestinal tracts open into a common pouch, which gradually becomes obliterated and divided (normally) into two separate tracts. In the case I am describing the rectum, instead of coming down and forming a normal opening, retained its embryonic connection with the urinary tract, which itself was not completely closed down to the normal end. A considerable defect remained. At least five inches of the urethra were absent, the urinary tract opened into the perineum, and out of it came the contents of both the bladder and the rectum.

The patient was a youth of seventeen who came to me in 1933. On examination I found that the sphincter (the muscle of control) of the lower bowel was present beneath the skin (Fig. 87B). Although it contained no opening and had never functioned, pricking it with a needle caused it to contract, indicating that it would resume function if the bowel were cut off from the urinary tract and brought out through it, as in the normal body. I decided to carry out such an operation. A curved incision was made in the perineum about two inches in front of the ring of muscle (sphincter) beneath the skin. After some of the muscles of the perineum were divided, the concealed rectum was disclosed; it was freed by blunt dissection, and the connection between the rectum and the urethra brought into view. An incision was made into the bowel, revealing the opening into the urinary tract through which the bowel movements passed. This abnormal connection was divided, leaving an opening into the urethra, which was then closed. With a finger in the rectum, it was freed from surrounding structures. An opening was then made by two incisions in the form of a cross through the skin over the center of the ring of muscle (sphincter) beneath the skin, a circle of which was then cut out (excised). The rectum was caught with clamps and drawn down through the ring of sphincter muscle (Fig. 87 C) and held there by stitches through the skin (Fig. 87 D), thus producing a normal external outlet (anus) for the rectum. After additional operations had been carried out to correct the defects in the lower urinary tract and make a urethra, the patient obtained an excellent result. Five years after the operation he reports that he is entirely cured and is leading a happy married life.

A search of the literature showed that this was the first time that anyone had carried out the operation described above. Never before had a bowel that emptied into the urinary tract been cut off and brought out through the sphincter muscle, which, in these cases,

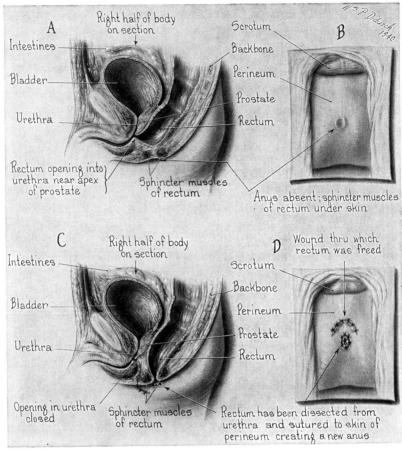

Fig. 87. A mid-line section (*A*) showing the anal opening absent (*B*), the rectum communicating with the urethra just below the prostate (*A*). At the site of the anus is a dimple in the skin beneath which the circular muscle (sphincter) that normally surrounds the bowel is present *C-D*. The operation performed to sever the connection between the rectum and the urethra, and bring the bowel out through an opening made within the sphincter. The stitches holding the rectum to the skin are shown.

lies beneath the skin ready to function as soon as the rectum is brought out through it, as was done in the operation described above.

Hermaphroditism

Those unfortunates who have the organs of both sexes—known as intersexuals—have intrigued intellectuals since time immemorial; in fact, quite a few intellectuals have been intersexuals. Hermaphrodites have commanded the attention of lawmakers, historians, mythologists, poets, sculptors, painters, and physicians since the earliest times.

Aphrodite, as a result of a celestial union with Hermes, brought forth an extraordinary child endowed with the attributes of both father and mother. Unable to determine the sex, they decided to affix both their names, and their child has gone down in history as Hermaphroditos, to whom recent biologists have given the unromantic title of "intersex."

This anatomical combination of both male and female was encountered long before the age of Greek mythology. Some of the great Hebrew writers have affirmed that in the first chapter of Genesis there is authority for believing that Adam was a hermaphrodite. During the time of Pope Innocent III, Catholic priests openly advocated this interpretation of Holy Writ to mean that Adam was both male and female. Whether Eve came as the result of auto-impregnation is not clear.[1]

That social problems of great perplexity and seriousness were caused by the frequent occurrence of hermaphroditism is plainly shown by the laws and regulations that from time immemorial have been made against these unfortunates, and by their frequent representation in art as creatures presenting both male and female attributes. We find them first as individuals of double sex for whom special legislation was necessary, and later we find them enrolled among the gods and worshiped by many nations.

[1] In one of the original Books of Moses, Genesis 1: 27, is found the passage: "Male and female created He them." In an early Jewish commentary (Midrash, Genesis, Rabbah 8: 1) "Rabbi Jeremiah ben Elazar said: 'When the Holy One, Blessed be He, created the first man, He created him אַכְדְרוֹגִינוֹס.'" (Greek ανϑρόγυνος, later called hermaphroditos and translated hermaphrodite by English writers). Query: What did those who thought Adam was a hermaphrodite think the nature of God was?

Great confusion concerning the origin of the word "Hermaphroditos" has been caused by Ovid. Unfortunately, his fascinating story, written about 7 A.D., describing the affair between the son of Hermes and Aphrodite and the nymph Salmacis has been accepted as the authentic one by most writers. There is evidence of the existence of Hermaphroditos and his legendary divine origin from Hermes and Aphrodite in several works before Ovid. It seems amazing, therefore, that the *Oxford Dictionary* and the *Encyclopaedia Britannica* go back no further than Ovid, but accept his fantastic version.

In the Middle Ages hermaphrodites were forbidden to be judges, advocates, or university rectors because they had been branded by nature. In Thomas Johnson's translation of *The Works of That Famous Chirurgeon Ambrose Parey* (1678) we find an interesting comment on an old English law which commanded these individuals to "chuse the sexe which they will use, and in which they will remaine and live, judging them to death if they be found to have departed from the sexe they made choice of."

In 1602 the Parisian parliament condemned a hermaphrodite to death because he had made use of the sex that he had abjured. Nicholas Vendette reports a Scottish hermaphrodite who was to be buried alive because he had impregnated his master's daughter after he had decided to live as a woman. There is also a case on record in which the question of legal male inheritance was not settled until the individual had lived as a female for fifty-one years. This person was married (as a woman) when twenty-one, but her husband, finding coitus impossible, left her after ten years. Afterward, though dressing as a female, "she" had relations with other women. She finally lived in the home of her brother, with whom she eventually came to blows. She prosecuted him for assault and he charged her with seducing his wife. Examination ensued, and at this ripe age she was declared to be male.

In Greek art Hermaphroditos is found depicted in many ways. He is seen in marble, in terra cotta, in cut gems, in murals, and as an adornment for vases. One of the earliest statues of a hermaphrodite is that by Polycles, who lived during the fourth century B.C. (Fig. 88).

At the Brady Urological Institute many intersexes have come for treatment, often uncertain what their real sex was. One patient, now twenty, had been reared as a female and attended a fashionable girls' school until two weeks before admission to the hospital. The girls in the school were so attracted to this patient that "she" began to wonder whether "she" was really a girl and went to a physician,

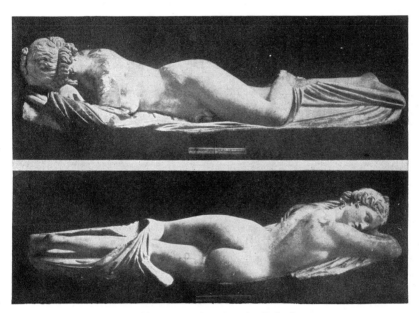

Fig. 88. Hermaphroditos by Polycles

who discovered the true sex and referred the patient to me. In the meantime the patient had doffed high heels, lingerie, and other feminine garb, discarded make-up, and had the hair clipped. Masculine clothing and shoes were worn rather awkwardly. When the patient was stripped, I thought I had before me a girl, but careful examination revealed the true sex, and operations to restore conditions to normal were performed. After the final operation a love affair sprang up between the patient and the nurse in attendance, and before long they were married. The couple has since visited me, and they are apparently very happy. The condition that this patient presented is known as masculine pseudohermaphroditism.

True hermaphroditism (*hermaphroditismus verus*) is that condition in which the patient presents both male and female sex glands. The scientifically proved cases of this type are rare. I discovered the tenth to be reported in medical literature. This patient, eighteen years old, was a college student almost six feet tall, and a splendid athlete. There was an external genital defect for which he sought operative restoration to normal. A rupture was also present in the lower left groin, but I had no doubt that the patient was entirely masculine. When I operated to cure the rupture, an incision into the sac disclosed a complete set of female organs, with an ovary functioning monthly. Opposite, in its normal position, lay a testicle. The patient was a true hermaphrodite. He was entirely unaware of the condition and had normal masculine instincts. I removed all the female organs and carried out the other operative procedures necessary to make him normal. Success was achieved. Three years later he married, and is now a happy and successful man of prominence.

A case that did not end happily was the following: A "boy" was brought to us years ago for operation on account of a genital defect. Dr. William C. Quinby, now professor of urology at Harvard, discovered that the patient was a girl, and advised the father to allow him to carry out operations to make his child normal. The father asserted that he had six girls and that this "boy," although only ten, was a valuable worker on the farm. He refused to have another girl added to his family and departed with the patient.

Twenty-one years elapsed. A small but sturdy-looking man appeared at the hospital with a pretty girl. It was our patient, now thirty-one. The pair had asked a priest to marry them. Our patient had been called aside by the priest and told that he could not do so because the father, many years ago, had told him that the patient was a girl. As the priest was deaf to all importuning, both of them had come to me. The patient asserted that "he" felt confident a mistake had been made at "his" first visit here. "He" had grown up as a male, had had many affairs with women. "He" felt certain from experience that "he" was well prepared to be the husband of the girl to whom "he" was engaged. She also asserted her complete confidence in "him." "He" demanded a thorough examination to disprove the diagnosis. After a careful study I had to tell "him" that no mistake had been made. The two left in tears.

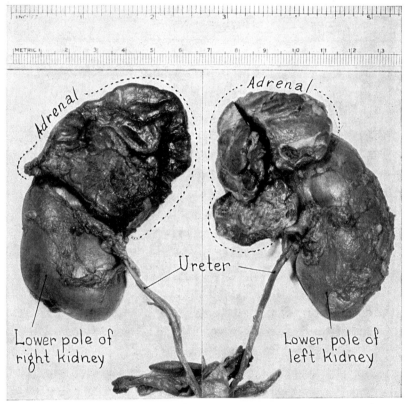

Fig. 89. An autopsy specimen showing adrenals sixteen times normal size from the body of a female who had shown male characteristics (virilism)

Three days later I was summoned to the ward. There lay our patient, desperately ill, having taken a lethal dose of bichloride of mercury. Postmortem examination revealed the cause of the extraordinary abnormalities that were present. The adrenal glands, which lie immediately above the kidneys, had grown to sixteen times their normal size (Fig. 89). They were almost as large as the kidneys.

The adrenal gland in the earliest stage of development is large compared with the kidneys and the sex glands, which lie close by. With the growth of the fetus, in most cases the adrenals diminish rapidly while the sex glands develop their male or female character and descend to their normal positions. Occasionally, from some as yet unexplained cause, the adrenals continue to grow, sometimes reaching great size. This condition of adrenal overgrowth (hyperplasia) occurs almost always in females, and causes amazing abnormalities. The genital organs are arrested in their development and the patient develops masculine attributes (virilism). Many of these cases are pronounced males at birth; they often grow to maturity and marry as such. The literature contains several amazing cases in which these females have lived vigorous masculine lives and had apparently happy wives who were surprised when the true condition was disclosed after death. Since early times the social and legal complications that have arisen among these "female pseudohermaphrodites" have been frequently described in literature.

The only treatment is to attack the offending organ—a greatly enlarged adrenal. As shown in Fig. 90, I have developed a method by which the adrenals can be simultaneously exposed. By the use of a special retractor, made in our machine shop, the spinal muscles are pressed together, giving a large exposure of the depths of the opening in which the adrenals lie. As shown here the adrenals are greatly enlarged. In some cases I have cut away a considerable part of each. Now I prefer to remove one adrenal. In one of these cases the patient has already lost much of the facial hair and a female contour is gradually developing. Various male characteristics are getting smaller. It is sometimes necessary to amputate the penis-like clitoris and open up a concealed vagina. One of these patients is now happily married.

Another condition that produces similar conditions is that of adrenal tumor. A girl of eighteen had been apparently normal until she was ten. Signs of virilism (masculinization) then developed. This was characterized by a growth of hair on the face, a deepening of the voice, and failure of feminine bodily characteristics to develop. A masculine torso and other male attributes were present. Beneath

the ribs on the right side a round mass was felt. An X-ray taken after
air was injected into that region through the back showed a tumor

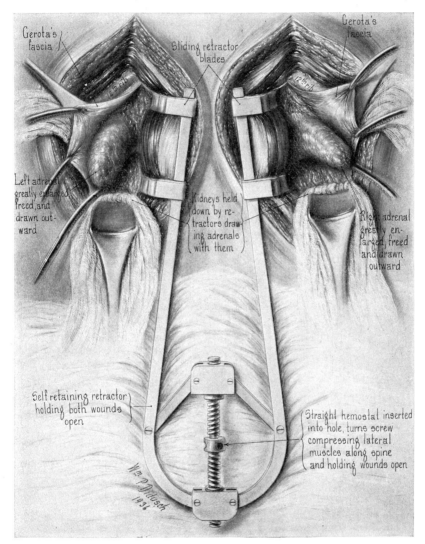

Fig. 90. The author's double retractor used to draw the spinal muscles together for
the simultaneous exposure of both adrenals

above the kidney. At operation the bilateral simultaneous exposure
of the adrenals was carried out (Fig. 90). The right adrenal was
normal, but on the left side a tumor larger than an orange was

present (Fig. 91). The pedicle containing the artery and vein was clamped off, as shown, and the tumor was easily removed. In a few weeks the facial hair began to fall out. The torso became feminine

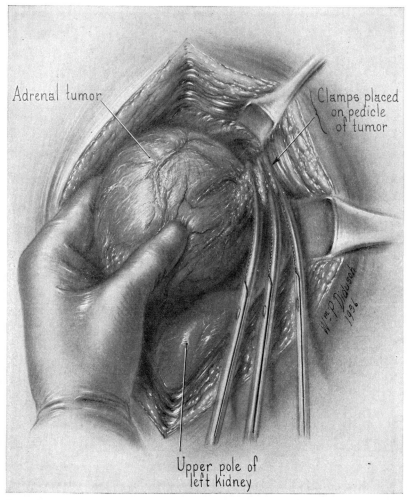

Fig. 91. The tumor of the left adrenal has been brought out through an incision. The blood vessels supplying it have been clamped before dividing and tying.

in appearance, certain masculine attributes began to disappear, and life became more normally feminine.

On a visit to Pittsburgh several years ago I saw two "sisters" who on examination had been thought to be so masculine in their appurtenances that the doctor had decided to put them both in male attire. One was fourteen and the other six. At that time very little had been accomplished by operative attack on enlarged adrenals. After a long consultation with the physician I could not honestly tell him I thought he was making a mistake, so these two girls are now growing to maturity in trousers and lead masculine lives. They may even marry females.

Another interesting experience was that of two children who were brought to me in 1935. One, three years old, had been reared as a girl. The other child, six months old, had been diagnosed a boy. On careful examination we found both were girls, although important radical genital operations were necessary to make each of them fairly normal females. In both instances the adrenal glands were thought to be responsible for the masculinization and the suppression of the feminine characteristics. An operation to remove one of the greatly enlarged adrenals will eventually be carried out with the hope of promoting their complete feminine development.[2]

An Operation on a Tiger

In the spring of 1923 a member of the Anatomical Department came over to the hospital and said that a sick tiger, supposed to have appendicitis, had been brought in from the zoo, and he wondered whether I would be interested in trying to cure him.

Getting together members of the urological and general surgical staffs, I went over and found a beautiful Bengal tiger in a cage. He was accompanied by a veterinarian who said the animal had been vomiting, and he thought the tiger had either appendicitis or intestinal obstruction. As it was impossible to examine him, we injected five grains of morphine in that portion of his body farthest removed from his head. This enraged him greatly. I was chief anesthetist and Franklin P. Johnson assisted, and it was some time before it was possible to administer enough ether (on brooms, which

[2] Details of these and other cases have been presented in my book *Genital Abnormalities, Hermaphroditism and Related Adrenal Diseases*, Williams & Wilkins, 1937.

I stuck beneath his nose) to get him anesthetized. He destroyed several brooms and makeshift cones before I got him under. By slipping a heavy rope around each paw and raising some of the iron bars, we were able to draw the tiger out of the cage and get him on a large table. There was no way to tie him down, but with eight men holding onto the ropes attached to his paws we got him stretched out.

The surgical team, consisting of Dr. Holman, Dr. William F. Rienhoff, Jr., and Dr. Cecil Bagley, applied soap, shaved his abdomen, and painted on iodine as meticulously as for the most important case in the operating-room. The animal seemed to be well anesthetized, but suddenly he opened his mouth and gave forth a growl that so terrified some of the crew that they dropped the ropes. Applying ether more vigorously, I again got him under, and the team was persuaded to return. The operation was commenced. About this time Dr. Lewis Weed, professor of anatomy, thought the room was very hot and turned on a big electric fan immediately behind Dr. Bagley, who thought the roar was the tiger's, and jumped over the instrument table. When order was restored, the operation proceeded. The appendix appeared normal, but there seemed to be a thickening between the stomach and intestine, which was thought to be responsible for the vomiting. On this account a gastroenterostomy was done to provide an exit for the stomach contents directly into the intestines. We thought this would cure him, but the poor tiger's condition grew rapidly worse, and he soon ceased breathing. Believing that this was due to too much ether, and that we should give the tiger the usual chance of restoration by artificial respiration, Johnson straddled the tiger, applied his great strength to the ribs, and succeeded in making him breathe, but only for a short time. Autopsy showed that what the tiger really had was multiple abscesses in his chest.

Operative Fees

In common with other surgeons I have had a goodly number of amusing experiences connected with operative fees. Some twenty years ago while on a trip to New York I was called on the telephone from Philadelphia. A patient requested the privilege of having a brief examination at my hotel in New York City. I asked him to wait to see me at our hospital, where I could examine him completely, but he insisted on coming to New York.

His prostate was extremely large and unusually soft. I thought he had simply a huge enlargement that could be shelled out by the usual method. I told him he would have to stay in the hospital about three weeks, and he agreed to pay me $500. "I'll only be able to pay that," he remarked, "if I don't have to stay longer than three weeks. If I do, will you deduct my hospital expenses from your fee?" I agreed.

When the prostate was exposed, it was seen that instead of a simple enlargement the patient had a malignant tumor (sarcoma) of the prostate, a rare condition that I had never seen, and beyond hope of radical cure. All I could do was to remove the obstruction. The patient had taken one of the best rooms in the hospital, on a corner with a southern exposure, and costing $12 a day. At the end of three weeks he was far from well. The following week his board bill was on me, $84 was deducted from my bill, and the same amount the next week. During the third week, as I saw my fee rapidly disappearing, I suggested that he move into a cheaper room. But he said, "No, I need the sunlight and I prefer to stay here," so he stayed on and on at $12 a day (on me). When the wound had firmly healed, my work having been done, and he should have been ready to go home, pleurisy developed. I proposed transferring him to the medical department, but he would not have it. When my fee had been completely eaten up and I suggested that he had long since recovered from my operation and could easily be treated at home, he insisted that he preferred the treatment at the hospital and stayed on from week to week at my expense. When he left he owed me nothing and I owed the hospital $350, which he insisted upon my paying. He was deaf to my arguments that his case had proved entirely different from what I had contracted to operate for and that his stay had been unduly prolonged by complications of a medical character.

Shortly after this a huge man appeared at my office and after examination demanded to know how much the proposed operation would cost. I looked him over, noted a shabby coat, a worn cravat, a large brass watch chain, and the general get-up of a man in meager circumstances. I said "Can you pay $100?" "Well, with difficulty I may be able to get that much together." The operation was carried out, and the patient left in a few weeks. About a month later a physician from Williamsport came to the operating-room and said to me, "Our city has been convulsed over a trick our richest citizen, Mr. Thomas, played upon you." I replied, "You can't mean Mr. James Thomas, because he is a very poor man—I could tell from his shabby clothes." He burst out laughing. "He has been going around Williamsport telling everybody about those clothes. He went to a pawnshop and rented an old cutaway coat, a red tie, and a large brass watch chain. He thinks your bill is a huge joke, and so do some of his friends in Williamsport."

Another patient from Pennsylvania, from whom I had removed a tuberculous kidney, went home without paying his bill. Some months later, in going over my accounts I detected this fact. No one knew what his circumstances were, so we sent a bill for $500. The next week I received a letter in which the patient thanked me for my generosity for making my bill so low and enclosed a check for $5. To letters explaining that he had made a mistake no reply was received.

In 1900 an officer of the United States Navy appeared at my office complaining of pain in the right kidney. Ureteral catheterization showed suppuration in this kidney. The X-ray had just come to Baltimore, and the only machine was at a private sanitarium where a young medical man who has since become famous was the operator. To obtain a satisfactory picture of the kidney region it was necessary at that time to expose the patient for thirty minutes. He lay under the X-rays for a half-hour, but when the plate was developed it was pronounced unsatisfactory. Four such exposures were made before satisfactory results were obtained. A few months later we were amazed to note reddening of the skin of the abdomen, which grew steadily more angry, and finally broke down. An ulcer as large as a small saucer appeared. This was our first experience with X-ray burns. Up to that time it was not known that they were dangerous to tissues, and radiologists frequently exposed their hands before the X-ray tube to determine the strength of the current. Several of these men subsequently lost their fingers, one of the most tragic cases being that of Dr. Frederick Baetjer, chief of the X-ray Department, Johns Hopkins Hospital. He underwent scores of operations during which surgeons attacked cancerous degenerations by removing the fingers, the thumbs, the skin of the hand and forearm, and glands up to the armpit. After about sixty operations he was finally cured and lived, with his mutilated hands, to do a great work in roentgenology.

As the large burn on my patient showed no tendency to heal, it was finally necessary for me to cut away the ulcer and cover the raw surface with a large graft of skin, which I took from his right thigh. The result was satisfactory, and I sent a bill for $500 for my operations and many months of treatment. I received a brief note saying that he considered my bill a fair one and would pay it as soon as he had collected that amount from the X-ray man, whom he expected to sue on account of the burn. I wrote that I would not accept payment under those circumstances and would cancel my bill if he would not sue — and he didn't, nor did he offer to pay me anything.

In the summer of 1904 I was in Cape May with Mrs. Young and the children. There were no garages, but I persuaded a man who ran a bicycle shop to let me keep my Stanley Steamer in his stable, for which I was to pay $10 a month. During the course of the month he sold me a dollar's worth of oil and assisted me one day in replacing a punctured tire. I happened to notice that his small daughter had a minute tumor of dilated blood vessels on her upper lip, and I told her father I would be glad to remove it. He had expected to take the child to Philadelphia for the operation and was delighted to save that expense, as I told him I would make no charge for the operation. I made elaborate preparations for the procedure and got two physicians to help me, one for the anesthesia and the other for instruments, and so on. Supplies (ether, antiseptics, ligatures, and the rest) cost me about $5. It took me almost an hour to do a neat job and get a closure that would leave no unsightly scar on the upper lip. The ultimate result was splendid and the family was overjoyed. When we were leaving for Baltimore, I told Mr. Jones I wanted to settle my account. He said "I've got it all worked out— $10 for the storage of your automobile, $1 for oil, and 25 cents for helping you repair that punctured tire—but you've been very good operating on my child, so just give me $11 and I'll call it square."

One afternoon when my office happened to be quite crowded, a late arrival came forward and said: "Dr. Young, I cannot possibly wait until you have looked after that crowd. I must see you at once." He was a short, thickset man, quick in speech and action. I saw that he was an interesting man, but explained that I had to take patients as they came and could not play favorites. He protested that he was an extremely busy man, and had come a long distance; he was very nervous. His personality was so impressive that I did arrange to see him shortly, when he burst out as follows: "My name is Robert Wolf. I am a desperate man. I have suffered greatly for many months. I have seen physicians all over Europe and in this country. I am no better. If I don't get well in two months I shall kill myself. I have come here as a last resort. I want your very best attention." On my assuring him that he would have every possible attention, he said: "I have heard that before, but I have got no results. In order to be sure of your interest I stopped by the Packard Agency and ordered for you a limousine. Here is a check for $6,000 to pay for it. The car will be here in a month. Please accept this as a retainer from a desperate man and don't refuse it." On my insistence that I had done nothing for him that deserved anything, that my practice was not that of the legal profession and I did not require a retainer, and that I did not want his automobile because I did not deserve it, he insisted that I keep it, saying: "What is money to me when I am desperate? I have an income of $1,000 a day, and what is six days to me when I am determined to kill myself if I am not relieved?" The result was that I never worked so hard over any patient in my life, and before the two months were up his pain had left. He was well.

Robert Wolf, at eighteen, when he had just finished high school, killed a man in self-defense. He could not prove his justification, and was sentenced to the penitentiary. While there, to put it in his own words; "I was put in the shoemaking shop and became an expert shoemaker. When I left, that was all I knew, so I took a job at that work. In a year or two I had saved some money, so I started out for myself. In a short time I had several shoemakers working for me. In a few years I had built a shoe factory, and at the age of thirty-two I found myself a prosperous manufacturer with a capital of $1,000,000. I took stock and decided that I did not want to make shoes the rest of my life, so I sold out my business and bought the *Ohio State Journal* of Columbus, at that time the most influential Republican newspaper in the state. Now at the age of forty-two I own a string of newspapers and have an income of $1,000 a day. I discovered the presidential possibilities of Taft, started the boom that ended in his election to the Presidency. I have been a big factor in the development of my state, but I am a desperate man. You seem surprised at my method of attracting your attention. I believe in extreme measures when your heart is set on accomplishing something. A few years ago I received a telegram saying that my son, who was a pupil at a preparatory school at Dobbs Ferry on the Hudson, was sick with an inflamed middle ear. His case was said not to be serious, but I took the first train to New York City, and when I got there called up the best specialist on the ear that I could obtain. As there was no early train to Dobbs Ferry, I chartered a train and took the specialist to the school. When I arrived there, we found that there had been a turn for the worse, the mastoid had become involved, and meningitis or brain abscess seemed imminent. The otologist said that an early operation alone would save him, and this was carried out. As a result, my boy is alive today. You can understand why I am no believer in half-measures."

IN 1912 a big, burly man with a huge head and a strong face appeared at my office. With him was a Baltimorean. "I have with me Mr. James Buchanan Brady," said the latter, and as I seemed quite ignorant, he added: "The celebrated Diamond Jim Brady. He has been to surgeons in Boston and New York. They have all refused to operate, because his case is said to be too complicated, and he has come here as a last resort. He's a rough diamond, but a fine fellow." Brady wore a neat, well-fitting morning coat, but in his tie was a huge diamond, and diamonds also sparkled from his vest, watch chain, cuff links, and the head of his cane. He looked his nickname.

Brady's case did indeed present a formidable series of complications: diabetes, Bright's disease, generalized urinary infection, inflammation and obstruction of the prostate gland, difficulty and frequency of urination, in addition to an old cardiac disease (angina pectoris) and high blood pressure. Examination showed a chronic inflammation of the prostate, which formed a bar at the neck of the bladder and obstructed the outflow of urine.

I told Mr. Brady that this great difficulty in urination could be cured by an operation. He said he had been told that on account of his heart disease and diabetes he could not stand an operation. I explained that I had recently invented an instrument with

JAMES BUCHANAN BRADY
After a portrait by George B. Shepherd

which the operation could be done entirely through the urethra, and without making any external cut, and that he would not have to have general anesthesia, which was considered dangerous in his case.

I showed him the instrument, which consisted of a tube with a short, curved inner end. On the under surface of the straight tube was a large hole or window into which the obstructing prostatic bar would drop as the instrument was withdrawn. An inner cutting tube would then be pushed in, cutting through and removing the entrapped bar. This simple instrument, which I called a prostatic excisor or punch, had already been used in many cases, as has been noted before (see Fig. 28, page 119).

Mr. Brady was delighted to hear that he would not have to take a general anesthetic, that the operation could be done in such a simple way without any external cut, and he readily agreed to enter the hospital. I explained to him that, unfortunately, I was preparing to go to London to present a paper to a medical congress and would have to leave in four days. Brady said that after I had done the operation, he would trust himself to my assistants.

I am giving the operation performed on Mr. Brady in intimate detail because some newspapers claimed that I cut out his overworked stomach and gave him a new one; other accounts credited me with having removed his gall bladder.

On April 7, 1912, after injecting cocaine into the urethra, the punch instrument was passed, the prostatic bar caught in the window and cut out by pushing the inner tube home (Fig. 29). Two more cuts were made and in a few minutes Brady was off the table, pleased that the operation had been carried out so quickly and without pain. Owing to the infection present, his convalescence was stormy. He had a chill and fever, his temperature increased each day, and when I went over to tell him good-by on the morning of the fourth day, his fever was high and I was not sure but that a severe sepsis would develop, or even blood poisoning. I told him how much I hated to leave him, but he said he understood and expressed his gratitude. I left him with many misgivings, uncertain whether he would recover.

When I left Baltimore, Brady knew nothing about my plans or who was to accompany me. We were greatly surprised when his secretary met me at the station in New York and insisted on conducting Bessy and me, three children, a French maid, and an Irish nurse to the Vanderbilt Hotel, where the secretary said Mr. Brady wished me to stop. On our arrival at the hotel we were met by the manager and other functionaires and conducted to the royal suite, consisting of drawing-room, sitting-room, and a series of bedrooms, with maids in attendance. The matron was there to arrange our clothes. We were assured that as friends of Mr. Brady everything would be at our disposal. His secretary then presented us with eight tickets for the all-star performance of *Robin Hood*, which was to be given that night as a benefit for The Lambs club. It was to be a gala performance, and I noted that the tickets cost $25 apiece. He said that Mr. Brady thought we might like to take some friends. The secretary then said that Mr. Brady wanted him to take the children to see "The Great White Way" after sundown, and that he would return in the morning with motors to take us to our ship.

On board ship, Mrs. Young found her stateroom almost filled with flowers and candy. In mine was a case of champagne, Scotch, rye and Irish whisky, red and white vintage wines, various liqueurs, Havana cigars—small, medium, and large—cartons of cigarettes of several makes, most of the month's magazines, and the New York newspapers—all this from a man whom I had known only a few days and who was in Baltimore so sick that I was not sure he would recover.

While in Europe I was glad to receive cables announcing his continued improvement, and his final discharge from the hospital with a perfect result from the operation. The other conditions of long standing required my attention off and on during the five years Mr. Brady lived. I frequently went to New York on this account, and enlisted the services of one of my assistants, Dr. Oswald S. Lowsley, then an intern at Bellevue Hospital.

Brady was born on the Bowery, of a drunken father and a mother who ran a saloon and tended bar. His mother never drank; she impressed her son with the evils of drink, and made him promise never to touch liquor. He went to work at the age of twelve as a messenger boy in the Grand Central Station. He soon made up his mind that there was a great future in railroad equipment, and it wasn't long before he became a traveling salesman for a supply house. He determined to be the best-dressed man in the business. As he traveled all over the country, he carried with him well-tailored business suits, cutaways, dinner suits, and dress clothes. He wore a large diamond pin, which he had bought with the first money he saved. He usually dressed for dinner, even in the West, where his frequent appearance in tails, white waistcoat, and white tie created a sensation. He became a marked man, and this pleased him. His stylish business suit and diamond pin gave him an entree, and often led to a discussion about jewels. He bought more and more diamonds. When he found a businessman keen to talk about stones, he would casually pull out a chamois bag and toss out a dozen or so large sparklers. The name "Diamond Jim," which he soon acquired, went before him, and when he arrived at a new town, railroad men upon whom he called had all heard of him, and his welcome was enthusiastic. His personality was ingratiating, and he was a free spender. His prospective clients were treated to champagne dinners and their wives received candy and flowers. Brady prospered, and before long he became one of the best-known railroad men. His success was such that he rose rapidly in the great house of Manning, Maxwell and Moore.

The Mellons of Pittsburgh then became interested in him, and his prodigious salesmanship won for him the head of the sales department for their great corporation, which had an output eventually of one hundred standard steel cars a day. To sell these was Brady's job.

The men who let the contracts were the chief purchasing agents and the presidents of great railroads. Brady set about to make these his devoted friends. Through scouts he kept tab on their movements, and when they arrived in New York, Brady arranged to meet them with a Rolls Royce with two liveried men on the box, and this motorcar was at their beck and call as long as they were in the city. Rooms, usually at the Waldorf, had been reserved for them by Brady, often the royal suite, already stocked with wines and liquors and decorated with flowers. Mr. Brady's secretary would appear in the afternoon with front-row tickets for the principal shows. The secretary would quietly inform the visitor that if he wished either a dinner or a supper party he would be glad to arrange it at Mr. Brady's expense, and have present dancing girls and, after the shows, almost any of the stars of the footlights that struck his fancy. If he had a penchant for dancing, a small orchestra would be on hand. Brady discreetly kept away, but after a week or so, when the railroad executive left New York and found all the bills had been paid, he did not forget James Buchanan Brady.

This was not all he did for the railroad executives and also for the scores of his friends with whom he had no ax to grind. He bought so much candy that he finally purchased a large interest in Page & Shaw. On all the holidays—national, state, and religious—multitudes of presents were sent out from Brady: cravats, scarfs, and gloves from Budd's; jewels from Tiffany's; glass and china from Ovington's; flowers from numerous florists; and candy by the cartload. The wives and lady friends were not forgotten, and through his astute agents he found out what people liked and what gifts would be the most acceptable.

The stories of Brady's experiences are numberless. One with the president of the Reading Railroad seems worthy of recording. Mr. Baer well deserved his name; he was so unapproachable that no salesman ever got into his private office. Brady's firm had never been able to accomplish anything with Mr. Baer, or to make any sales to his railroad. Brady was sent to Reading to see what he could do. When he presented his card, Mr. Baer's secretary politely informed him that it was useless for him to expect to meet Mr. Baer, as no one was admitted to his private office unless the caller had been requested to come. Brady casually remarked: "Well, I have nothing to do. I'll simply sit here and wait. This is a nice place to read the newspaper." In a little while Mr. Baer came in. Brady remained until midday, when Mr. Baer went out for lunch. Brady did the same, but soon returned, although the secretary again told him that it was useless for him to wait. At five o'clock Mr. Baer went home for the day. Brady also left, but was back bright and early the next morning and again on Wednesday, Thursday, and Friday. The secretary each day had expostulated at the folly of Mr. Brady's remaining when it would be impossible to see Mr. Baer, but Brady answered, "I have nothing to do." Saturday morning came. The secretary was called to Mr. Baer, who asked: "Who is that big, burly man sitting in my office? I've seen him every day this week. What does he want?" "He is James Buchanan Brady, vice-president of the Standard Steel Car Company, and he hopes to have an interview with you." "Didn't you tell him," said Mr. Baer, "that I never see salesmen, that I buy from whom I wish and never admit anyone to my office unless I call for him?" "Yes, Mr. Baer, I have told him that at least a dozen times." "He's a damned impudent chap," said Mr. Baer. "Send him in here. I'll give him a dressing-down." Whereupon Brady was admitted to the office of Mr. Baer, who turned fiercely upon him and said: "I understand your name is Brady. Don't you know I never see salesmen? Why the hell have you been waiting this entire week in my office?" With a broad smile, Brady remarked, "I have been waiting to tell you, Mr. Baer, that you can go straight to hell." It is not difficult to picture the scene that followed. The ultimate result was that when Brady left the office an hour later, he had with him a signed contract for $5,000,000 worth of steel freight cars.

After I returned from Europe, Mr. Brady gave a large dinner in my honor at the Vanderbilt Hotel, to which he had invited a number of railroad presidents and other men prominent in business affairs. Raymond Hitchcock was toastmaster and it was a rollicking evening. They poked a lot of good-natured fun at Diamond Jim, and he enjoyed it immensely.

Mrs. Young and I frequently saw Mr. Brady when we went to

New York, and found him remarkably generous and self-effacing. He would never come to the hotel to dine when Mrs. Young was with me, nor accompany us to the theater, remarking, "I am not of your class; I don't want to embarrass you." Although a large man, he was a fine dancer, employed the best of teachers to give him all the fancy steps, and at night clubs would occasionally do a tango with the première danseuse while all other dancers stood aside and applauded.

Wherever Brady went he was a marked man. At the theater the spotlight would be turned on him. He always occupied the center seat in the front row, and actors and actresses, as they came upon the stage, would usually salute him. Not infrequently most of their remarks and actions would be directed to him as the play progressed. He was recognized as the greatest patron of the stage and as the best friend the actors had; many of them owed their start and success to him. Brady's opinion of a play was taken by the critics to be one of the best. If he approved of it, they knew it would succeed; if he disapproved, the producers often took it off.

Brady's jewels were his greatest passion and interest. They were taken care of by the firm on Maiden Lane who made his jewelry. They had a huge safe filled with Brady's collection. There were some thirty-five sets, a different one for each day of the month, and then some. Each set filled a small morocco case and consisted of about twenty-five pieces. For example, his pearl and diamond set. There was a large pear-shaped pearl pin with a row of diamonds around the stem; five buttons for his waistcoat, each with a large pearl surrounded by diamonds; cuff links of a similar design; a gold pencil with a huge pearl in the end and diamonds festooned around its shaft; an eyeglass case with a large pearl surrounded by diamonds; a similar design on his pocketbook and his watch, and in the head of his cane. The largest jewel of all consisted of a huge pearl surrounded by diamonds that was the top button of his drawers, which Brady smilingly said was "only seen by his best girl." Each evening at six o'clock his jeweler would arrive with several cases for

Brady to choose from for the following day and also his jewels for the evening. I have often been with Brady when he had at least $250,000 worth of jewels on his person, and yet he never had a guard. He did, however, take the precaution, when he arrived at his home in the early hours of the morning, to send his chauffeur to open the door and see that no one lurked in the entrance hall or adjacent areaways. The lady in whom Brady happened to be interested for the moment was usually bedecked with pearls, diamonds, or emeralds, but as far as I could observe he gave little concern to their safekeeping. When he left her at her home she was not required to divest herself of the gorgeous string of pearls, the bracelets or rings.

Brady had in his sets some remarkable jewels. He had given much attention to their collection for many years and was constantly improving their quality and size. In his portrait he is wearing his diamonds set in onyx. The ring was one inch square and had a $20,000 stone in it. This portrait was painted for me by George Shepherd, in whom I became interested while he was a student at the University of Virginia and sent to Paris to study. Brady's diamond set contained some of the loveliest stones I have ever seen. The star-sapphire set was exquisite, as was his ruby set. There was a beautiful cat's-eye set that he loved very much. Another remarkable one he called his transportation set. Here almost every form of locomotion was illustrated. The stickpin was an airplane; the waistcoat buttons, carwheels; the cuff links, cars of various types; his watch was decorated with an automobile, his wallet and eyeglass case with other forms of locomotion, many of considerable size. When he burst forth with his "transportation set," he created a sensation. Brady's love for his jewels was no more astonishing than that of a bibliophile for his old, uncut first editions or manuscripts in some dead language that he cannot read. I believe he had as much justification for his hobby as many other collectors have for theirs.

One of his friends who objected seriously to Brady's galaxy of jewels finally persuaded him to give them up. Brady did so, but every day went down and had them paraded before his eager gaze by the jeweler who kept them. His friends noticed a tremendous change in his temperament. His gaiety had disappeared, and his friend who had persuaded him to give up his jewels came to him and begged him to put them on again. Immediately Diamond Jim was his old gay self. While his jewels, his motorcars, his famous dinners, his dependent actors and actresses, and his intimate acquaintances among the great heads of railroads of the entire United States were sufficient to mark Brady as an extraordinary man, he was at heart simple and retiring, and one of the most considerate and generous men I have ever met.

Although Brady interested women greatly and had many affairs, I believe there was only one with whom he was greatly in love—a beauty of the stage, Edna McCauley, a reigning stage favorite. Brady had her installed in a lovely South Branch bungalow and she lived in great style. On one of his visits Brady brought down with him one of the Lewisohns, who repaid Brady's hospitality by running off with the beautiful Edna and disrupting Brady's happy home. He was disconsolate for a long time, and his attachments in the future were transitory. Only once did Brady refer to it to me, and then with fire in his eyes and anger in his voice. His long and intimate friendship with Lillian Russell has been described at length in the biography of Diamond Jim by Parker Morell. Mr. Brady never spoke of this to me.

Brady had spent hundreds of thousands of dollars on actors and actresses and in lavish entertainments. He admitted that often this had been mistaken generosity. Thinking of the money Brady had squandered, it occurred to me that he might be persuaded to build a hospital as a monument to himself. I had already prepared the plans of a urological hospital several years before, when Mr. William H. Grafflin offered to give me $200,000 for that purpose. The plan fell through when the trustees were persuaded that as there was no endowment, the building would have to contain too many private rooms to make it self-supporting. The plans were far from perfect, but they gave me a talking-point.

Mr. Brady had come again to me for a check-up. I pointed out to him the great need of an institute devoted to urology that would contain not only wards for public and private patients but laboratories for clinical and research work. Such a hospital would carry Mr. Brady's name forever. From it would come a great series of clinical and scientific papers that would reach all quarters of the earth and carry on each publication the name of James Buchanan Brady. I contrasted this with the ephemeral character of the fame and pleasure he got from the plays he backed, the actors and actresses he supported, and the sportsmen he banqueted. Here was an opportunity for him to hand his name down to posterity by this institute as Rockefeller's was by the institute that bore his name and Hopkins's was by the Johns Hopkins University and Hospital. I saw that Brady was greatly impressed, and having used every argument, I left him to think it over.

In the same ward a short distance away was Mr. George Stephens, president of the Chesapeake & Ohio Railroad. He had come to see Brady a few days before. Brady told me that Mr. Stephens was suffering with pain in the bladder; I looked in with a cystoscope, discovered a stone, crushed and removed it. Mr. Stephens was convalescent and very grateful. I told him about the proposal I had made to Brady and asked him to help me. Quitting the ward, I absented myself for an hour and then came back. I went first to see Mr. Stephens, and he told me that immediately after I had left the ward Brady had come to his room. "I think he is going to do it." I then went to see Mr. Brady and he immediately told me that he was greatly impressed by the opportunity offered to build an institute that would perpetuate his name, and that he would do it. It is needless to describe my joy. Elsewhere I tell in detail the design and construction of the James Buchanan Brady Urological Institute on the grounds of the Johns Hopkins Hospital, and its dedication in 1915. Brady often sent patients to be treated at his institute—

some intimate friends, others poor people who had won his sympathy. The fact that they all were taken care of without expense was greatly appreciated by Brady, who often said that the pleasure he got from building the institute was great and that he was sorry he had not done it years before.

For four years he enjoyed comparatively good health, continuing his active direction of the sales department of the great Standard Steel Car Company. He dressed every evening, generally in full dress, and was to be seen dining with friends or at the theaters and night clubs afterward. He got to bed late, but being a sound sleeper, he woke at nine o'clock ravenously hungry and "polished off" a huge breakfast. I have seen him eat six cantaloupes and quantities of eggs. At his other meals large steaks or many chops would disappear rapidly. His principal libation was orange juice, of which I have seen him consume two quarts. At a small dinner at my home one of my guests said: "Mr. Brady, I have always heard you were a great 'sport,' but you refused a cocktail, sherry, Sauterne, champagne, and cognac, and took neither cigarettes nor cigars. I don't believe you're much of a sportsman." Whereat Brady shyly remarked, "No, I don't drink or smoke, but there's one other little thing I'm very fond of."

Although our operation had removed his obstruction to urination and given him comfort, his heart continued to disturb him, and eventually the angina became so serious that he was put to bed. Tired of the excitement in New York, in the spring of 1917 he moved to Atlantic City, and at the Shelburne, in apartments decorated with flowers, overlooking the busy boardwalk he loved so well, he died on April 13, 1917.

Brady's funeral was one of the most notable in New York. Both St. Agnes Roman Catholic Church on East Forty-second Street and the streets surrounding it were crowded. The railroads were represented by their presidents and great officers, the theaters by leading stars. More impressive were the crowds of poor who wept as his coffin passed by, and told near-by onlookers of the kindnesses that Brady had bestowed upon them.

He was indeed one of the most extraordinary men I have known—a rough diamond, it may be said, brought up on the Bowery, self-educated, with unusually flashy tastes, but one of the most persuasive men in America. His affection for me and gratitude for what I had done for him, and his pride in the Urological Institute built in his memory, were always great, and to me it is a huge satisfaction to have known him so well.

CHAPTER 8. THE JAMES BUCHANAN BRADY
UROLOGICAL INSTITUTE

HAVING secured Mr. Brady's promise to build a urological institute, I decided to go abroad to study hospitals and equipment. St. Peter's Hospital for Stone for years was the only hospital in the world devoted solely to urology. In it had worked many men who had become famous, but the hospital was still small and inadequate, with few laboratories and no provision for research. There was little to be learned there, but elsewhere in London new hospitals had gone up that were well worth study. In Paris, the Hôpital Necker had a celebrated department of urology where the famous Guyon had built a fine museum. I had spent a summer there twelve years before. Here we picked up many suggestions and at the Hôpital Lariboisière, in the Salle Civiale, was an excellent and more modern urological department. At old Saint-Louis, with its classic buildings, was a noted museum of moulages—reproductions in plastic material—of every type of disease, perfect in color and of great value in teaching. With a Paris architect I had a chance to study the plans of a beautiful new hospital that had been built in the Alps by J. Pierpont Morgan. There were no hospitals in Austria or Germany of interest to us.

With voluminous notes and many blueprints, I returned to America and set to work with the architects Archer and Allen and the collaboration of Dr. Winford H. Smith, director of the Johns Hopkins Hospital, to perfect our plans. It was decided that in addition to wards for public and private patients, there must be rooms for the reception of patients, history-taking, clinical and laboratory examinations, and X-ray facilities, besides an abundance of laboratories devoted to bacteriology, pathology, and chemistry. Provisions were to be made for departments of photography and illustrative art, and for a machine shop. For experimentation, space and operating rooms for animals of different types should be provided. The Urological Institute was to be so designed that it would work in close co-operation with the outpatient urologic dispensary already located in the basement of the surgical building, where an excellent lecture room and museum for specimens to be used in teaching were at hand. After many months of consultation, drawing and redrawing plans and specifications, at last they were complete.

Ground was broken November 15, 1913, and on January 21, 1915, the James Buchanan Brady Urological Institute was opened to patients. The first floor provides for varied activities. It connects directly with the outpatient urologic clinic, which occupies spacious rooms and is well equipped for clinical and laboratory work, minor operations, and examination of the interior of the bladder with the cystoscope. Cases found of special interest are taken through the corridor connecting with the first floor of the Brady Urological Institute, where are provided rooms for the reception of patients, history-taking, and examinations of all sorts, some by X-ray. Adjacent are laboratories for microscopic, bacteriologic, and pathologic work, photography of patients and specimens, and also photomicrographs and a department of illustrative art, and offices for the director and associates as well as special rooms for research. This floor furnishes a diagnostic clinic for public and private cases as comprehensive and convenient as any I know of. The histories, which are voluminous, are kept in a soundproof room in which the record clerks work. In the basement is a well-equipped machine shop, and also provision for animals of different types, with rooms for sterilizers and tables and instruments for experimental work with them, always under anesthesia.

From the second to the fifth floors are wards for public, semiprivate, and private patients, each equipped with a day room and a sun porch. On the sixth floor are recreation rooms for patients and bedrooms for the resident staff. The top floor is given up to laboratories for chemistry, bacteriology, and various problems of research.

The eight floors that comprise the Brady Urological Institute furnish a complete special surgical unit with practically every requisite necessary for the clinical and experimental study of cases.

The Dedication of the Institute

It was not until May 4, 1915, that the formal dedication was held. Invitations had been sent to distinguished men in medicine and surgery and also to many of Mr. Brady's friends, as well as to citizens of Baltimore. Brady arrived with quite a retinue on the morning of the ceremonies in a stylish cutaway, wearing what was to him a modest collection of diamonds, and a top hat. I wore a sack suit and noticed his quick survey of my attire and apparent surprise.

Dr. Edward L. Keyes, Sr., of New York, delivered a beautiful address on "Opportunity." He traced the progress of medicine and surgery and pointed out the advantages of this new institute and the opportunity it afforded for research and advancement. In the audience were many ladies, and although they were unable to follow the scientific portions of Dr. Keyes's address, they were repaid by an amusing incident. When Dr. Keyes raised his hands to give a more vigorous emphasis to some remark on "Opportunity," his suspenders broke and his trousers started to slip down. During the remainder of his brilliant discourse the audience had difficulty in maintaining its serious interest, owing to Dr. Keyes's struggles to keep his trousers up.

The audience was invited to visit the institute and meet Mr. Brady, who glowed with pride in his monument.

In the evening in the ballroom of the Hotel Belvedere a banquet was held. The table was oval and the center was filled with flowers, ferns, and plants. The Governor of Maryland sat at Brady's right and I on his left. Around the table were distinguished men of the bench, the bar, and the medical profession, Raymond Hitchcock and other notables from the stage, and many intimate friends. There were the usual speeches, Hitchcock's being the most amusing, particularly his comments on finding Brady in such serious company. When Mr. Brady was called on, he arose and said, with evident emotion, "The sky was never so blue and the grass never so green as they are this day for me," and sat down.

When his Urological Institute began to function, I explained to Mr. Brady that we would need at least $25,000 or $30,000 a year for maintenance. Asserting that he hoped I had overestimated the amount, he offered $15,000 a year, and gave that regularly for two years. In the meantime our expenses in running the laboratories and research departments amounted to much more, but I footed the bills and bided my time so as to present Mr. Brady accurate figures showing how much the operation really did cost.

When Brady came down with his serious anginal attacks, he told me that he had made his will and left the Institute $300,000, which would provide the necessary $15,000 for maintenance. Realizing that I had tarried too long, I immediately got together my accounts, put them in brief and effective form, and presented to Brady at his hotel in Atlantic City a statement that showed we really needed $50,000 a year to run the laboratories, research departments, and public wards in the best possible manner. Brady considered the proposition and said, "All right; I will add a codicil to my will and leave you enough to produce that amount annually." Returning to Baltimore, I wrote at length my recommendations and my understanding of his agreement, and as Dr. Thomas R. Brown was going to Atlantic City to see Mr. Brady professionally at my request, I entrusted my letter to Dr. Brown and asked him to bring me a report from Mr. Brady after he had read the letter. On the following day Dr. Brown reported that he had delivered the letter to Brady, that he had not seen him read it, but later on in the day Mr. Brady had told him to tell me that he had read my letter and would carry out his promise to me.

A few days later I went to Atlantic City to see Mr. Brady. I was met by a secretary, who said: "Mr. Brady received your letter. He has made the codicil to his will leaving the money to provide the endowment that he promised you. It has been attended to, but Mr. Brady dislikes greatly to talk about wills or anything else that refers to his possible death. I request that you say nothing to him about it, but you have my assurance that it has been done."

I did as instructed, and on numerous visits I never referred to the subject to Brady himself, but often asked the secretary whether he was positive the codicil had been added to the will. He always told me I could rest absolutely assured that everything was all right. He told me this at least eight times.

I saw the secretary after Mr. Brady's funeral and asked to see the will. He seemed disturbed at my mentioning the matter, said he could not show the will to me then, but that it would be opened the following day and that I could be present. Imagine my surprise when the next morning I saw in the *New York Times* a detailed account of Brady's will in which the amount left the Johns Hopkins Hospital for the maintenance of the James Buchanan Brady Urological Institute was $300,000, the sum Brady had provided in his original will. No change had been made, and there was no codicil found.

I made an attempt to see the secretary, but he evaded me. I had no written documents; I had only the memory of Brady's promise and the secretary's statements. Dr. Brown had not seen the contents of my letter and could be of no help. I have given this in intimate detail because I want those connected with the Brady Institute to know that I did not overlook the necessity of getting an adequate endowment. To this day I have never been able to understand how Mr. Brady's intention was frustrated.

During the years immediately after the World War we had no great difficulty in obtaining donations for research and clinical purposes. One of the first of these was for $50,000, which came from two of our patients, Mr. Willis Sharpe Kilmer and Mr. Robert W. Kelley. Afterward Mr. Kilmer contributed additional amounts totaling over $50,000; and Mrs. Robert W. Kelley has materially assisted us since her husband's death. But our work was geared to high standards and expenses were heavy, at times as much as $35,000 a year being expended on the laboratories, research, and clinical departments in addition to Mr. Brady's endowment.

Then we had the good luck to obtain a large endowment from four splendid friends, men who appreciated the high character of the work done at the Brady Urological Institute from personal experience. These were Mr. William N. Reynolds, Mr. Robert W. Kelley, Mr. Henry K. McHarg, and Mr. Hobart J. Park. Their total contributions eventually amounted to $400,000. This fund, which they insisted upon calling the Hugh H. Young Research Fund, at first yielded more than $22,000 a year, but with the depression of some of the securities and the diminution of interest rates, a marked reduction in income resulted. At this point we had the good fortune to receive a donation of $15,000 from Mr. August Heckscher and $30,000 from the Chemical Foundation through the kind offices of Mr. Francis P. Garvan and his secretary, Mr. Buffum. Additional sums have come from time to time from grateful patients and friends. But we have faced yearly the necessity of begging and borrowing and going into our own pockets to continue the active work in our laboratories and clinical departments. Being poor—as compared with richly endowed institutions—has made us work the harder to produce more in order to impress philanthropic men with the value of our work.

The staff of the Brady Urological Institute, as originally constituted, was:

CLINICAL

Director
Hugh H. Young

Chief of dispensary
John T. Geraghty

Dispensary assistants
Frederick W. Hobelmann
Albert Keidel
Joseph E. Kerney
Frank Hinman

Roentgenologist
Charles A. Waters

Resident urologist
William A. Frontz

Assistant resident urologists
Edwin G. Davis
J. E. Burns

Interns
Francis T. Williams
Don F. Cameron
Howard L. Cecil

Supervisor of nurses
Elizabeth C. Thomas

Chief of records and bookkeeper
Elder H. Slade

Secretaries
Philip Meisel
Roland Abercrombie

Machinist
Howard Hughes

Male nurses
William A. Robbins
Walter Oliver

RESEARCH

Bacteriologist
E. O. Swartz

Chemist
George Peirce

Pathologist
David M. Davis

Physicist
William S. Gorton

Medical consultant
Norman M. Keith

Experimental surgeon
William C. Quinby

Artist (*later*)
William P. Didusch

Plastic modelist (*later*)
Vladimir Fortunato

Photographer (*later*)
Charles F. Elvers

The Clinical Organization

In the organization of professional services of the Brady Institute a careful study was made of the Phipps Psychiatric Clinic at the Johns Hopkins Hospital, and of the Peter Bent Brigham Hospital. Following the plan in operation at these two hospital units, I proposed in the design of the Brady Institute that private offices be furnished. Dr. Winford H. Smith kindly made this recommendation to the Medical Board and the trustees. As a result, when the Brady Urological Institute was opened I moved my effects bodily from private offices in the city to the institute. Friends warned me that this would interfere considerably with my private practice. Many ambulatory patients, especially those who would drop in on their way to or from business, found the trip of two miles or more to the Brady Institute much too far and went elsewhere, but the gain in conservation of time and the ability to keep closely in touch with clinical and laboratory work more than compensated.

With the growth of our clinical organization, the offices and laboratories on the first floor became more and more crowded. Mr. Sylvester Labrot contributed almost $10,000, with which additions and revisions were made. Now each member of the visiting staff has a private office and a secretary, and concentrates most of his time at the institute. This rearrangement of rooms furnished a large studio for Mr. William P. Didusch, who has broadened his art work to include motion pictures. The Department of Publications, in charge of Miss Bertha M. Trott, is also located on the first floor of the institute. Here also the X-ray work is done, under Dr. Charles A. Waters and Miss Mary A. Goldthwaite, as well as the pathological work under the technical charge of Mr. Charles F. Elvers.

The Research Organization

These departments were presided over by full-time salaried men of experience. They offered special courses for small groups of students, directed their special laboratories, and engaged in research. As many problems overlapped, these laboratories were co-operative and mutually helpful. The animal department was utilized by all, as was also the machine shop.

In 1916 Dr. Edwin C. White came on the staff as chemist, and in 1920 Dr. Justina H. Hill as bacteriologist in chief.

Undergraduate Teaching

With the rapid development of medical science and art in every direction the undergraduate student has been veritably swamped by the learning to be acquired. Here we make no effort to give detailed instruction to undergraduate medical students, nor to make them expert in urologic technique. If we can sufficiently instruct them in the fundamentals that are of utmost importance to good knowledge of medicine and surgery, we have accomplished enough. If at the same time we can inspire them with the importance and the beauty of the subject, some will be likely to return, demanding to be initiated into the intricacies of the art.

Working on this basis, the undergraduate is given instruction for a trimester as a student assistant in the ward and the outpatient dispensary. Weekly clinical lectures and quizzes on cases coming to this outpatient clinic are held, and ward rounds for an hour once a week for every student in the surgical group during each trimester are given. At these ward rounds the usual methods are employed, stress being laid upon the importance of careful manual examination and delineation by free-hand drawings or diagrams of the findings. Dr. Osler's apt remark, "The difference between the good doctor and the poor one is that the good doctor knows how to make a rectal examination," is often quoted, and the student is urged to make careful charts of the rectal examination of all the cases that he meets in the various hospital wards. In urologic ward rounds we stress the importance of the careful study of the history, the pathology, the etiology, and complications, the diagnostic methods that have been used in working up the case, and the surgical operation that is to be employed.

Long convinced of the lasting value to students of ocular demonstrations, I have prepared methods by which the various problems presented by each case may be shown in every possible way. For this purpose we have developed what is called the "urologic bus." This vehicle is a carriage sufficiently small to be taken along on teaching rounds. It is provided on each side with shelves, on which are placed anatomic and pathologic models or specimens that have been previously selected in accordance with the cases and diseases to be seen at ward rounds. The interior of the "bus" contains a series of photographs mounted on large cards inserted into frames that hang by a cord from a pulley, being counterbalanced by a lead weight. When withdrawn from the central compartment the proper pictures may be brought to view by spreading the fanlike group of metal frames containing them.

A typical case upon which rounds were held may be cited:

A public-ward patient had a stone in a double kidney on the left side. A student gave a complete history and described the clinical and laboratory findings. The X-ray film showing a stone high up in the left kidney region was exhibited. The pyelogram, which showed that the kidney was double, the lower half containing no stone and secreting healthy urine, was also shown. The case was further elucidated by showing a chart carried in the "bus" depicting cystoscopy, ureter catheterization, and the taking of a pyelogram—an X-ray picture of the kidney filled with a fluid that gives a shadow—on the combined urologic and X-ray table; a card containing drawings explaining the embryology of the kidney and the development of double kidney and double (bifid) ureters; a card showing the operative technique of exposure of the kidney and the operation for double kidney in which the diseased half is removed and the healthy half left in place (heminephrectomy); the specimen (from the shelf of the "bus") removed at operation; and other specimens from previous operations and from autopsy cases.

The convalescence was then described. The kidney function tests before and after operation were presented with charts showing curves of elimination, and finally the healing wound was exhibited.

By such presentation the students obtain not only the usual history and description of diagnostic methods, but also full and complete ocular demonstrations of the pathology, embryology, and surgery of the case, so that (in my opinion) a much more lasting and complete picture of the disease is impressed upon the student's mind by my plan of teaching with the "urologic bus."

In these rounds we also make use of a series of drawings by Mr. William P. Didusch, as well as models that have been prepared by Dr. Vladimir Fortunato.

For several years Dr. Fortunato had been preparing a number of anatomical and surgical models for other members of the faculty. Finally the funds gave out and his services were about to be lost to the Medical School. I had found his work very helpful in recording rare clinical and pathological conditions, so I cast about to find funds to keep him in Baltimore. Thereafter he worked several years for the Brady Institute alone.

When the American Medical Association met in Chicago, I decided to make an exhibit of Dr. Fortunato's moulages. A huge box would be necessary to transport them. Dr. Fortunato conceived the idea of using a coffin box, on the inner surfaces of which he was able to fasten his models and so avoid injury to them in transit. When the lid was screwed on, four men were required to carry it by the coffin handles to the truck that transported it to the station. Dr. David M. Davis had charge of the installation of the exhibit and accompanied the "coffin" on the train. At the station difficulties were encountered when the express company demanded a death certificate. At Chicago, as a truck carrying the coffin was pulled down the platform Irish laborers on an adjacent track stopped their work, removed their hats, and stood reverently with bowed heads.

Recently, motion pictures have been much used to supplement our clinical demonstration of cases. We have now an extensive library of films of our operations, photographed by William P. Didusch, comprising almost every important disease of the genitourinary tract and the operations employed. In this list are many rare conditions and amazing sexual abnormalities associated with hermaphroditism. We have now numerous motion pictures in color of those patients who come in female dress, are discovered to be males, and undergo operations that transform their status so that they finally leave in masculine attire. Some of these "strip-teases" are most amusing.

The great advantage of motion pictures of operations is that with modern apparatus, wonderful illumination, and high-powered lenses very fine details of the essential portions of an operation are obtained, and when they are projected on the screen, the student is able to see the intimate technique far better than he possibly could while looking on in the operating room. By judiciously selecting only important details, an operation requiring an hour or more can be adequately displayed in a colored motion picture in eight or ten minutes. It is thus possible to bring to a class of students all they need know of the details of important operations, far better than they could get in many visits to the operating-room and occupying far more of their very valuable time.

These motion pictures are not shown at ward rounds, but in an adjacent classroom, to which we are able to bring patients from the public wards with conditions that illustrate the subject under discussion, and also pathological specimens.

By the use of the "urologic bus" that moves from patient to patient with the progress of the bedside clinic and carrying pathological specimens, X-rays, photographs, and drawings illustrating similar cases and operations, a very practical method has been devised for use in conjunction with bedside teaching. With the showing of motion pictures two or three times during a trimester, the graphic method of teaching is greatly amplified, and the busy student's knowledge of our special branch made far more comprehensive than it was ever possible before I introduced the "bus" and the motion pictures.

In addition to the teaching that I do, my associates give instruction in urology to members of the second, third, and fourth year classes. It includes work in topographical anatomy, pathology, bacteriology, physiology, and clinical and laboratory urology.

The Education and Training of Urologic Surgeons

In days gone by, when the graduate in medicine went into a hospital, he rarely remained more than a year, and this was divided between medicine and surgery. In some cases, after six months in medicine if he wished to specialize in surgery he would remain twelve months in that work, but it was rare indeed for a man to stay more than a year and a half or two years in a hospital. As a result, when these men left they had only a smattering of the line of work in which they might spend their lives.

With the opening of the Johns Hopkins Hospital in 1889, Dr.

Halsted decided to break with tradition and keep his resident surgeon very much longer. When I came on the surgical staff, Dr. Joseph C. Bloodgood had already been on the staff four years. After that he remained four years more as resident. Dr. Osler had adopted the same plan of keeping his residents for several years. Dr. William S. Thayer eventually remained in the hospital for nine years. As a result of this plan, the resident surgeon soon became very expert, and it was not necessary for the chief surgeon to do all the difficult cases and most of the others.

In Philadelphia, Dr. J. B. Deaver's residents remained in the hospital for eighteen months. As a consequence Deaver did practically all the work, not infrequently operating upon from twenty to thirty cases himself almost every day of the week. In order to do this, it was necessary to have outside assistants, one of whom would have the patient anesthetized and prepared for Dr. Deaver to make the incision and do the important part of the operation, the patient then being turned over to another older assistant, who would complete the operation and close the wound. In this way patients passed rapidly through a procedure somewhat similar to that on automobiles going down the assembly line. I do not mean to insinuate that the work was not high-class: there was no more expert surgeon than Dr. Deaver, but he had far too much to do, and his residents far too little actual operating to do.

With Dr. Halsted's plan, Dr. Bloodgood was able to do any and all of the operations and the "Professor," as we called him, could devote himself to rare or unusual cases; to conditions in which he was greatly interested; to subjects on which he was making advanced studies, and so on. As a result of this splendid plan, Dr. Halsted developed consecutively expert surgeons who have gone forth to head departments at other universities and to illuminate surgery.

I spent three years on Dr. Halsted's staff, and had my turn in the operations that came to the resident, so when my opportunity to organize a staff of my own at the Brady Urological Institute came, I decided to pattern it somewhat after Dr. Halsted's plan, but to go even further. The man who is chosen to go through the residency at the Brady pursues the following course:

After his graduation, in which he must have made excellent marks either at the Johns Hopkins or some other medical school, he is appointed from the Urological Department to spend twelve months as a rotating intern in urology, surgery, and gynecology at the Johns Hopkins Hospital. The next year he serves as a fellow in pathology under Dr. William G. MacCallum. During the next year he works in a general surgical service, preferably with Dr. T. F. Riggs at St. Mary's Hospital, Pierre, South Dakota, where, as resident surgeon, he assists in Dr. Riggs's splendid operations and has an opportunity to do many himself. He then returns to the Brady Urological Institute as second assistant resident. During this year he takes an important part in operations, the conduct of the clinic, teaching, and research. The next year he becomes first assistant resident in urology, doing more important work and having an opportunity to make publications. From there he goes to Ancker Hospital in St. Paul, Minnesota, as resident urologist under Dr. F. E. B. Foley, one of the most skillful of American urologists. His year there adds greatly to his surgical and urological skill and may furnish subjects for publication. He then comes back to be resident urologist at the Brady Institute. During this, his last year, he takes an important part in the direction of the institute in teaching and research and does nearly all the operations on patients in the public wards. These men have given so many years to this long and arduous preparation to become residents that I consider it my duty to see that they get as much operative experience as possible. On this account my associates on the staff and I rarely operate upon cases in the public wards, although we occasionally assist in very difficult or interesting cases. As the entire staff is present daily at the institute, group discussions of cases, particularly the important or puzzling ones, are held with the resident and the younger men on the staff.

The value of these long but fruitful years of training is shown by the operative results of the successive residents, not infrequently better than those of the visiting staff. In a recent publication Dr. Samuel A. Vest, who finished his residency three years ago, reported the cases of perineal prostatectomy operated upon by the last five resident urologists. There were two hundred and thirteen cases, with only three deaths, a mortality of 1.3 per cent. Some of our residents have done over fifty consecutive perineal prostatectomies without a death, although public ward patients often are derelicts whose cases have been neglected and are supposedly more serious risks than private patients.

During the long course of training in the various hospital departments the house officers become very expert in diagnostic and clinical procedures. Thirty years ago when we wished to make an intravenous injection it was thought necessary to make an incision through the skin, dissect out the vein, open it with a knife, and insert a cannula (metal tube). Even then one dared to introduce only a normal saline solution. Transfusions of human blood became possible only after Dr. John J. Abel of the Johns Hopkins Medical School found a way to prevent clotting of blood taken from a donor by adding a remarkable anticlotting substance obtained from a peculiar South American frog and known as hirudin. A little later sodium citrate was brought out, and gave a much simpler method of preventing coagulation. Even then transfusion was often extremely dangerous because of the incompatibility between the blood of the donor and that of the recipient. But again a great advance was made. Methods were discovered and perfected by Dr. Moss of the Johns Hopkins Hospital by which bloods could be typed and so accurately matched that one was able before operation to choose from a number of prospective donors blood that could be introduced without danger. Well do I remember a patient in my early days at the hospital to whom we gave an intravenous transfusion of blood from a brother. His condition was desperate and we felt justified in taking the chance of introducing his brother's blood, which we hoped would be compatible. Unfortunately it was not,

and a violent disintegration, known as "laking" of the blood, occurred, and he soon died.

With the introduction of Ehrlich's salvarsan for the treatment of
syphilis by intravenous injections it was soon discovered that
transfusions could be done by simply inserting a needle through the
skin into the vein. The house officers rapidly became so expert that
it was rarely necessary to make an incision to find the vein. Not
infrequently their splendid work has saved the life of my patients.

Only recently a patient well over eighty with a serious cancerous
condition that made it necessary to carry out an emergency operation was so greatly shocked that respirations had ceased and the
heartbeat was very feeble. By great skill one of the younger house
officers was able to get a needle into a vein and inject the blood of a
donor, thus averting impending death.

Patients in critical condition often require the assiduous atten-
tions of house officers for days at a time during which they get very
little rest. Their esprit de corps and devotion to duty are splendid,
and it gives me much pleasure to acknowledge my great indebtedness
to them for their fine work on innumerable occasions. I must speak
particularly of Dr. Gordon M. Dean, who came from Aberdeen,
Scotland, to spend long years with us in preparation for the professorship in the Department of Urology at the University of Aberdeen that had been promised him upon completion of his service
at the Brady Urological Institute. Dr. Dean came to the residency
in urology after a brilliant record in the laboratories and wards in
preparation for his final year. He was an indefatigable worker, and
gave to the patients entrusted by us to his care the most meticulous
attention; in fact, he went much further than was expected of him,
and frequently interrupted his hours of sleep to visit patients who
were in a serious condition. I had two patients, each suffering from a
desperate condition in the urinary tract that was complicated by a
serious gastrointestinal disturbance. One of them lived a month,
and during this time Dr. Dean worked himself almost to exhaustion.
The other patient, with even more serious abdominal complications,

died after several weeks. By this time Dr. Dean was an ill man. He came down with an abscess of the middle ear that required operation. This was followed by pneumonia, which nearly ended fatally. When he had apparently recovered, I insisted on his going to Florida for a long rest. He seemed to be improving steadily, when suddenly a cerebral attack, probably meningitis, carried him off. I have often blamed myself for allowing him to give so much of his time and his vital force to these desperate cases.

For many years interns, residents, and other house officers at the Johns Hopkins Hospital were not allowed to marry. A cousin of mine, who was working his way up to the residency in urology at the Brady Institute, was much in love. He had become engaged to a charming girl while he was a medical student at the University of Virginia. Mrs. Young was devoted to Charles Bidgood and his fianceé, Mary Carrington. As Charles spent year after year in his term of service at the hospital, Mrs. Young became more and more disturbed by the strict rule that prevented these two from marrying. She decided to make an issue of it. She soon won Dr. William G. MacCallum to her point of view, persuaded him to visit with her the hospital board, and ultimately succeeded in having the rule rescinded.

Since then many hospital house officers have married either before or during their service as residents. The hospital has wisely allowed them to secure apartments adjacent to the grounds, and gives them direct telephonic communication with the hospital switchboard. The financial circumstances of many of these men are straightened, and not a few are heavily in debt. Their wives frequently secure positions to bring in enough money to support their homes, and occasionally assist in the preparation of scientific papers. Often two or three of these couples occupy one of the old residences that have been transformed into makeshift apartments on streets bordering the hospital grounds. Allowing the house officers to marry was one of the best moves the hospital has made. The fact that these changed conditions are due to the insistence and interposition of Mrs. Young is not generally known.

The importance of the uniquely long period of training that residents graduating from the Department of Urology at the Brady Institute have to follow is shown by the fact that in recent years three have gone almost directly from the residency to be heads of departments and professors of urology at important medical schools and two have immediately become associate professors.

Soon after I started to practice in Baltimore Dr. William Huger came to be my office assistant and when I came down with tuberculosis, he took charge of my practice, as mentioned previously. Huger also had charge of the genitourinary dispensary. Other doctors acted as assistants at my office and in the dispensary, some of whom subsequently went to the Union Protestant Infirmary. Several went to the Hopkins Hospital as assistant resident surgeons in urology. These men were Hugh H. Trout, Joseph Hume, Alfred I. Mitchell, Harry A. Fowler, John T. Geraghty, Louis C. Lehr, Charles M. Remsen, A. R. Stevens, John W. Churchman, Alexander Randall, John R. Caulk, Montague L. Boyd, H. W. Plaggemeyer and Arthur B. Cecil.

After the construction of the Brady Urological Institute Dr. Frank Hinman was the first resident urologist. Those who have followed him as resident urologists are as follows: William A. Frontz (deceased), J. Edward Burns, Edwin Davis, Winford O. Wilder, Raymond F. Hain (deceased), Howard Cecil, William D. Jack, Clyde L. Deming, Herman A. Gailey, David M. Davis, Franklin P. Johnson, Charles Y. Bidgood, Eugene Clay Shaw, Winfield W. Scott, J. Everett Sanner, Robert W. McKay, Edwin P. Alyea, Edward C. James, Howard C. Smith, Marshall P. Gordon, Lloyd G. Lewis, Gordon M. Dean, Walter W. Baker, Hugh J. Jewett, Samuel A. Vest, Wyland F. Leadbetter, John E. Dees, Henry C. Harrill, and Carl E. Burkland.

With three exceptions these men have practiced as specialists in urology in various parts of the country. Nearly all of them are visiting urologists in their respective hospitals. The majority of these men have been professors of urology in their medical schools and a few are associate professors. Among the medical schools in which these men have held professorships are Cornell Medical School, Bellevue Medical School, University of Rochester, Yale University, University of Pennsylvania, Jefferson Medical College, Johns Hopkins University School of Medicine, Howard University, University of Virginia, Duke University, Emory Medical College, Tulane University, Washington University, University of Nebraska, University of Oregon, University of California, College of Seventh Day Adventists, Baylor University, University of Aberdeen, Scotland. Another group of men who were assistants at the Brady Urological Institute, but did not complete their residency, have won important urological positions, most of them professorships in urology or heads of departments in urology at the following institutions: University of Buffalo; University of Georgia; Loyola University; University of Pittsburgh; Western Reserve University; University of California; University of Syracuse; Yale University; Marquette University; George Washington University; University of Cincinnati; University of Manchester, England; University of Edinburgh, Scotland; Union Medical College; Peiping, China; University of Puerto Rico; University of Toronto, Canada. The Brady Urological Institute contributions to medical literature by this group of men are great.   They have played a very important part in the development of urology.

The James Buchanan Brady Urological Institute has had its twenty-fifth anniversary. There was no celebration; we hadn't the time or money to waste. The immense amount of work done by the staff during these fruitful years totals four hundred and forty-one published papers, in addition to a great many unpublished ones, lectures, and addresses.

The Journal of Urology

Within a year after the dedication of the Brady Urological Institute it was apparent that there was great need of a journal for the publication of papers by members of the staff on urologic subjects. The question of starting a special journal of urology was discussed with prominent urologists in other parts of the country. I made arrangements with the Williams & Wilkins Company of Baltimore to publish the *Journal of Urology*. The editors were John T. Geraghty, David M. Davis, Herman O. Mosenthal, and Hugh H. Young, editor in chief. It seems sufficiently interesting historically to quote our announcement, which appeared in the first issue:

FOREWORD

The title of this publication "The Journal of Urology—experimental, medical and surgical"—expresses briefly the aims, hopes and ambitions of the editors.

Recent years have been very prolific in the production of splendid papers on the urinary tract, its adnexa and correlated subjects. Many of those from the departments of physiology, pharmacology, chemistry, pathology and bacteriology have been scattered through the various special journals on those subjects. The embryological and anatomical researches have likewise appeared in journals devoted to these fields. Medical articles on the kidney, adrenals, urine, etc. and the many diseases which are secondary or correlated, and surgical papers of a similar scope, have found lodgment in dozens of diversified journals all over the country.

The situation is such that one who is interested in all forms of research in this field, anxious to keep abreast with what the internists are doing along these lines and at the same time desirous of following the progress of surgical urology, is overwhelmed with the magnitude of the task and fails to discover much that is important. The medical and surgical urologists have much in common. Both are dependent on the progress made in experimental researches, and all concerned could be greatly broadened by a knowledge of what each is doing. A realization of another's problems is often a fertile source of suggestions for subjects of research. The scientific branches, the laboratory men, are often greatly aided by contact with the difficulties of the clinicians, and the latter often point out unsuspected uses of great value for apparently sterile discoveries.

The diseases encountered by the surgical urologist are most often intertwined with complicating or secondary lesions in which the internist's help is required. The more each of these varied interests can know about the other the better it should be for all.

It is evident that some common meeting place is extremely desirable— some medium in which all types of papers upon the field of common interest may appear—archives of urology—historical, embryological, anatomical, biochemical, pharmacological, pathological, bacteriological, surgical and medical, experimental and clinical.

Such is what we hope to accomplish in the Journal of Urology, and we bespeak for it the support and active assistance of all who come within the wide scope of its work.

Realizing that authors may often desire to publish their work also in one of the more special journals, we shall be glad to allow this if made simultaneously. Wishing to stimulate investigation, we are fortunate in being able to make use of the generosity of a friend in the shape of a "Research Fund," which will be utilized to assist worthy authors of the most meritorious research papers, to be decided by a special editorial committee.

H. H. Y.

The first issue appeared in February, 1917, and contained one hundred and thirty-eight pages. The eight papers comprised one each on the artificial cultivation of cells of bladder tumor cells outside the body; the embryology and surgery of double ureter; the bacteriology of the seminal vesicles; a study of urea in the blood; drainage of the kidney in wounds; the physiology of the ureter; the effect of calcium on urinary secretion; and a description of new laboratory apparatus. This number, composed largely of experimental and research papers, gave evidence of the scientific character that we hoped to maintain in the *Journal of Urology*.

When the second number appeared (April, 1917), America had entered the World War, and most of us had joined the A.E.F. Regardless of this interference, six numbers, totaling five hundred and seventy-nine pages, were issued in that year.

In 1918, although many of the urologists were in France, the *Journal of Urology* had twenty-five original articles covering almost five hundred pages.

In 1920, at the annual meeting of the American Urological Association it was proposed to publish a journal devoted to urology in which could be put the papers and discussions presented at the annual meetings. Realizing that it would be difficult for us to maintain the *Journal of Urology* if a second journal came into the field, I proposed to the association that they take over the *Journal of Urology* without reservations, make it their own, do with it as they pleased, and appoint a new board of editors. Some who had expected violent opposition from the editor of the *Journal of Urology* were amazed at my offer to step down and give over to the American Urological Association the journal I had started and run for three years. My confidence in fair dealing from the association was justified when, after accepting my offer, a board of editors was chosen and I was asked to continue as editor in chief. The other members of the editorial board were William F. Braasch, Henry G. Bugbee, Herman L. Kretschmer, and William C. Quinby. These men have taken a great interest in their work, personally reviewed many of the papers, particularly those concerning which there was doubt as to the desirability of publishing them in the *Journal*, and throughout the twenty years that have passed have continued to function in an important editorial and administrative capacity. We have a delightfully harmonious and sympathetic board.

The next year it was possible for us to enlarge the *Journal* greatly and bring out two volumes as large as the single annual volume we had published formerly. This arrangement provided that every member of the American Urological Association was to be a subscriber to the *Journal of Urology*, and our financial status improved at once. After that more than sufficient papers were offered for each volume, and we were able to pick and choose, thereby increasing the standard of our papers. Pari passu the *Journal* had a splendid effect upon the American Urological Association. The publication of their transactions in a journal greatly improved the papers and discussions.

At the end of the tenth volume there appeared a cumulative index of fifty-one pages listing three hundred and fifty-five articles. Among these were epoch-making papers, not only in clinical urology, but in related scientific branches of medicine.

In 1928 we published our twentieth volume. The cumulative index of the preceding ten years then occupied eighty-six pages and embraced an even more important series of papers. The two yearly volumes had grown to approximately seven hundred and fifty pages each. With the thirty-eighth volume a cumulative index of eighteen volumes was presented, containing one thousand, seven hundred, and eighty-three papers. In 1934, Dr. William A. Frontz, who for seventeen years had been a very efficient associate editor, died, and Dr. J. A. C. Colston was made associate editor. He has played an important part in the supervision of the *Journal*.

In the meantime the American Urological Association had decided to offer space in the *Journal of Urology* for the publication of transactions of branch societies. The restriction was made that these papers must be carefully reviewed by an editorial committee and only those papers found to be worthy of the *Journal* would be accepted for publication. This plan has resulted in improvement of the local programs. Members have become far more careful in their work, particularly in the preparation of their papers.

In 1938 the editorial staff prepared a pamphlet that discussed the preparation of manuscripts. Fundamental rules concerning the composition of papers, the presentation of cases, and the use of illustrations were given. Examples were offered to guide writers in the preparation of papers and tell them what was to be avoided. Examples of bad practice were given. The desirability of being succinct, brief, to the point, was stressed, and suggestions on the use of the literature were offered. This pamphlet, which went to all members of the association, has had a pronounced effect in improving the papers offered for publication. Nevertheless it is often necessary for the editorial board to condense—usually with very beneficial result—papers in which the author has been too prolix.

During the past year a marked increase in the number of splendid papers offered for publication has made it necessary to increase the pages in each volume. This would not have been possible had not the growth of the American Urological Association and the enlargement of the *Journal* made it possible to increase considerably the list of subscribers, and also that of advertisers. The *Journal*, which formerly had difficulty in keeping out of the red, gradually wiped out the deficit and finally showed a fair profit. This has made it possible to publish during 1939 two volumes, one of nine hundred and fifty pages and the other of thirteen hundred and eleven pages. The December issue contained over four hundred pages, almost as many pages as those in the first volume, which comprised the first year. Also, the annual subscription has been reduced from $5 to $4.

I have not space to analyze critically the two thousand, five hundred, and seventy-eight articles that have appeared in the *Journal of Urology* during the twenty-two years since its beginning in 1917. The *Journal* has achieved an important position in the world's medical literature, and is usually accepted as being the outstanding journal devoted to urology. In it have been published the great majority of the important papers on urology and allied subjects during those twenty-two years. Its effect in improving the character of urological work and elevating the position of urology has been incalculable. Men in the experimental and research branches of medicine have been stimulated to undertake problems related to genitourinary diseases. My prediction in Volume I as to the need of a journal that would welcome papers "historical, embryological, anatomical, biochemical, pharmacological, pathological, bacteriological, surgical and medical, experimental and clinical" has been completely justified.

AT THE International Medical Congress of 1913 in London I heard the celebrated German chemist Ehrlich present a paper on "chemiotherapy" (now shortened to "chemotherapy"). This was the new name he gave to the science of chemical treatment of infections. He told of his new chemical compounds of arsenic, especially salvarsan, by which he claimed to have obtained complete sterilization in various types of infections in animals and human beings by the injection of one large dose of the drug. To these methods Ehrlich gave the imposing name "therapia sterilisans magna." He predicted that in a few years many infectious diseases would be curable by intravenous injections of chemical compounds.

I returned to America greatly impressed by the magnitude of Ehrlich's researches, and the remarkable character of his results inspired me to add to the Brady Urological Institute, then in the course of construction, a laboratory for chemical investigation. It occurred to me that we might try to add to phenolsulphone-phthalein (our thalein kidney function already described) substances that would make these compounds antiseptic and thus enable them to sterilize kidney and bladder infections while passing through the urinary tract. Various compounds of phenolsulphonephthalein used in this experimental work were furnished by Dr. H. A. B. Dunning, who had prepared them in his chemical laboratory.

252

The United States entered the World War, and I left for France. While I was in London I visited the chemical laboratories of Browning and secured from him quantities of various antiseptic dyes to send to the Brady Institute. With these Edwin C. White and Edwin Davis continued the researches. In collaboration with Harrell, Davis showed that with one of the drugs which I had sent, acriflavine, good results could be obtained in the treatment of gonorrhea. Later, when Davis came to France, this method of treatment was introduced into some of the venereal camps of the A.E.F.

On a visit to the Institut Pasteur I met Frouin, who showed me his work on septicemia in mice, which he was treating with a drug compounded from metallic tin. He had found that in the tin mines workers were not subject to boils. He came to the conclusion that the tin was probably responsible for their freedom from these infections. Boils are caused by staphylococci, very virulent bacteria. He inoculated some of these organisms, which he had obtained from a boil, into the peritoneal cavity of mice, and found that the animals invariably died of blood poisoning (septicemia). He then took another series of animals that had been similarly inoculated with fatal doses of these bacteria and gave them in the same way (intraperitoneally) injections of solutions of a compound of tin (stannoxyl). Many of these animals were saved. He then began to use it in staphylococcic infections in human beings. Soon after this a member of the United States Reparations Commission upon whom I had operated in America—to remove a tuberculous kidney—came down with a severe staphylococcus infection of his leg. A large boil formed, and we treated it by stannoxyl injections with excellent results; this was in Paris, where I happened to be during the summer after the war.

I was also impressed by two other investigators. Lévy-Bing had shown that novarsenobenzol, the drug we used for syphilis, when introduced intravenously often had a remarkable curative effect on deep-seated gonococcus (the cause of gonorrhea) infections. D'Hérain had shown that sulphate of copper in 2 per cent solution injected intravenously would often cure bronchial infections, particularly those due to the streptococcus.

My own experiences with chemicals in preventing our soldiers from contracting venereal diseases (prophylaxis), and the resultant remarkably low venereal rate that the American Expeditionary Forces showed, convinced me that much was to be gained by more actively following antiseptic therapy in the treatment of infections, and that much could be learned by the study of new compounds. I was anxious to begin anew at the Brady Urological Institute our studies in chemotherapy.

The Story of Mercurochrome

While I was in France Dr. White had continued his preparation of dye compounds, and on my return in January, 1919, we again took up the bacteriological and clinical study of these drugs. Dr. White eventually produced more than two hundred and fifty compounds. Most of the older antiseptics kill bacteria quickly, but they also kill tissue cells. We started out with the desiderata of obtaining a drug which, while antiseptic or germicidal, would not be poisonous to the system, would not form a precipitate in body fluids, would be effective in blood and in urine, and would do little harm to tissues. It was necessary to study these drugs in our bacteriological laboratory to determine their germicidal strengths in various solutions and in animals, in order to see how nearly they approximated our requirements. The bacteriological work was done by Dr. E. O. Swartz. Many compounds were discarded because they were too toxic or too irritating; others, because they formed a precipitate in the body fluids and were thus rendered inert; others, because they were deleterious to tissues and internal organs. Out of the entire list only three were put aside as being very valuable. These were Nos. 205, 220, and 253 of the series.

No. 220 excited our interest on account of its extraordinary properties. It was a deep-red dye (dibromoxymercuryfluorescein) highly soluble in water, and was relatively not injurious to tissue cells. We gave the name "mercurochrome" to the drug because of its mercury content and its color. Mercurochrome in weak solutions inhibited the growth of bacteria, but in common with other mercurials, it required some time to kill the organisms. When injected into the veins in considerable quantity, mercurochrome produced no lesions in the internal organs of animals.

I set about to try local applications of the drug clinically and we obtained results better than I had seen before in the treatment of local infections. In a short time a sufficient number of clinical cases had accumulated to enable me to make a long report, with White and Swartz. We showed that in mercurochrome we had an antiseptic dye that penetrated deeply into the tissues and caused little or no irritation. It could be used in the urethra in a strength of 5 per cent with impunity, and common bacteria like the staphylococcus and the colon bacillus were killed in one minute by a solution of 1 : 1,000. The original drug was difficult to prepare for clinical use and was slightly irritating. Later Dr. H. A. B. Dunning prepared a satisfactory water soluble sodium salt that had almost the germicidal strength of our compound and was much more practical. This has been the compound that has been used in practice. Subsequently, studies showed that when very large numbers of bacteria were present, killing would take much longer. We described a series of infections of the bladder and kidney successfully treated, and about fifty cases of gonorrhea. We predicted that the drug would be a valuable addition in the local treatment of genitourinary cases.

Later, papers in medical journals appeared showing its value as a mild antiseptic and first-aid treatment of superficial wounds, in local applications, of the nose, the throat, the ear, and also in gynecology and obstetrics.

In an important series of bacteriological studies, J. H. Hill found that in experimental wounds heavily infected with staphylococci (the most common pus-forming bacteria) cultures made at once from the surface of those treated with a 7 per cent solution of tincture of iodine showed no growth of bacteria, while similar cultures from wounds treated with a 2 per cent aqueous solution of mercurochrome showed a marked reduction in the number of organisms. But when such wounds were examined twenty-four hours after treatment, those treated with iodine often contained as many as twenty times more bacteria than were found in those treated with mercurochrome.

These and other careful experiments conclusively proved that the stronger antiseptics were sometimes much less effective, because they killed off tissue cells. These dead cells produced an excellent pabulum for the growth of bacteria. The solution of mercurochrome in water did relatively little damage to the cells and there was no layer of dead cells for the bacteria to grow on, and the antiseptic dye's action was continuous. The ultimate action of mercurochrome is consequently often superior to that of tincture of iodine. In addition to the fact that 2 per cent solution of mercurochrome causes only a minimal amount of tissue reaction and does not impede healing, it does not cause pain or "sting." Because mercurochrome does not injure the tissue cells, I have used it frequently as an application to operative wounds before closure. In this way bacteria that drop in from the air or are introduced by the surgeon's instruments or hands are inhibited from growing. After its use in hundreds of cases, we feel confident that applications of mercurochrome materially cut down infections. A recent article by Edwin Davis has shown that when these applications of mercurochrome are made to prostatectomy wounds, fever, suppuration, and delayed closure occur rarely.

In our paper we had stated that mercurochrome could be introduced intravenously in a 1 per cent solution in doses of 5 milligrams per kilogram of body weight without injury to the internal organs. Piper of Philadelphia confirmed our findings by animal experiments, and then attempted to save the life of a woman with puerperal septicemia (childbed fever) by intravenous injections of 1 per cent mercurochrome. There was an immediate drop in the temperature and the condition of the patient improved, but only for a time.

Piper also tried the drug on four other cases, but did not obtain a cure, and in a publication he said: "While these cases are certainly not definitely conclusive that in mercurochrome we have found a specific cure for blood stream infection, we feel that we may, perhaps, after more extensive observation, find a way to increase the dosage so that our results will be better."

Dr. Piper came down to see us and we reviewed his interesting work. Shortly afterward an excellent case appeared in which to try out intravenous therapy. One of my patients, following ureteral catheterization, developed a chill and fever and became very sick. Blood cultures showed a heavy blood-stream infection. He was seen by a medical man in consultation with Dr. Colston and myself. He was very weak, he had a high temperature, and cultures showed 140 colonies of colon bacilli in each cubic centimeter (fifteen drops) of blood. The consensus of opinion was that he would not live many hours. Colston and I decided that it would be a good case in which to try out intravenous mercurochrome. Accordingly, Colston gave the patient 34 cubic centimeters of a 1 per cent solution (about one ounce) into one of the large veins of the right arm. This was followed by a chill, considerable rise in temperature, and rapid pulse; for a time the patient was very ill. But in a few hours his temperature began to drop rapidly and in twelve hours he was completely conscious. He said he felt well, and demanded something to eat. A culture from the blood showed that it was sterile. The heavy infection had been completely wiped out by a single injection into the veins and, in addition, a pronounced infection of the kidneys had disappeared.

This amazing result excited us greatly, and we rapidly extended our clinical use of the drug. In a paper with J. H. Hill we reported our first case and also another patient in a desperate condition with blood poisoning who got well promptly after intravenous mercurochrome. There were also three cases of acute infection within and around the kidneys that cleared up with similar treatment. In a footnote we reported that Dr. E. B. Piper had written us that he had cured three cases of staphylococcus and two of streptococcus septicemia with mercurochrome. We conceded that there were several failures to cure blood poisoning, and concluded that "when blood cultures show a generalized septicemia, mercurochrome can now be offered with the hope of sometimes preventing an otherwise surely fatal ending, and that certain localized infections may now be safely subjected to the experimental use of intravenous injections of mercurochrome."

This paper aroused widespread interest, and papers from other clinicians appeared confirming our statements. Letters came to us citing numerous cases in which mercurochrome had been used intravenously. One year later we were able to present an analytical study of two hundred and ten cases that had been treated with mercurochrome at the Brady Institute and elsewhere. Among these were fifty-seven cases of septicemia, in twenty-eight of which cure was claimed, and in eight, great improvement. In only eighteen cases was the treatment called a failure. Some of the cases were described as showing a remarkably rapid disappearance of the blood-stream infection in apparently hopeless cases. There were twenty-two cases of pneumonia, twenty-two infections of the kidneys and lower urinary tract, thirty-seven infections with the gonococcus, in all of which a high percentage of good results was claimed. The rest of the report dealt with local infections of varied types in which good results were attained. We concluded: "In thus presenting a new form of therapeutics in such a varied series of cases we realize that we will perhaps be accused of offering a panacea for every infectious disease. We are quite willing to meet this criticism with the series of cases here recorded which, we believe, justifies the assertion that in mercurochrome, intravenously administered, a remarkable addition to therapeutics may be claimed."

This paper led to a wide usage of the drug, and some incautious clinicians used it in larger doses and with less care than we had employed. We had shown by injections of the drug in animals that no injury to the kidneys or other internal organs resulted from an injection of mercurochrome in much larger doses than had been used in human beings, but to be sure that such was the case I asked Dr. Raleigh Penick, assistant of Dr. William G. MacCallum in the Department of Pathology, to study the cases of blood poisoning that had come to postmortem examinations. After analyzing seven cases in which mercurochrome had been given and ten in which it had not, Dr. Penick found that in those cases which had received mercurochrome the lesions were exactly the same as in those that had not received the drug. What some observers had said was kidney "damage" due to mercurochrome was a condition produced by the bacteria in the blood stream and typical of blood poisoning. It was not due to the mercurochrome.

When given in large doses, mercurochrome causes pronounced reactions: nausea, vomiting, and frequent and occasionally bloody bowel movements, but reactions follow all powerful drugs. Salvarsan, so remarkable in its cure of syphilis, not infrequently is followed by pronounced bodily reactions, but the results are so splendid that even occasional fatal reactions have not prevented the continued use of salvarsan. As I point out later, sulfanilamide is often followed by severe reactions.

While I was in Belfast visiting Andrew Fullerton, professor of surgery at Queen's University, he took me to see a patient whose life he said had been saved by mercurochrome. One of their distinguished men, Sir James Reid, after a slight surgical operation had suffered blood poisoning accompanied by high fever and chills. The patient's condition was so desperate that Mr. Fullerton called in the professors of medicine, pathology, and bacteriology, all of whom saw no hope of saving the patient. Fullerton then produced *Young's Practice of Urology*, which I had recently sent him, and pointed to cases similar to Sir James's in which I described the successful use of mercurochrome intravenously. He suggested the drug in this case. The three consultants remarked that they had seen accounts of severe reactions in American medical literature and they opposed the use of the drug. Fullerton asked them what they had to offer and they all admitted they had nothing to suggest and that the patient was going to die. Fullerton told them he knew me personally, had confidence in my statements, and thought he ought to try mercurochrome.

By the time he had told me the story we had arrived at the country home of Sir James. He lay in a large four-poster bed and greeted me cordially. When Fullerton asked him to tell me his remembrance of the case before and after the drug was given, he said: "From day to day I felt myself becoming weaker and my brain more cloudy. One day I realized there were a lot of doctors in the room, but I could not see them nor hear what they said. I felt a needle prick in my right arm. A little later I had a severe chill and completely lost consciousness. I do not know how long I remained in this condition, but finally I was awake, my mind was clear, I felt thirsty and asked for a drink. Later, I asked for food. In a short time I was well."

In Rochester, New York, I met Mr. Eastman, the developer of the Kodak. He said: "I'm delighted to meet you, because your drug saved the life of one of my dearest friends in Africa. We were hunting. He shot a lion, thought the beast was dead, approached too close, and was fearfully mauled and bitten. The doctor predicted that he would surely die from blood poisoning, but by the liberal bathing of his wound with mercurochrome his life was saved."

Another African hunter told me that he had come down with tropical fever and his life was despaired of. He was taken to a Dutch missionary physician, who gave him an intravenous injection of mercurochrome that dispelled the infection and resulted in a rapid cure. The missionary had employed mercurochrome in many cases of infectious diseases.

To reinforce our clinical cases by further experimental demonstration of the value of intravenous mercurochrome, I sent two members of our staff, J. H. Hill and M. E. Turner, to work under the director of the Hygienic Laboratory of the United States Public Health Service in Washington. These bacteriologists inoculated twelve hundred mice with the pneumococcus, a germ so virulent that in the minutest dose it invariably killed the animals. When mice that had received a lethal dose of the germ were injected with mercurochrome, 20 per cent were saved. These results confirmed our clinical reports.

Experiments were made to determine just how mercurochrome acted to cure blood-stream infections. Hill and Colston showed that after intravenous injections of mercurochrome the further growth of bacteria in the blood was arrested; the blood became bacteriostatic. This gave the cells of the blood and tissues a chance to throw off the infection. It has since been shown that sulfanilamide acts in much the same way.

The work of the Brady Institute on the use of mercurochrome to combat local and general infections was the first important effort to apply Ehrlich's principles of chemotherapy. In the many papers we wrote in presenting cases from our clinic, in letters from correspondents, and also in the huge literature on the subject that soon accumulated, there was abundant proof that this form of intravenous therapy was, in given cases, followed by marked improvement or cure of local or generalized infections. That there were many failures was freely acknowledged, as was also the fact that often in order to get results fairly large dosage was required, and this was accompanied by reactions. These reactions are not serious, and we at the Brady have never had a death attributable to the use of mercurochrome. We continue to use intravenous mercurochrome, and papers by others appear from time to time citing successful cases. Among the recent reports was an article from the Mayo clinic by Emmett, who described excellent results in cases of acute infections of the kidneys. A similar paper appeared from the clinic of George R. Livermore in Memphis, and the same conclusions were reached. We have reported additional instances in which the use of mercurochrome in deep-seated gonococcus infections has often been followed by sterilization in cases that had persisted for years. Dr. O. S. Culp has studied our cases of gonorrheal arthritis treated with intravenous mercurochrome, and has found that in 69 per cent of them the infection was rapidly cleared up, and in others it was much improved.

Sulfanilamide

Although an impartial review of the large number of reports on the intravenous administration of mercurochrome justified the conclusion that excellent results were often obtained in general and local infections, still the fact that it had to be given intravenously and could not be successfully employed by mouth markedly interfered with its general adoption. When sulfanilamide, a drug that could be given in much larger quantity by mouth, appeared, the stage was set for its adoption by the medical profession. When Dr. Perrin Long at the Johns Hopkins Hospital reported on the work that had been done by English clinicians and in conjunction with Dr. Eleanor Bliss presented interesting experiments on animals, it was thought that the drug was effective only against a special type of streptococcus. Very promptly studies of the effect of the drug in animals infected with bacilli and other organisms commonly found in the urinary tract were made by J. H. Hill in the laboratories of the Brady Urological Institute. The drug was also used clinically in our wards by Vest and others in similar infections in human beings, with excellent results.

In our outpatient dispensary sulfanilamide was applied to the treatment of gonorrhea in 1937. In a short time Dees and Colston, with the assistance of Henry C. Harrill, reported that they had obtained remarkable results in fifteen cases of acute gonorrhea. The external evidence of the infection often disappeared with great rapidity, and there was far less involvement of deep-seated organs. The publication of this paper led to a wide use of sulfanilamide not only in gonorrhea but in other forms of venereal disease, so that in the short space of three years a tremendous literature on the use of these drugs in genitourinary infections accumulated.

A vast amount of research has been carried on in the quest for better drugs. Sulfapyridine was produced, and was shown to give remarkable results in the treatment of pneumonia. In our out-patient dispensary it has been found to be very efficient in the treatment of gonorrhea.

The most recent similar drug is sulfathiazole, which in some ways appears to be more promising than its predecessors as a urinary antiseptic. We may look forward to the experimental and clinical study of a long line of such drugs. Until we know much more ac-curately than we do now the exact chemical and physical changes that occur after the internal administration of antibacterial drugs, we must judge by the results without knowing the exact mechanism by which they are obtained.

This incomplete review of the immense amount of laboratory and clinical publications that have been made in the treatment of local and general infections with chemical compounds administered intra-venously, or more recently by mouth, shows the great progress that has been made since Ehrlich in 1913 predicted that some day infectious diseases would be treated successfully by chemotherapy.

DURING the winter of 1916 and 1917 I was greatly enraged by the Germans and felt strongly that we should prepare for war. I was convinced that military training for the youth of the country was absolutely essential at this time when we were certain to be plunged into the war, and I wrote articles on the subject in the *New York Times* and the *Baltimore Sun*.

President Wilson was recalcitrant to all suggestions that we adopt universal military training or other measures of preparedness, so a group of Baltimoreans decided to visit Washington and present our views to him. A small company of lawyers, doctors, and business-men appeared by appointment in his executive offices. The political and general aspects of the importance of military preparation were presented by Mr. John E. Semmes, a forceful speaker, but as he got carried away with his subject he talked rather acrimoniously, and I could see that the President was considerably nettled. I had been asked to present the medical aspects of universal military training. I briefly sketched the advantages to the youth of the country that could be obtained by adopting methods similar to those in use in Switzerland and other countries which had universal military train-ing of their young men. When I finished, President Wilson replied. Showing great heat, he said: "Had your arguments, Mr. Semmes, been presented in more temperate language, they would have been more effective. I cannot help feeling greatly exasperated at what

HUGH HAMPTON YOUNG
Colonel, M.C., A.E.F., D.S.M.

has been said." He proceeded to say that he knew far more about the subject than we did. After a few words he closed the conference and virtually showed us the door. Whether we had any effect is hard to say, but after that much more vigorous notes were sent to Germany, finally an ultimatum; the German Ambassador was given his papers; and declaration of war was demanded by Wilson of the Senate on April 6, 1917.

I went to Washington and offered my services to the Surgeon General. A base hospital had been formed at Baltimore that had many of our best men in medicine and surgery, many medical students who went as enlisted personnel, and a large corps of our best nurses. It was suggested that I could be of most help if I remained to aid in organizing additional hospital facilities in Baltimore and that I might even have a special urological reconstruction hospital at which some of the seriously wounded would receive special attention.

Colonel Goodwin, representing the Medical Corps of the British Army in Washington, called for one thousand well-trained young surgeons to be sent to the aid of the British in their evacuation hospitals, which were seriously undermanned as a result of losses at the front. From the Brady Institute, David M. Davis, J. A. Campbell Colston, and William D. Jack volunteered, and left at once. Many others went from the hospital, and from all parts of the country these men were hastily got together and sent across.

My desire to go increased. The drawback to enlisting was the fact that we had no research fund at the Brady Institute. It was necessary to contribute myself and persuade others to contribute in order to keep the laboratory and scientific departments going. A minimum annual sum of $15,000 was necessary. It was not at hand, and until the money was raised I felt that my responsibility at the hospital was too great for me to think of going. One morning I was awakened from my sleep with an idea—why not put my radium to work and have the fees contributed to the research fund? I felt confident that by this means my associates could get $10,000 or more a year to keep our laboratories going. I jumped out of bed, got a hasty breakfast, took an early train to Washington, and went up to the headquarters of the Medical Corps of the United States Army. This was on May 24. I had been approached by three young medical men, previous assistants of mine, who begged me to take them if I went. When the Surgeon General asked me what I would like to do, I said I wanted to go at once, to take with me three assistants, and to operate on special urological cases in the British hospitals, in addition to making a study of the progress that had been made in urology and venereology in the armies of our Allies. The papers were fixed out at once; in fact, I wrote them.

I was told that the earliest possible transportation would be provided. I found that General Pershing was going to leave on Monday morning, May 29, on the steamer *Baltic* of the White Star Line, and after a little persuasion my group was given sailing orders for the same ship. Uniforms were hastily made. In four days I secured two uniforms as well as an overcoat. Dr. Franklin Martin accuses me, in his biography, of having taken a uniform that had been made for him by the military tailor, but I still protest ignorance of any such theft.

When I got to the hospital on Saturday, our chief clerk, Philip Meisel, begged me to take him, saying that he thought it would be preposterous for me to go abroad without a secretary. It was then almost noon. Could the proper papers and passports be secured in time for Philip to leave Baltimore the next day? I thought of my friend Hampson Gary in the State Department at Washington. I explained the whole matter to him over the telephone. Gary said he would do the best he could. He sent word to me that the chief of the Passport Bureau would wait until two o'clock Saturday afternoon, and that if I could have the young man over there before that hour, the papers could be made out. He said, however, that the whole affair was quite irregular, as thousands were waiting for passports. I wrote letters endorsing Meisel, who then left for Washington. The next morning when I went to the hospital I asked Philip if he had his passport. "No," he said, "because I did not have any photographs they refused to give me a passport." I hastily called up Gary, explained to him that such a requisite had not been made clear to me, that it was absolutely essential for me to take Philip with me, and he must sail from New York the next morning with me on the *Baltic*. "Photographs are now being made at the Brady Institute, and he can be in Washington within two hours. Please get the head of the Passport Bureau and ask him for your sake and mine to fill out the passports." After an hour the phone rang. Gary was on the line. "After great difficulty and many telephone calls I discovered that the head of the Passport Bureau is on his farm in Virginia with a group of Senators who are to lunch with him." I explained to him the urgency of the situation. He cursed furiously, then: "Tell them to send the damn fellow over. I will make out the passport for him at three o'clock, but don't ever speak to me again."

On the way to New York on Sunday afternoon I had the good fortune to meet Mrs. Hiram Dewing. She was an old friend, had been a bridesmaid at our wedding, and her brother was president of the International Mercantile Marine. The *Baltic* was one of their ships. I told Sue my troubles. I had not been assigned to any particular room on the *Baltic* and had no transportation or accommodations for Philip. I asked her if she would be so good as to get hold of her brother and beg him to give us accomodations. About midnight my telephone at the Vanderbilt rang. It was Sue. "After much effort I finally caught up with my brother, who is visiting on Long Island. He has agreed to come to the city and see that your stenographer has transportation." Philip appeared the next morning at six o'clock and informed me that it was necessary to obtain visas from both the French and British consuls. I had been ordered to be at Governor's Island at ten o'clock. The British and French consular offices did not open until ten o'clock, and we were miles from Governor's Island. Much more telephoning to be done. Assistants were reached, and after many minutes spent in persuasion they agreed to open the offices earlier than usual and to visa the passport.

Philip and I were at the docks of Governor's Island at ten o'clock and went aboard a tug that was to take us out to meet the *Baltic*. Captain Louis C. Lehr, Lieutenant Montague L. Boyd, and Lieutenant Howard L. Cecil, the other members of my team, were also present. Knowing that we had no travel orders for Philip, and in fact no right to take him aboard, I advised him to secrete himself in the hold. In a little while the large tug began to fill up with husky-looking men. Lehr, Boyd, Cecil, and I were all dressed fit to kill in our new uniforms, but the crowd that came aboard were in citizens' clothes, and very rough-looking ones at that. They wandered about the boat in groups and finally one of them, with a large pipe in his mouth and an old slouch hat, stopped in front of us and said, "Look at the sawbones, all dressed up." Feeling that the United States Army was being insulted, I immediately jumped up and said: "What do you mean by addressing in this way officers of the United States Army? Who in the hell are you?" "I am Colonel Parker, of the 104th Infantry, a member of General Pershing's staff, and those men over there are other officers. We were ordered to leave secretly in citizens' clothing so as to prevent German spies from finding out on what boat General Pershing and his staff are to sail." Greatly crestfallen, I explained that we had been given no instructions not to appear in uniform. Colonel Parker then departed, and soon a sturdy-looking man of middle age with a strong Roman face came up and said: "I am Major Harbord, General Pershing's chief of staff. Major, let me see your papers." After scrutinizing them he said: "They seem to be correct. I cannot find that you have made any mistake. It seems strange that you should have been ordered on this tug for General Pershing's party. I will show your papers to General Pershing." He then departed. In a little while Major Harbord reappeared to say: "Come with me and bring your group of officers. General Pershing wishes to see you," and in a few minutes we were before the future Commander in Chief of the United States Army. We were duly presented, and the General said: "As soon as you are aboard, procure some citizens' clothes. In case our ship is torpedoed, we do not wish submarine

officers to discover that my staff and I are aboard." I assured him
that we would carry out his orders, and we backed off, much relieved.

The tug soon pulled out. We went out into the harbor and waited
in the fog until the *Baltic* hove in sight and stopped. The transfer to
the *Baltic* was a perilous affair. She loomed high above our tiny
tug. The sea was rough and both tug and ship rolled violently. The
gangplank rose at a steep angle. General Pershing went aboard first
and as the ship lurched I feared that he would be thrown into the
sea, but they dragged him aboard, and his party followed him
up the steep ascent. We four then went aboard, followed by Philip,
who scrambled up the gangplank like a scared monkey. I told him
to secrete himself until we were well out to sea. Without a ticket,
without accommodations, without any connection with the A.E.F.,
with no travel orders and only a hastily secured passport, Philip was
aboard at last, unauthorized. A representative of the International
Mercantile Marine came up and presented a note from President
Franklin assuring me that a stateroom had been secured for Philip
and that he would see that I had one of the best staterooms on the
ship.

General Pershing's officers had been selected because of their
ability, training, and fitness to begin the organization of the A.E.F.
in France. The Medical Corps was represented by Lieutenant
Colonel Merritte W. Ireland, who had been with the General in
Texas, Major George P. Peed, and Captain Henry Beeuwkes.
Colonel Ireland kindly invited Lehr and me to sit at his table.

There were only a few civilians aboard the *Baltic*—too many
ships had been lost from torpedoes to make sea travel attractive.
There were a few actresses going over to join the Red Cross, and
some Canadian and American newspapermen. One of these was
Mr. Charles H. Grasty, formerly editor of the *Baltimore Sun*, and
at that time on the staff of the *New York Times*. I explained to him
our need for civilian clothes and he got some for us from various
passengers. They didn't fit and we put up a shabby appearance,
but not much worse than General Pershing and his staff, most of

whom looked like tramps. They expected to throw their "civies" overboard as soon as they were permitted to don uniforms.

We were assembled after dinner and addressed by General Pershing. He said he wished the voyage to be as profitable as possible, that United States Army officers would deliver lectures and the officers of the French and British armies would talk to us on the development of their specialties in war. He wished everyone to study French, and for that purpose classes would be organized, with instructors.

Colonel Ireland said General Pershing wanted me to deliver an address on venereal disease as a problem of war. How many days would it take me to get ready? "Give me four days, Colonel, as I wish to make a lot of charts with which to illustrate my talk." The steward got me a collection of large seating cards, about three feet square, on which were the names of those occupying the various dining-room tables on previous voyages. On the backs of these, with red and blue pencils, I succeeded in making about a dozen charts with which I was able to discuss the frequency of venereal disease in civil life and its problem in the army. General Pershing sat in the front row, and at the end of the hour thanked me for "a very interesting talk." He said he considered venereal disease one of the most important problems confronting the Medical Corps, that he personally was greatly interested in the subject, and while in Mexico had adopted extraordinary measures to prevent venereal infection among his troops.

In a few days we were at Halifax, where some British passengers were taken aboard. We traveled far south, then went far north. It seemed that we must be going around the north of Ireland, but another turn to the south at last brought us to a point where we were close to the west of France. With no lights showing after sundown, we were not even permitted to light a match or smoke a cigarette on deck. We were commanded not to undress when we went to bed, and to wear life-preservers night and day. We had frequent messages by radio from ships that had been torpedoed, and wondered why our ship, which to us seemed the most important of all, received no naval escort. It was not until we had almost reached France that destroyers first showed up, two British and then two American. They circled around us at great speed and displayed their extreme agility in all sorts of remarkable maneuvers. The next night, when we were right in the midst of the German U-boat zone, I was informed (subsequently) that during three hours our captain had heard the calls of ten ships being attacked by German submarines.

It was an excited group that drew up to the dock at Birkenhead, opposite Liverpool. The ship had hardly made fast to the dock when a battalion of Welsh Fusiliers came down the circuitous road into the dockyard. They were headed by a sergeant major who led a magnificent goat bedecked with ribbons. Across the goat's forehead was a large silver plate with the coat of arms of the organization, which had been presented by Queen Mary. The Welsh Fusiliers date back to the days when yeomanry wore queues that were oiled. In order to prevent greasing their uniforms they wore two strips of wide silk braid that extended from the collar for several inches down their backs. Although the queue had long since been replaced by a boyish bob, the Welsh Fusiliers still wore the black tapes.

Some British officers with much gold lace on their uniforms came aboard and were received by General Pershing. He went down the gangplank accompanied by the British officers and held a review, carefully inspecting the Welsh Fusiliers, including the goat.

CHAPTER II. STUDYING VENEREAL DISEASES
WITH THE BRITISH ARMY
IN ENGLAND AND FRANCE

WE SOON entrained in a special for London. We accompanied General Pershing and his staff to the Victoria Hotel, where we met Colonel Alfred E. Bradley, who was to become Chief Surgeon of the American Expeditionary Forces. He looked over my orders to report to the Chief Surgeon of the British Army, and said he probably would need us in France before long. In the meantime he thought it would be well for us to make a careful study of urological surgery and the venereal-disease situation in England and the British Expeditionary Forces. He said that a report on these subjects would be of great importance to the A.E.F.

In the British Army the campaign against venereal disease was confined largely to pamphlets and lectures. Prophylaxis (preventive treatment) had not been adopted. When we told the British of the wonderful results obtained by this means in the United States Army, they said they had seen our publications, but that their people were conservative, that the use of prophylaxis was considered as condoning an immoral act, and that violent opposition was engendered whenever any such proposition was made. As a result venereal disease was very prevalent. Finally by calling prophylaxis "early treatment" it had been possible in some commands to carry it out partially.

The Canadians had an active visa office at No. 3 Southampton

Street, to which all their soldiers arriving in London on leave were required to report. It was presided over by an American clergyman serving with the Canadians, who was a colonel in the Sanitary Corps. His interest in the prevention of venereal disease in the army camps in Canada had brought quick recognition, and prompt transfer to the important visa office in London. He personally met every Canadian soldier on leave and had a long talk with him on the dangers of venereal disease and the importance of avoiding it by continence. If he did not succeed in this, he was to report to the visa office, where prophylaxis was efficiently carried out by methods employed in the United States.

The Chief Surgeon of the Australian forces was greatly interested in the venereal problem. He believed that prophylaxis was more effective than lectures on continence. He told me that he had been visited by the Bishop of London, who after talking to him said, "General, from what you've said, it seems to me that you think there are no chaste men," to which the Chief Surgeon replied, "Yes, Bishop, there are chaste men, but all of them are impotent."

The chief medical officer of the New Zealand forces thought venereal disease was a proper punishment for sin. "In New Zealand," he said, "all venereally infected soldiers are taken to an island, where they are penned up, and the populace knows why they are kept there—a just retribution." The New Zealand High Commissioner, after hearing that the Medical Corps of their army would not accept prophylactic methods, organized a visa office and a venereal prophylactic station in his own headquarters. When I called there, I was shown to a certain room. Seated behind a large desk was a charming curly-haired blonde. Feeling confident that I must be in the wrong place, I explained that I was looking for the Department of Venereal Prophylaxis. "This is it," she said, "and I'm in charge." Miss Rout had served with the New Zealand Red Cross and had done efficient work in Egypt. She had a wide knowledge of the venereal peril and had been entrusted with the visa office and prophylactic work. I asked her what was done to prevent venereal disease among their troops. "To each soldier on leave," she said, "I give a box of these prophylactic tubes." She opened a box, and I counted six tubes. "You give each one six?" "Yes, every New Zealander needs at least six his first night in London. We have some particularly sturdy specimens, and to these I give, in addition, a few of these," and with that she reached in her desk drawer and pulled out some condoms. "We buy the best quality," she said as she stretched them to considerable length.

It was reported to us that as the Colonial troops received 5 or 6 shillings a day, they were much more sought after by loose women than the British soldier, who got only sixpence a day. I reported this information to Colonel Bradley, and we went to see General Pershing. After the General had heard my report on the venereal-disease situation and the Colonial troops, he asked me to see Ambassador Page and get him to request the War Department in Washington to withhold half of the American soldier's pay, emphasizing that it would help immensely in our crusade against venereal disease. I saw William H. Buckler of Baltimore, one of the secretaries at the American Embassy. He took me to see the Ambassador, who listened with keen interest to the report General Pershing had asked me to make. He asked me to help him phrase a cable requesting Washington to withhold a portion of each soldier's pay.

After four days in London, General Pershing left for France. That morning the Germans staged their greatest raid on London. Twenty-one planes came across, and their bombs killed about six hundred persons. They bombed a railroad station, perhaps hoping to get General Pershing and his staff. One bomb struck a car filled with passengers, most of whom were killed.

I was invited to attend the annual meeting of the National Council for Combating Venereal Diseases, which met at Queen's Hall. Lord Sydenham presided, and presented a letter from His Majesty King George, who spoke of the seriousness of the situation and the importance of an active crusade against venereal disease. Sir Alfred

Keogh, Commander in Chief of the Medical Corps, British Army, said that while the condition in the armies was serious, that of the civil population was distinctly worse. Sir William Osler was at the meeting, and at his suggestion I sent to the London *Times* my impressions as a medical officer sent to investigate these conditions in the B.E.F.

One day on the Strand I was looking at some fascinating military haberdashery. A major of the Canadian Expeditionary Forces stopped, and we began to talk. He was an interesting fellow, and we went off to lunch together. At the British Y.M.C.A. house he had been asked if he would like to spend a week end in the country and, having nothing else to do, he had gladly accepted. After passing through a lovely park he arrived at an old Georgian mansion. The butler conducted him to his room, laid out his evening clothes, and then took him to his hostess, Lady ——. His dinner companion was a charming widow. She also sat next to him at a game of bridge. The party broke up about midnight. He was just getting into his pajamas when the opening of his door attracted his attention. His dinner companion was standing there. She said: "You men in the army lead such dangerous lives, and may never return from the next offensive. It's our duty to make your leave enjoyable, so here I am." After his bags were packed on Monday morning the butler said: "I beg pardon, sir. May I speak frankly? Perhaps you don't know the terrible losses this family has suffered. His Lordship and the eldest son died during the first year of the war. Her Ladyship has great difficulty maintaining this estate. It would be helpful if you would leave a contribution of a hundred pounds."

On Sunday we had a day off and Lehr and I went to Cherkley Court, Lord Beaverbrook's home in Surrey. This old house was in a great forest of yew trees that had been planted by Cromwell to furnish wood to make crossbows for his archers. There were places for twelve at the table, but Lady Beaverbrook remarked that two guests, a Mr. Lord, as I understood her to say, and his daughter would arrive late. When they came, I was introduced to them but did not catch their names. The father took his seat next to me. To my left was Lady Beaverbrook, who was so lovely and charming that my head was constantly turned in her direction and I had no conversation with the taciturn man on my right. In a lull of the conversation Beaverbrook called out, "What do you think about that, Bonar Law?" I realized then that my neighbor was the Chancellor of the Exchequer and the member of the War Cabinet next to Lloyd George in importance. I lost no time in making up for my indifference. He talked interestingly, particularly about the first stage of the war, in which the British forces had fallen back so precipitately that it was feared they would be driven to the English Channel; in fact, preparations had been made to concentrate the British fleet off the French coast to bring the remnants of the army back to England. (Just as they had to do in May, 1940.)

As Cherkley Court was far in the country and transportation difficult, Lord Beaverbrook invited Lehr and myself to spend the night. Although we had neither razors nor toothbrushes, we stayed. The next day we were driven back to London by Lady Beaverbrook. Her husband talked interestingly about the deplorable situation in Europe. Mr. and Mrs. Oliver Hoare, also guests, left in a dilapidated Ford. They invited us to dine with them on the following Friday. On our return to London we were very busy, and on Friday morning I had a vague remembrance that we had a dinner engagement. I asked Lehr, "With whom are we dining tonight?" "With a couple of Hoares," said he.

Lehr and I crossed over to France to study venereal disease in the B.E.F. We found several large hospitals devoted entirely to the treatment of these infections. All men found to have venereal disease were immediately evacuated from the front, or wherever their organizations were located, and sent to the nearest venereal-disease hospital, where they remained an average of forty-six days. There were twenty-three thousand hospital beds at that time occupied by these cases, amounting to approximately two whole infantry divisions in the British Army. The loss of man power to fighting forces was tremendous—70,495,000 soldier days per year.

After four terrible years of war some Tommies were frankly glad to get into a venereal hospital and enjoy for six weeks or longer surcease from the agony of the front. Indeed, the men were so demoralized that some tried to get another infection as quickly as possible, and occasionally the infection was intentionally transmitted from one to another with a matchstick.

We had an opportunity to visit an old friend, Colonel Gordon Watson, chief surgeon of the Fifth Army B.E.F. He lived with a jovial mess of colonels in a villa in the outskirts of Hazebrouck, some eight miles from the front. We spent a day visiting evacuation hospitals and ambulance dressing-stations along their sector. I was particularly eager to see what was done to those patients who suffered severe genitourinary wounds. In the casualty clearing-station at Remy Siding, Colonel Watson said; "This is an interesting case. He's one of our observation balloon men, and during the last four weeks his balloon has been shot down five times. Each time he has made his escape in a parachute with little difficulty. Last time, while he was descending to earth the German aviator circled around him, firing his machine gun at him. Since then he's been very nervous, and we're giving him a rest cure before he returns to his balloon."

We could not refrain from visiting the scene of the great battle for Wytschaete Ridge, which the British had taken after blowing up the German lines with huge mines that had been planted after months of mining beneath the German position. I counted five great craters over a hundred feet across and many feet deep. While we were inspecting those a Boche plane passed over, and shortly afterward we were subjected to a little shelling, my baptism. The Colonel made a dive into an old German pillbox, and Lehr and I quickly followed. When we emerged we were all covered with slime and could not help laughing at each other.

We proceeded to Ypres, where the sad ruins of the celebrated Cloth Hall and the great cathedral alone remained amid the general desolation of the once proud city. Ahead could be seen the quagmire with isolated pillboxes in which the British Army managed to subsist. The wounded had to be evacuated on duckboards (walks) that virtually swam on the surface of the morass. The Red Cross brassards of the stretcher-bearers were no longer respected by the Germans, and the terrible mortality that had been inflicted on the Medical Corps necessitated holding the wounded by day and evacuating them by night. Even then they were subjected to pitiless fire. To fall off the duckboards often ended in drowning in the marsh. Once the wounded arrived at the ambulance heads and were transported to evacuation hospitals, the medical service afforded was wonderful, and the great hospital trains that thundered down to Boulogne carried medical personnel equipped to make the wounded as comfortable as possible, even providing for continuous antiseptic irrigations of wounds and supplying splints and other surgical appliances. Arrived at Boulogne, the wounded were quickly distributed to the many thousand hospital beds provided by the numerous hospitals at that port and in adjacent cities, where the greatest surgeons in England and also nonsurgical specialists, who had deserted their luxurious homes on Harley Street, labored night and day in the great medical organization of the British Army. At these base hospitals even the severely wounded were allowed to remain only a few days. Owing to the tremendous numbers that were brought in from the front every day, it was necessary that they be transported quickly to Great Britain. For this, hospital ships and trains, magnificently equipped, had been provided.

On this trip we met many of the thousand young surgeons sent from the great hospitals and medical schools in America to serve as operators in the British hospitals in France. These were the first Americans to enter the World War. Instead of serving in the capacity for which they had been sent over, these surgeons were soon shipped by the British to divisions at the front as battalion, regimental, and ambulance surgeons to replace British officers. The misuse of this picked corps of one thousand surgeons was much resented by the Medical Corps of the A.E.F. We eventually withdrew many of them and brought them to our hospitals in France, but not before numbers of them had been killed, wounded, or captured.

Lehr and I went on to Paris and reported at General Pershing's headquarters, temporarily located on the rue Constantin. Colonel Bradley, Chief Surgeon of the A.E.F., told me that it had been decided to order me and those with me to Paris.

We then hastened back to London to pack up. When Lehr and I arrived at the Stafford on St. James Place, Boyd, Cecil, and the stenographer (Meisel) were in a state of great excitement. Boyd and Cecil had already received their orders to proceed to Paris, but as they had no money with which to pay their hotel bill, the proprietor was standing guard to prevent them from leaving. They assured him I would soon return, and in the meantime they would leave Meisel as hostage, but the proprietor refused to have a stenographer left as security for the considerable bill of four officers. The arrival of Lehr and myself was oil on the troubled waters. Cecil and Boyd promptly departed on a 1 A.M. train as soon as I agreed to be responsible for all bills.

The following morning we found at Brown Shipley's orders for Lehr and myself to depart immediately for France. We had to present the formal request from General Pershing and be discharged from the British Army. Then something had to be done about Philip Meisel, who had no status whatever. He was not in the army and had no valid reason for being in England. As he was a civilian, the army refused to have anything to do with him, and the officials said it would be impossible to give him a permit to go to France. Besides this, there was the difficulty of obtaining a French visa. Finally, as a result of alternate imploring and cursing and much scurrying back and forth to various headquarters—French, British, and American—I managed to secure a special order allowing

Meisel to accompany me to Paris. The boat train we had to take left at ten-thirty in the morning. We had been so busy the day before that we had failed to go to Brown Shipley's to get money on our letter of credit. While Philip and I completed the packing, Lehr was sent to the bank at nine o'clock to secure funds. We waited impatiently for him to come back. Ten o'clock, and still no Lehr. Finally, at ten minutes after ten, he dashed up, hastily paid the hotel man, and we were off to Charing Cross Station, where we just caught the boat train. Turning to Lehr, I asked why he had taken so long at Brown Shipley's. "Hujus, I had a hell of a time. When I got there at nine o'clock, I found only the night watchman, who told me through a chink in the door that they didn't open until ten. I explained to him our desperate situation, and he finally allowed me to get inside. He was opening the mail, and occasionally extracted pound notes sent in for deposit. I begged him to let me have £40 on my letter of credit from the pile before him. He was deaf to my entreaties until I slipped a £5 note into his palm. Securing the banknotes, I hastened to the door while the porter ejaculated, 'You Americans are extraordinary people.' "

CHAPTER 12. STUDYING VENEREAL DISEASES IN THE FRENCH ARMY

IN JULY the Chief Surgeon notified me that I had been put in charge of all the urological and venereal disease work. It was the first time a consultant had been appointed director of any division of medicine in the army. The position afforded a wonderful opportunity for radical departures from previous methods in vogue in the Allied armies, with the possibility of great accomplishments in urology and venereology. My official title was Director of the Division of Urology.

Colonel Bradley asked me to prepare a program for a Division of Urology for the A.E.F. After giving him a detailed report of our studies with the British Army in England and France, I proposed that we should make a similar study with the French Army, to which he agreed. As I was leaving headquarters I met a colonel of the regular Medical Corps, who said, somewhat sarcastically, "What are you over here for?" "I've got a big job," said I "to make the underworld safe for democracy."

While studying the venereal-disease problem in Paris, I had the good fortune to meet Clément Simon, a young syphilographer who stood high among army venereologists. I told him of my proposed inspection trip and suggested that he accompany us.

On July 22, 1917, Lehr, Simon, and I left for the zone of the French armies. We soon reached the pretty village of Meaux, only twenty-four miles from Paris, the nearest point of the German advance, from which they were driven back many miles in the First Battle of the Marne. A little farther along, near Senlis, we came across the first venereal-disease hospital. In the afternoon we reached Compiègne. At a venereal clinic some of the nurses were women of high social position, and countesses were engaged in giving urethral injections. Here was the headquarters of the great French Army. We were invited to dine at the mess of the Intelligence Corps—a rollicking group of young officers. We met a Captain Lehr from Alsace, one of the most celebrated of the secret service. We discovered that he and my Captain Lehr were cousins. Speaking and looking very much like a German, he had recently traveled all over the Reich. He told us thrilling stories of hairbreadth escapes.

At Compiègne we also visited Alexis Carrel in the hospital he had organized in the Hôtel du Rond-Point-Royal and where he had made his great advances in the treatment of wounds with the Carrel-Dakin solution. We saw many large wounds that were kept flushed with this benign antiseptic solution flowing intermittently from many minute rubber tubes into the depths of the wounds, thus ferreting out the infection, cleansing the tissues, and finally rendering the wound sterile, so that it was possible to do a clean operation and close the wound completely. Heretofore, extensive wounds had to fill up by granulation—a process that required many months and led to great scars. Carrel had not only greatly shortened the convalescence, but he had markedly reduced the mortality and even made it possible to save patients with severe compound fractures of the great bones, which previously had required amputation. By his wonderful discoveries at the Rockefeller Institute, Carrel had greatly honored France, but when he returned home and demonstrated his methods at this French hospital, instead of being enthusiastically received he was savagely combated by the most important surgeons in France. He was almost in tears when he told me how contemptuously he had been treated in the country of his birth.

Speeding on towards Epernay, we passed the Montagne de Reims, on the south slopes of which were thousands of acres of vineyards and peasants working among them, heedless of the savage war going on a few miles away. At Epernay we saw the great champagne cellars. One firm had fourteen miles of tunnels in the great cliff of chalk, and in it were nine million bottles of champagne. When he saw my astonishment, the proprietor told me that when the Germans arrived he had seventy-five million bottles; they drank up much of it, and the resultant drunkenness of the German soldiers possibly contributed to the victory of the French on the Marne.

We moved on to Vitry-le-François, where we found that a great hospital had been organized in cavalry barracks and stables. The celebrated syphilographer Lévy-Bing was in command. With great pride he took us through the huge rock barns, on the plastered walls of which he had allowed some of the great artists of France, who happened to be among his syphilitics, an opportunity to give full rein to their bizarre imaginations. On these walls were a dozen great pastel paintings about ten by twenty feet, depicting the sad plight of the *vénériens* as they appeared stripped for their initial examination and went through various stages of treatment.

We discovered that the French had made great progress in simplifying the treatment of syphilis. In the American and British armies the old salvarsan (606) was still being used. A half a pint or more of the drug in solution was slowly passed from a suspended receptacle through a tube into the vein of the forearm—a procedure that required much time and was often painful. On alternate days the unfortunates usually had their buttocks injected with mercurial oil. Lévy-Bing used the new French preparation—novarsenobenzol, which was so nonirritating that it was only necessary to use fifteen drops of water to dissolve a dose, which was then injected with a small hypodermic syringe into the vein. On alternate days, instead of the painful mercurial oil he used another intravenous injection, equally small in amount, of oxycyanide of mercury. So expert had these specialists become that the speed with which they worked was positively unbelievable. In three hours I saw one young medical officer make intravenous injections in three hundred patients. Lévy-Bing showed me statistics which proved to my satisfaction that his treatment was greatly to be preferred to the methods in use in the British and American armies. It was decided then and there that these methods should be adopted in the A.E.F.

As we proceeded along the French front we made brief excursions to see interesting medical and military organizations nearer the battle line. These included a visit to the Chemin-des-Dames and the destroyed city of Soissons, and Reims with its great cathedral still towering proudly to the sky after being struck by seven hundred shells.

At Bar-le-Duc we found a hospital of many thousand beds devoted to the treatment of syphilis and complicated cases of gonorrhea. It was only when a gonorrheal infection involved deep-seated organs and the patient became quite ill that he was evacuated from his organization to one of these special hospitals. This plan of the French varied sharply from that of the British, who sent every man, even those with slight gonorrheal infections, back to a hospital often over a hundred miles away. The French had so improved their regimental medical services that they were able to care for cases of gonorrhea while the soldier remained with his organization on a duty status. This removed a tremendous load from their hospitals. Up to that time there had been two hundred thousand cases of syphilis and eight hundred thousand cases of gonorrhea in the French Army, and to hospitalize all of these was impossible.

In order to obtain further information in this most active part of the French front, both as to the treatment of cases of gonorrhea with their regiments and also to obtain details concerning urological wounds, we took the "sacred way" down which five hundred thousand wounded had passed from the great fortress of Verdun. We spent the night at a little château on the banks of the Meuse, and were awakened by a terrific explosion that shook the house violently. The next day we found, just before entering Verdun, that great stores of shells stacked along the road had been blown up by long-range German artillery. Along one side of the road were dozens of draft horses stark in death where they had been blown by the exploding shells from the road along which they were drawing munitions. The force of the explosion was so terrific that giant poplars lining the roads had been broken off like matchsticks.

In the citadel of Verdun we found a beautifully appointed hospital of one hundred and seventy-five beds in long tunnels deep within the hill. Some five thousand troops could be accommodated in the vast corridors in this great cliff. There was a bakery capable of producing bread for sixty thousand daily, and a charming theater, where we saw a riotous play given by soldiers at rest in the citadel. Some were celebrated comedians from Paris. As we took our seats the band stood up and played "The Star-spangled Banner." Our underground rooms were well ventilated and seemed luxurious. The commandant's mess provided an exquisite menu, with vintage wines and Havana cigars. It was thrilling to meet at the table Captain d'Artigue, whose heroic resistance had saved Froide-Terre, the last of Verdun's encircling forts. He had lost almost all his officers and men. With the field telegraph out of commission, his only method of communication was by carrier pigeons; he gave me original copies of many messages he had sent by way of these wonderful birds. The Fort de Vaux had recently been recaptured, and we visited it with the commandant, passing along deep trenches in the walls of which were decaying arms and legs of bodies that the fresh troops had been unable to remove as they feverishly dug themselves in. At the Fort de Vaux we found an excellent small hospital, and from the parapet we plainly saw German soldiers moving up and down their trenches.

We hurried on to Toul, another great fortified city of ancient France, and afterward the center of great American hospitals. From there we went on to the old royal city of Nancy, where we had an excellent opportunity of studying the problem of venereal disease among the civil population of this beautiful city of a hundred thousand people, from which almost all the men and youths had gone. Nancy was veritably crowded to overflowing with women who had concentrated there from occupied areas. Many had lost husbands, brothers, and sweethearts. They were fed up with the war, overpowered by *cafard* (the blues), and crazy to be diverted. All moral restraints had gone to the winds, and at medical headquarters we were informed that venereal disease was rife. The cases among civilian women gave the French Medical Corps a serious problem, because almost none of the civilian physicians remained in the city. Valuable notes on venereal disease were being amassed.

After visiting the headquarters of the Eighth French Army and various hospitals, including one with a capacity of six hundred patients that was built entirely underground, we retraced our steps to within two miles of the front and visited Gondrecourt, headquarters of the First Division A.E.F. This division of over twenty-five thousand men was distributed in the towns and villages and farm buildings in a training-area fifteen miles in diameter. They were housed in barns and stables, as were the battalions of the very noted French division, the Chasseurs Alpins, which had been sent there to instruct the Americans in the art of war. The French were bedded on hay directly on the floor. The Americans had individual cots, but the weather had become so cold that many of the soldiers had "chucked" these and also taken to hay on the floor. Colonel Bailey K. Ashford, the division surgeon, listened with the greatest interest to the recital of our studies with the British and the French and made valuable suggestions, which were afterwards incorporated in our report.

At Bazoilles we encountered Base Hospital No. 18, from the Johns Hopkins Hospital. Our old pals were very unhappy. The C.O., a hard-boiled regular, got the doctors up at five o'clock for setting-up exercises and sent them across country on a ten-mile hike with a sergeant while he went back to bed. This did not improve the relations between the C.O. and some of the very distinguished medical men who formed the Hopkins unit.

Remote from the zone of the armies were a series of urologic centers to which were sent the wounded requiring special operations upon the genitourinary tract, and therapeutic care. In most instances initial operations had been carried out in the evacuation or base hospitals. At one of these "centers," devoted almost entirely to genital wounds, we found great progress had been made by the chief surgeon, Cathelin, in the difficult plastics required to repair mutilations of the genitalia. We saw many patients in which the result looked excellent. "But," remarked Cathelin, "the most important thing is to know the functional results. Among the nurses I have a group of patriotic young women who, when I request them, take a patient in whom complete reparations have been made to a charming little room I have prepared as an adjunct to the hospital and bring me the next day a faithful report as to the success of the operation. Ours is the only hospital in which the functional value of the member after operation is obtained."

WHEN I returned to Paris, I reported to Colonel Bradley, who requested me to prepare recommendations for the organization of a
urological service of the A.E.F. The plan I suggested was acceptable
to him and together we presented it to General Pershing. I quote
from my war diary:

Saturday, August 11, 1917: At ten o'clock Col. Bradley and I were
received by Gen. Pershing. Col. Bradley presented the document which I
had prepared and the General read it very carefully, expressing the greatest interest. The plan proposed was:

Imperative need for consecutive treatment of syphilis. Investigation
of recurrences in French armies shows conclusively the absolute necessity
of consecutive treatment of syphilis for a period of a year or two. This
makes it essential that adequate provision be made by means of proposed
regimental infirmaries so that men with syphilis may be treated properly.
If this provision is made, there is no reason why all cases of syphilis
should not be treated there. In the French army, gonorrhea is treated in
the regimental infirmaries; and with improvements, which we can easily
carry out, there is no reason why both gonorrhea and syphilis should not
be well and thoroughly treated at regimental infirmary dispensaries, on
an ambulatory basis, as in private life.

Advantages: This will keep the men in their regiments. At present
the British send all venereal cases to base hospitals in France or in England and 18,000 men or more constantly are away from their organizations,
living in idleness and with hospital comforts and food; a premium is thus
placed on getting venereal disease, and the British medical officers complain that it is often taken advantage of by the men.

Long transportation will be avoided. By treating the men near the front, early treatment, so important in all these diseases, will be secured.

Both French and British authorities complain that women are often infected by venereal patients en route to venereal hospitals at the rear; this will also be avoided.

Other needs for a regimental infirmary: A better study of camp hygiene, food, presence of vermin, early detection of infectious skin diseases and better treatment of slight ailments, particularly the "common cold" and grippe.

Proposition: To provide small, well-equipped regimental infirmary dispensaries, each consisting of an easily demountable hospital barrack of about five sections, including twelve or fourteen beds, a small office, a small treatment room and prophylactic station.

Personnel: In constant attendance there will be a medical officer who will remain with the infirmary and not change places up and down the line with the battalions. He will be under the officer commanding the regiment located for the time being at the camp. He will look after the health, hygiene and sanitation of the men and the camp, under the direction of the regimental surgeon. A training station at the base, which would rapidly acquaint them with their manifold but simple duties, can easily be organized, and the men adequately prepared for their work, which will not be difficult or require specialists.

The question of requiring soldiers on leave in Paris to reside in the official army hotel is worthy of more consideration. It is proposed that great liberty be allowed and that the men simply be required to return to the hotel for the night by 1 A.M. It is urged that this would be no hardship, and unquestionably such a plan would make it possible to carry out prophylactic treatments earlier, and that thus much venereal disease could be avoided.

The Y.M.C.A. proposes the establishment of a central restaurant and the organization of an army hotel. They are now willing to cooperate with the Medical Department in providing prophylactic stations and abundant facilities for medical supervision in their hotels.

Civil population: Extensive studies show that there has been much demoralization in the civil population and a great increase in venereal diseases. In the town of Nancy the chief medical officer of the Eighth Army (French) reports that syphilis is eight times as prevalent, proportionately, now as before the war.

The French are making strenuous efforts by means of *"Services annexes,"* which are under the command of medical officers, to treat the civil population for venereal diseases.

Investigation shows that while something can be accomplished by working through the police, most of the work must be done by the establishment of dispensaries and small hospitals organized to treat all kinds of diseases among the civil population, who are now left without medical attention. The confidence and cooperation of the population should be secured, and women with venereal disease induced to come for free, private, secret and adequate treatment. If such a service is established by the A.E.F. not only will a great work be accomplished for this stricken region of France, but the fountain source of venereal infection of our soldiers will be brought under control. Prophylactic stations could also be organized in these small dispensaries, particularly if adjacent to encampments of American troops. This work should be done in connection with the American Red Cross, and a visiting nurse organization.

The Chief Surgeon then explained in detail the proposed scheme and requested me to give at length the arguments for it, and to demonstrate the method of operation. With maps, plans, etc., I proceeded to detail rapidly the methods employed by the French and English, the manifest objections, the very inadequate treatment provided, the absolute necessity of our providing much better medical care, supervision and treatment, and the need of new and far more thorough method of organization as proposed in the regimental infirmaries. I also went over the importance of the work among the civil population and pointed out that in order to accomplish results it would be necessary to organize small general medical dispensaries as proposed in the scheme which I outlined, under army supervision, and manned by army medical officers, the rest of the personnel and equipment to be furnished by the Red Cross. The proposed army hotels and the order requiring men to report and lodge there, and the medical dispensary and supervision as well as the plans for amusement, athletic sports, etc., were dwelt upon.

The Commander-in-Chief discussed the whole question with us at great length, evinced the keenest interest and a wide knowledge of the subjects presented, and said he considered these problems among the most important from the standpoint of efficiency and preservation of effectiveness in the army, and gave his most hearty consent to the entire plan.

This interview resulted in General Order No. 34, which contained these provisions: All commanders to develop a higher morale in their commands, to try to inculcate temperance, in order to prevent the ravages of venereal disease, to provide amusements; medical officers to give frequent lectures on hygiene and venereal diseases and to carry out an inspection of all soldiers twice a month; soldiers to obtain visas upon going to cities on leave or duty; establishment of regimental infirmaries, with equipment for proper treatment of venereal disease, with soldiers on a duty status or at special work camps; every man contracting venereal disease to be court-martialed and deprived of pay, and officers to be disciplined.

The organization of the Division of Urology was begun by sending Captain Montague L. Boyd to the First Division and Lieutenant Howard L. Cecil to Saint-Nazaire.

The modern treatment of syphilis is based on Ehrlich's great discovery of salvarsan (606). Up to 1914 this was manufactured only in Germany, and inasmuch as stocks of this drug began to run low, the prices in the United States soared until in a short time $6 or $8 a dose was exacted by the representative of the German firm that held patents. This serious situation eventually resulted in an investigation by a senatorial committee, at which Dr. George Walker, afterwards urologist to our base ports, appeared and presented a strong indictment against the representative of the German manufacturer, who jumped up and called Dr. Walker a liar. Walker replied with a blow on the chin that floored the German, right in the committee room.

The situation in this country was relieved somewhat by the arrival of the submarine *Deutschland*, which dived beneath the British warships guarding the entrance to the Chesapeake and made its way to Baltimore with its cargo, largely composed of salvarsan, which brought fabulous prices.

After a while the drug was being produced in the United States, but in such limited quantities that we could not secure any for the A.E.F. The French were manufacturing the drug in sufficient quantities to supply their own and the British armies and had developed in novarsenobenzol a very efficient modification similar to Ehrlich's second formula (neosalvarsan) that had the marked advantage of being less toxic than salvarsan. This is the drug we adopted for the treatment of syphilis in the A.E.F.

The Chief Surgeon A.E.F. commissioned me to visit Billon

Frères, the French manufacturers. They said they could supply our needs and proposed to charge us the same that they did the British, but I had found out that the British were paying twice as much as the French did. I demanded that we be charged no more than the French, inasmuch as our forces were intimately associated with theirs and we had come over to save France. The manufacturers finally agreed, and instead of $6 a dose—once the price in the United States—we contracted to pay an average of 16 cents. Working with the same firm, we developed a compact gelatin-covered prophylactic tube that could be carried by those whose positions were far from prophylactic stations.

In order to carry out our new plan for the treatment of venereal diseases without sending soldiers away from their commands, I was authorized by the Chief Surgeon to furnish each regiment with a urological set equipped with the finest syringes, needles, and other special instruments and apparatus for urological and venereal work. When these sets were ready, I notified the medical purchasing officer in Paris and he told me they would be sent to the main base supply depot in southwestern France, from which they could be requisitioned by the supply depot of the intermediate zone, and from there would go by requisition to the supply depot and the zone of advance, from which they could be obtained, also by requisition, by the supply depot of the army corps and divisions. At this rate it would take six weeks before the drugs and equipment could reach the regiments. I asked if I might be allowed to take these supplies directly to the regiments, but the purchasing officer asserted that this was entirely irregular and could not be done. Returning to the zone of the advance, I saw the chief surgeon of the supply depot there, Colonel Reno, and explained my desire to get these much-needed things to the troops; he agreed to accept receipts from the regiments to which I proposed to distribute the boxes and said that he would make my accounts all right.

I returned to Paris, gave my personal receipt, filled a truck with the boxes, and distributed them to the regiments myself. With the receipts in hand, I returned to the supply depot, advance section, and asked for Colonel Reno. I was told by another officer that he had replaced Colonel Reno, who had been adjudged insane and sent home. When I presented my receipts for the infirmary sets, the new officer refused to accept them, saying that it was entirely irregular. I explained that Colonel Reno had told me that if I obtained receipts for the boxes which I distributed to the regiments, he would accept them and make it all right. But the new director of the supply depot said that such action would be entirely irregular, and intimated that when Colonel Reno agreed to do such a thing he was already insane.

I soon began receiving demands for an accounting of the boxes, but as I could not return them and they had cost more than twice my year's pay, I simply did nothing. I was wondering how long it would be before I was court-martialed when, to my great relief, an order was issued that supplies delivered to medical consultants need not be accounted for.

The drugs for the treatment of venereal diseases had been purchased and sent to the base supply, and the division urologists immediately sent in requisitions for their needs, but several weeks would elapse before they could be obtained through regular channels. Cases were at hand that urgently needed treatment. To meet this emergency I got the Red Cross to buy syringes, needles, and other apparatus and the drugs needed for the treatment of syphilis and gonorrhea, and took them personally to our headquarters at Neufchâteau. From there I distributed them to the regiments and other outfits that needed them. This work was outside my regular line of duty, but I was intent on seeing that treatment went on without interruption.

CHAPTER 14. MEDICAL SERVICE

FOR THE CIVIL POPULATION

OF EASTERN FRANCE

WHEN I presented the results of the inspection trip with the French Army, I reported that there was a large area in eastern France in which there were few doctors and in which the medical needs of the population had been cared for by the French Medical Corps. Now that our divisions were coming in, the French had left, and the treatment of the people would devolve upon the Medical Corps of the A.E.F.

I had stressed the fact that at Nancy syphilis was six times as prevalent as it was before the war. A large part of the population was composed of women, and as a result of the long continuation of the war, morality was at a low ebb. Undoubtedly there was much venereal disease in the whole region into which our divisions were going.

It was suggested in my report that we organize a special medical service with the double purpose of taking care of the general medical and surgical needs of the inhabitants and, particularly, of treating to render free from infection, if possible, venereal cases among the women. To accomplish this it would seem best to select a group of officers from the Medical Corps and supply them with transportation. I proposed that the American Red Cross be called on to assist in this undertaking, and eventually to build a small central hospital for cases urgently needing surgical or medical attention in an institution.

The Chief Surgeon approved the plan, which was presented to General Pershing along with the program proposed for the work of the Division of Urology. The General heartily approved, and I was commissioned to secure the co-operation of the Red Cross. The Red Cross voted the necessary funds. The Chief Surgeon furnished a list of about thirty unattached medical officers who had arrived in Paris. I selected six who appeared especially adapted for the work and who expressed enthusiasm. They had a fair knowledge of French, and were sent to one of the French hospitals for special training.

Each of the medical officers was to be assigned an automobile, a chauffeur, a nurse, and equipment for general medical and surgical work. Mrs. J. Earle Moore, who had spent two years in one of the French military hospitals, was to act as supervisor of nurses and secure other nurses. In conference with the doctors and nurses we prepared lists of equipment, instruments, and drugs, which were to be purchased by the Red Cross.

While these preparations were going on, I left Paris with Major Alexander Lambert, chief surgeon to the Red Cross, for a more intimate inspection of the region in which we were to establish the American Medical Service for the Civil Population, as we decided to call it. At Chaumont, to which General Pershing recently had moved his headquarters, we reported to the Chief Surgeon. We then called on Major Robert Bacon, formerly American Ambassador to France, and now liaison officer with the French. He introduced us to Dr. Dauve, president of the Medical Syndicate for the Department of the Vosges, who gave his approval of our plan. He was seventy-two years old and the only physician in that city of twenty thousand.

We made a tour of the region, which stretched from Chaumont to Nancy and from Bar-le-Duc down to Epinal. At Nogent, a town of thirty-five hundred, we found two old doctors. At Montigny, with a thousand inhabitants, we found one doctor aged sixty-seven. We passed through numerous towns without a single physician. At Neufchâteau, a city of four thousand, there was one physician aged

seventy-two. The *sous-préfet* of the district said that the civil popu-
lation was in urgent need of medical assistance and welcomed us
enthusiastically. We passed through the great watering-places of
Contrexeville and Vittel and continued on to Epinal on the Moselle.
Here we got the same story of the scarcity of medical service.
Turning northward along the valley of the Moselle, we reached
Nancy and called on the *préfet* of the Department of Meurthe and
Moselle—M. Mirmar, a distinguished man who displayed interest
in our proposal. There were nearly half a million people in his
department. Nancy, a large city, was crowded with women from the
surrounding district. At Bar-le-Duc we called on the *préfet* of the
Department of the Meuse, which extends up to Verdun. Before the
war there were a hundred physicians in this region and now only
nineteen. Large areas were without doctors.

We returned to Chaumont and gave a detailed account of our
trip to the Chief Surgeon. We proposed that we organize the medical
service with Neufchâteau as a center and from there send the teams,
consisting of a doctor, a nurse, a Ford automobile, and a chauffeur,
into districts radiating around Neufchâteau, to take care of that
section. Colonel Bradley enthusiastically endorsed our plan. Simon
and I returned to Neufchâteau to make the preliminary arrangements. We had no difficulty in securing billets for the medical
officers and a large apartment for the nurses. I also secured quarters
for a medical mess and a good cook.

The next day we returned to Paris, reported to the Red Cross,
and began preparations to move to Neufchâteau. On September 17,
although the chauffeurs had not been secured, we left Paris with
three Fords, the other six to follow with chauffeurs, nurses, and
supplies. At Gondrecourt we visited Colonel Ashford, and Captain
Boyd, who was to assist me in directing the work.

On September 23, in order to secure a committee of prominent
women to assist us in our organization, we called on Princess
d'Hénin. She lived in a château on a great hill about three miles
from Neufchâteau. The Princess was a handsome woman of middle

age and spoke English beautifully. Her grandmother was a Willing of Philadelphia who had gone to France as a girl and had never returned to America because she feared the terrible seasickness she suffered coming over. She eventually married into the French aristocracy, and her granddaughter became the wife of Prince d'Hénin, Comte d'Alsace and Senator of the Department of the Vosges. Portions of the château dated back to the Crusades. The view across the valley of the Meuse over beyond Domrémy-la-Pucelle, the home of Jeanne d'Arc, was exquisite. When we told the Princess of our proposed plan, she expressed great interest and consented to be chairman of the committee. We visited the ladies whose names she had given us, and all agreed to attend a meeting the next day. In halting French I explained our program. The Princess spoke enthusiastically and wrote a letter of introduction, which we had mimeographed and sent to the mayors and other officers of the cities and districts into which we expected to go. The *préfet* of Neufchâteau also sent out a circular letter explaining our program.

About this time we experienced the first hitch. Some of the physicians were afraid that by getting free medical service the people would be so spoiled that when the doctors returned after the war they would not be willing to pay for medical attention. It looked as if we would be prevented from inaugurating our medical service. I had discovered that in each city and town there was an official list of the indigent. I suggested that we charge the regular rates of the medical practitioners to all who were not on the list of indigents and that the money be held in bank for the families of French medical officers killed or wounded in the war. The difficulty was solved, and our plan was then accepted by the physicians.

Armed with our letters of introduction, we had no trouble in obtaining in each district a room for a dispensary that would be heated and maintained without cost. By this time the chauffeurs and nurses had arrived with the equipment, a central office and storehouse had been secured, and the districts around Neufchâteau laid out like segments of a pie. We met each morning at eight o'clock at our central bureau in the main square, and the teams started off to visit the dispensaries and their several sectors. The distance covered by each group was about forty or fifty miles.

At first the natives looked dubiously upon our visits, but soon they received the doctors and nurses with open arms. The number of patients grew steadily. The news of our organization spread throughout the whole department, and in a short time even the best people were among the many who came to the dispensaries. The first cases were largely trivial, but as the population grew more confident, serious maladies were encountered. In a short time the American Medical Service for the Civil Population was firmly installed in the hearts of the French and we went about our work with joy. Princess d'Hénin frequently visited the dispensaries and encouraged us.

The teams had been to work only a short time when a case of appendicitis was encountered. We waited until the other teams had come in from their circuits, then three automobiles with a complete surgical team, nurses, and operative equipment were dispatched to the home of the patient, where the operation was performed. Before long other cases requiring surgical operations were encountered. The need of a hospital for this work was evident, and we urged the Red Cross officials in Paris to hasten the arrival of some barracks that had been bought at our suggestion.

In about a month the hospital was completed. It consisted of ten barracks, well constructed and capable of handling about seventy patients. Ample space was provided for the reception of patients, clinical study and diagnosis, laboratories, and X-ray equipment. There were wards for both male and female patients and a splendidly equipped, well-lighted operating-room. Quarters for the nurses and the doctors were provided. Dr. Maurice Pincoffs came to direct the medical work, Dr. Richard Kieffer for the surgical department, and Dr. David M. Davis for the laboratories. Ultimately an impressive number of operations was reported. The medical work of the hospital was even more extensive. The work among the civil population was extended into districts more remote, and this necessitated additional visiting teams.

From time to time an officer of the regular Medical Corps left for service with the army divisions, and in June the remaining officers were sent to active duty at the front. Their places were taken by doctors who had come over in the service of the Red Cross, many of them not having been accepted by the army on account of some slight disability. I continued as director, but the active work with the divisions kept me away much of the time.

The American Medical Service continued to function until after the Armistice. Incipient epidemics of measles, scarlet fever, and meningitis were discovered early and kept from spreading to our troops. Many cases of venereal disease among the women were identified and treated, thereby preventing hundreds of infections among our soldiers.

Prince d'Hénin in a letter to Marshal Foch said, "I wish to tell you of the eminent services and incalculable benefit that have been afforded to the people in this region of eastern France." In his book *Experiences in the World War* General Pershing speaks of our medical aid "for the sole benefit of the French people" as "much appreciated by the inhabitants."

While I was launching the American Medical Service for the Civil Population in Eastern France, Louis Lehr was immured in Paris putting together our official report of visits to the British and French fronts. When I returned to Paris after an absence of a month, I found Louis restless and depressed. "Hugh, for goodness' sake, send me away from here. I'm sick and tired of the French cuisine with its fancy sauces. To show you how desperate I am, the other day, while I was having a liqueur at the Café de Paris, I said to a girl who had joined me at my table, 'Can you cook?' She seemed greatly surprised, and said that this was the first time a gentleman had ever asked her such a question—but she admitted that she was a good cook. We took a cab, went to the market, and then to her apartment, where I took off my coat, put on a checked apron, and assisted in the preparation of the meal. The chicken Maryland that we sat down to could not have been better prepared at the Baltimore Club. When I paid her the customary 20 francs and took my leave, she said that it was the most extraordinary experience of her career."

CHAPTER 15. PROSTITUTION IN FRANCE

AS SOON as we arrived in France we came face to face with the ancient institution of *réglementation de prostitution*, which the French considered the most scientific and effective method of combating venereal disease. They thought it was worthy of being adopted by the A.E.F. The United States Army was not without experience with regulated prostitution, both in the Philippines and more particularly in the recent expedition into Mexico in 1916. This force, commanded by General Pershing, found itself followed by a horde of prostitutes. In the somewhat loose organization of this mobile expeditionary force it was almost impossible to keep the men away from these women, and prophylaxis was difficult. General Pershing decided to corral the prostitutes, put them under the strictest military regulation, and carry out vigorous prophylaxis. After appropriate housing had been secured the prostitutes were surrounded by a barbed-wire fence, every woman was carefully examined, and only those found uninfected were retained for duty. The others were sent back home. At the entrance every soldier applicant was carefully examined and only admitted when found healthy. But even though both the man and the woman had been shown to be free from infection, when the soldier appeared at the exit gate he was given a careful prophylaxis according to rigid army standards. The results were indeed wonderful. No venereal disease was acquired in the army houses of prostitution, and the force returned to the United States with a wonderful record of freedom from venereal disease.

The consensus of opinion was that no such plan could be carried out effectively in France. I was asked to investigate the situation. The prostitute in Paris was required to carry a card of identification with space for a report of the examinations that she was required to undergo at weekly intervals. If found infected, she was forced to cease her occupation until declared safe. In many cases the prostitutes were transferred to a prison hospital devoted to the treatment of such cases.

These stations were scattered throughout Paris. To these I went to observe their methods. The forlorn girls in their tawdry make-up sat on anxious benches. One after another they passed the examining venereologist, who occupied a room in which there were several examining tables. A rough-looking assistant hustled the poor things on to tables, and the examiner went rapidly over each patient systematically—face, mouth, throat, skin of body, and so on— passing from one portion of the body to the other and from one woman to another, scarcely ever washing his dirty hands. Not infrequently active lesions of various venereal infections were palpated and then—on to the next case. I felt confident that venereal diseases were often transmitted from the infected to the uninfected, and that many a poor *fille de joie* acquired her infection at the hands of the examiner. Microscopes were seldom used. The whole procedure was fearfully crude and far from trustworthy. Not all the examining bureaus were as bad as this. Occasionally a man of scientific attainments, with bacterial knowledge and a desire to do careful work, was encountered. We decided that the French system of *réglementation de prostitution* could not be relied upon to prevent the spread of venereal disease.

While this investigation of ours was going on, the medical officers stationed at Saint-Nazaire, our first seaport base, having heard from the French Medical Corps about the virtues of their regulation of prostitution, apparently arrived at a different opinion. In fact, they were so impressed by what the French told them that an official document was drawn up and presented for consideration by the Chief of the Medical Corps, and by him sent up to General Headquarters. This document, and particularly the second endorsement, which is one of the most noted and amusing literary productions of the army, seems worthy of being inserted here.

PROPOSAL TO HAVE HOUSES OF PROSTITUTION FOR THE A.E.F.

From: First Lieut. H. L. C————, MORC
To: Commanding Officer, B. S. No. 1 (Through C. O. Base Hosp.
     No. 101).
Subject: Control of venereal disease in St. Nazaire.

1. Having received requests for recommendations for the control of venereal disease in St. Nazaire, I wish to submit the following:

(a) That a number of prostitutes be employed who will be carefully inspected, and that only those who have been found to be free of infection at the end of three weeks of careful observation be employed.

(b) That these women be under military control.

(c) That all the enlisted personnel desiring intercourse be compelled to use these women.

(d) That all the men, on visiting these prostitutes, be compelled to show a certificate from their senior medical officer stating they are free of venereal disease, the certificate to be dated the same day as presented.

(e) That every man be compelled to take a prophylaxis under the direction of a trained man at the house of prostitution immediately after intercourse.

(f) That all soldiers be prohibited from entering any other house of prostitution and that they be not allowed to go with any woman who is of ill repute.

(g) That any man contracting venereal disease be tried by court-martial, and if it is found to have been contracted in a place other than the military regulated houses, his punishment to be commensurate with the crime.

H. L. C————

First Indorsement

C. O. Base Hosp. No. 101, Oct. 6, 1917. To C. O., B. S. No. 1 (Through
     Base Surgeon)

1. Forwarded, concurring in the opinion of Lt. C———— that the

only certain method of controlling venereal disease in this district is by the employment of the measures recommended or by similar measures.

2. If the program outlined does not conflict with the French law to such an extent as to make it impossible, I recommend that the measures be taken to institute such a program in this city.

W. H. C———

Major, Medical Corps

Second Indorsement

Office of Surgeon, B. S. No. 1, Oct. 10, 1917. To the Base Commander, B. S. No. 1.

1. In theory, this plan may be accepted as ideal, but as a practical expedient it seems to require further development.

2. As it is proposed by an expert and ably supported by qualified observers, I recommend that a committee, composed as follows, be appointed to return working plans, detailed specifications and a general estimate of cost of installation and maintenance, including personnel and material required to reduce this theory to practice:

(a) Urologist to Base Hospital No. 101

(b) Commanding Officer, Base Hospital No. 101

(c) The Chaplain, 7th Engineers

(d) The Chaplain, 19th Engineers

(e) Local Secretary, Y.M.C.A.

(f) Surgeon, 3d Bn. 5th Reg. U.S.M.C.

3. The report of the Board should cover the following points, and answer the following questions, which must be carefully considered before the plan can be considered practicable and useful:

(a) Female personnel.

1. How and by whom are the prostitutes to be selected?

2. What will be their terms of engagement—by direct contract with a military department, benevolent army associations, or commercial contractor?

3. What will be the length of service?

4. What guarantee of submission to regulations and restrictions?

5. Will service be limited to military clients to the exclusion of outside practice?

6. How may restrictions to limit service be enforced?

7. How far will control of personal movements and surveillance of personal conduct extend?

8. Will military authorities distinguish the women of good repute from those of ill repute in the civil community and place the latter in restraint?

9. What, if any, personal liberties may be enjoyed by the prostitutes?

10. As acceptance to military service is conditional on physical competence, when disability arises in the military service will it be considered in "line of duty" or due to "her own misconduct"?

11. What will be the responsibility of the Government in the case of temporary or permanent disability or death in this military service?

(b) Male personnel:

1. Why limit this service to enlisted men? May not officers enjoy the same protection or be required to submit to the same restrictions as are imposed upon enlisted personnel?

2. What will be the exact clinical method of determining freedom from venereal infection, as it must be remembered that exacerbations of venereal disease appear after accepted clinical methods of examination have pronounced a cure?

3. In case of accidental infections, after all conditions have been complied with, will the ensuing disability be "in line of duty" and will the Government bear the economic loss?

5. What method will be employed to confine the attention of officers and soldiers to women in the military service, and how will the inclination to personal selection on the part of officers and soldiers be restrained?

6. Will enlisted men be confined to camp or permitted a restricted liberty under guard?

7. How will it be ascertained that a venereally infected soldier, who denies civil venereal patronage, has actually acquired his disease within the military zone?

8. In what numerical ratio to the strength of the command should prostitutes be provided?

9. What will be the disposition of women with honest and faithful service records who fail in their desire to please and to attract patronage?

(c) Material:

1. In what quarters will militarized prostitutes be sheltered—in camp, in barracks near camp, or in houses in town?

2. What tariff arrangements will be made—shall a flat rate be established or the charge for service be rendered according to grade?

3. In what form will tariff be paid—may post exchanges issue checks which can be charged on the pay rolls after the manner of post exchange purchases?

4. Who will adjust financial disputes arising from the charges of the female for non-payment and the denial of the male of satisfactory service?

(d) Social:

1. Will there be different classes of physical environment as well as

personal attraction at different rates of compensation for different military grades?

2. Will there be any race distinction made among the applicants for service or will "Jim Crow" principles be applied and receive official recognition?

(e) Administration:

1. What personnel will be required for administration?

2. What will be the grade and sex of the personnel required for the internal and external economy of the operating plant and for the hospitalization and detention departments?

3. How many medical officers, nurses, chaplains, quartermasters and benevolent civilian helpers will be required for the first installation of the plant?

4. It is believed that the plan herewith proposed cannot be executed unless all of these and many other details can be provided for before a practical demonstration may be begun.

5. As the system includes not only the control of prostitution and the regulation of fornication it should be presented frankly and fearlessly as a military necessity of such vital importance that none need scruple at the moral conjectures it may suggest, and if it can be put into such practicable operation that it will control venereal disease.

6. But after all, it should be remembered that with any system of military control over the sexual indulgence of the soldier, instruction in the nature and consequences of venereal disease, and appeals to his sense of self-protection, should be largely depended upon. It should always be impressed upon him that continence is not only possible but that it is entirely feasible and wholly practicable—especially for old men and senior officers, who should devote much of their time gained from this practice of continence to the instruction of young men who find themselves more occupied.

C. S. Ford
Lt. Col., Medical Corps.

Third Indorsement

Office of the Base Commander, B.S. No. 1, Nov. 5–17.
To the C.G., A.E.F.   (Through C.G., L. of C.)

1. The recommendations for the establishment of a military house of prostitution at this base are not approved; *but not for the reason set forth in the second indorsement.*

L. A. B——
Col. Infantry, N.A.

CHAPTER 16. THE VENEREAL-DISEASE PROBLEM AT A FRENCH SEAPORT

THE First and Second Divisions of the A.E.F.—old regulars— had arrived in France and were quickly transported to the training areas near the front. Stringent methods of prophylaxis had been instituted, and the venereal disease in these two divisions, each of nearly thirty thousand men, fell to forty per thousand. The venereal rate in the regular army in the United States was about ninety new cases per thousand men per year. The rate was figured out daily in the entire A.E.F. from telegraphic reports, which all organizations were required to send to General Headquarters.

General Pershing told me that on top of the papers awaiting him at his office each morning was the venereal report of the various organizations, and this was the first thing he considered. He compared this with the report for the previous day, and if he found a marked increase in the rate in any organization, he immediately called upon the Chief Surgeon A.E.F. to investigate it.

On November 9 I was notified that the venereal rate suddenly had jumped to two hundred as a result of great infection among newly arrived troops at the point of debarkation—Saint-Nazaire— and that Genereal Pershing had ordered me to go there at once to investigate and report.

I found that port facilities at Saint-Nazaire were so inadequate that shiploads of men were kept on board ten days or more before debarking. Shore leave was granted daily to about 20 per cent of these men. Liberated in this tough seaport, they behaved just as other vigorous youngsters would after having been penned up for weeks while their ships zigzagged to avoid the U-boats.

The grogshops did a tremendous business. The liquors principally dispensed were West Indian rum and a poisonous drink known as Niger gin. It didn't take much of this rotgut stuff to inflame passions and obliterate all repressions. Next came a mass movement to the houses of prostitution. There were six of these *maisons de prostitution* in Saint-Nazaire. They were small, and housed only five or six girls each. The situation within was terrible. The line of soldiers awaiting their turn extended along the narrow hall to the individual doorways. The fearful business went on from hour to hour while the "madame" grinned in satisfaction at the great money-making prowess of her girls. One proudly told me that her most active girl had taken care of sixty-five the day before, and that the average was between forty and fifty per day. "But how can they stand such a terrific experience?"   "Oh, monsieur, they wear out in about four weeks. We ship them off to less popular joints, and before long they are completely used up and become street-walkers."

Why did not prophylaxis prevent infections from these sources? Those soldiers from the ships, on their return, found them so crowded that few received prophylaxis. Those from the camp were frequently so drunk that they could not make the distance on foot and often fell by the wayside, where they were picked up and placed in trucks like rows of sardines and delivered en masse to the camps. When asked whether they had been exposed, the inebriated could give no intelligent reply, and often when the Medical Corps attempted to give prophylaxis forcibly they had a fight on their hands.

The happenings in this nasty, crowded seaport were the most disgraceful in the history of the A.E.F. I visited the commanding officers of the Medical Corps and the base port hospital. They were so overwhelmed that they had almost given up. The inmates of these houses of prostitution had been subjected to weekly examinations by French medical officers detailed for the purpose. They were far more scientific than the civic employees I had seen in Paris. The women we saw did not seem to be infected, but I had evidence that eight cases of syphilis had occurred among our soldiers from contacts made in one of the houses. Re-examination showed that none of these women had active signs of syphilis. Where did the infection come from? Investigation showed that tending the front door was a French boy of sixteen. He was the pet of one of the women, and examination showed an acute syphilitic lesion. Early in her career she had had syphilis, and was no longer in an infectious stage. She could not acquire a new infection, but the germs deposited by her boy lover remained there to infect the American soldiers who passed through her room. From this one woman eight of our men had acquired syphilis in a single day.

It was apparent that the danger of regulated prostitution was not entirely from the diseases of the women themselves, but also from the fact that by receiving one individual after another without any douching or even arising from their beds, these women came to possess "septic tanks" filled with almost every type of venereal infection.

I hastened back to General Headquarters and prepared a voluminous report. I had scarcely finished it when I received a telephone communication from the office of General Pershing; he wished to see my report immediately. The General was leaving for Paris, and asked me to accompany him. Closeted with me in his private car, General Pershing went carefully through my report and asked searching questions. "Major," he said, "this is one of the most disgraceful things that has happened to the American Army. Drastic measures must be taken immediately. I have agreed to meet the chiefs of the Allied armies in Paris, but this is more important, and I shall take the earliest train to Saint-Nazaire and put into effect your recommendations."

The General's visit to Saint-Nazaire is well remembered in the army. Like an enraged bull he confronted the headquarters staff, the medical officers, the military police, all who were concerned. With every detail of my report in his mind, he confronted them with their dereliction of duty and their neglect of army regulations. He ordered more rapid evacuation of troops; the stagnation in camp was to end; the transports were to be disembarked as soon as they arrived; houses of prostitution were to be surrounded by military police and rigorously put out of bounds; the saloons were to be treated likewise; prophylaxis was to be rigidly enforced with all troops, both permanent and transient.

A veritable transformation occurred. Never again did such disgraceful happenings occur in Saint-Nazaire, or any other seaport. The venereal-disease rate, which had skyrocketed to disgraceful heights, fell rapidly to the previous low rate.

After General Pershing's visit to Saint-Nazaire, I was requested to prepare a general order incorporating the suggestions made in our report. With assistance I prepared the essentials of an order, which were elaborated and issued by General Pershing as General Order 77, the most drastic and far-reaching health order ever issued to an army.

GENERAL ORDER NO. 77

Headquarters American Expeditionary Forces.

France, December 18, 1917

... All Commanding Officers are directed to give personal attention to matters pertaining to the prevention of venereal disease. ... No laxity or half-hearted efforts in this regard will be tolerated. ... The number of effectives in a command is an index of its efficiency and this depends upon the efficiency of the Commanding Officers.

Ports of Debarkation

... At ports of debarkation ... every endeavor will be made to locate the habitations, rooms or apartments and sections of town occupied by women engaged in prostitution. All such places will be considered "off limits"; they will be described and conspicuously posted in each company ... and the visiting ... of these places by members of the A.E.F. will be prohibited. The provisions of this paragraph should be enforced by local commanders at all other ... places where troops are stationed. ...

... The ... Surgeon of a section ... will act ... with the Urologist ... designated from these headquarters to carry out the instructions of the Commander-in-Chief.

... The Base Commander will require the Commanding Officer of arriving naval vessels or transports carrying troops to render a report ... of all those on board, listing those who have evidence of venereal disease. The troops and members of the crew will not be permitted ashore until this report is submitted. ... All men reported as having venereal disease will be placed under restriction in camps and there will be detained, but no members of ships' crew with venereal disease will be permitted ashore. ...

... The Commanding Officers of all troops will insist that men of their command whenever exposed to venereal disease will report to prophylactic stations as soon as possible after exposure and always within a period of three hours. ... Men returning to camp will be questioned by the guard and if exposure to venereal infection is acknowledged, the men will be directed by the guard to a prophylactic station. ...

Should men return to camp in an intoxicated condition they will be seized by the guard and taken to a prophylactic station where treatment will be administered by the non-commissioned officer in charge of the station. Cases of drunkenness should be subjected to prompt disciplinary measures.

An accurate list of all men suffering from venereal disease will be kept in each organization. Regimental commanders and commanding officers of independent units will direct their medical officers to make daily reports to the surgeon of the proper Base Section, giving in each the number of new venereal cases reported during the preceding twenty-four hours. All men so reported will be confined to the limits of the camp except when employed on military duty, and intensive treatment followed out.

Upon the departure of regiments or other organizations from ports of debarkation, the senior medical officer of the Base Section will report by telegraph to the Surgeon, Lines of Communication, and to the Chief Surgeon, A.E.F., the designation and strength of the organization, name of the commander, and the number of cases of venereal disease discovered or contracted by its personnel during the stay of the organization at the port of debarkation. *These reports will be filed at these Headquarters with the personal records of organization commanders, and will be used as a basis in determining the commander's efficiency and the suitability of his continuing in command* [italics mine].

Commanding Officers at all places where our troops may be located will confer with the local French authorities and use every endeavor to limit to the lowest possible number the places where intoxicants are sold. ...

Soldiers are forbidden either to buy or accept as gifts from inhabitants, whiskey, brandy, champagne, liquors or other alcoholic beverages, other than light wines or beer. The gift or retail sale of these by inhabitants in the Zone of the Army is forbidden by French law. Commanding Officers will see that all drinking places where alcoholic liquors named above are sold, are designated as "off limits" and the necessary means adopted to prevent soldiers visiting them.

... Commanding Officers at ports, either in person or through some responsible representative, will deliver to each organization commander ... a sufficient number of copies of this order, General Orders No. 6 [ordering the establishment of prophylactic stations; court-martial of soldiers contracting venereal diseases, and forfeiture of pay] and ... No. 34 [ordering the establishment of regimental infirmaries for treatment of venereal cases with their commands, or employment of venereals in useful occupations], and other approved literature on this subject, so that all may have ample information and that there may be no excuse for non-compliance with existing regulations.

Though this order is intended particularly for ports of debarkation, it should be interpreted in general as applying to all places where troops are stationed.

Camp, regimental, battalion, and company commanders will be held to a strict accountability for the fullest compliance with the requirements of this order.

By Command of Major General Pershing:

Official:
ROBERT C. DAVIS
Adjutant General

JAMES G. HARBORD
Brigadier General
Chief of Staff

The effect of General Order 77 was electrical. Previously, when I called upon the general of a division and asked about the venereal rate, I was usually told that he was very busy and to see Lieutenant So-and-so. After General Order 77, whenever I inquired at the headquarters of even the most high-ranking officers, they immediately replied: "There's no subject in which I am more interested. Please let me know in what way we can co-operate more effectively." The concrete results throughout the A.E.F. were extraordinary, and before long the venereal rate had fallen to sixteen new cases per thousand men per year.

CHAPTER 17. WRITING THE *MANUAL OF*

MILITARY UROLOGY

THE Chief Surgeon had authorized me to prepare a book on military urology. We secured the services of excellent men in venereology, dermatology, and urology. We took rooms at the Hôtel Continental and established an office with stenographers and clerks. Time was pressing, and we worked night and day. Within six weeks we had finished our volume of two hundred and ninety pages, the first in the A.E.F. on any medical subject. It was submitted with this official memorandum:

France
January 8, 1918

From:　Major Hugh H. Young, M.R.C.
To:　The Chief Surgeon, A.E.F.
Subject:　Manuscript for Manual

　1. In accordance with your request, I submit herewith manuscript for manual dealing with venereal diseases, dermatology and urology, intended for the use of military surgeons of the A.E.F.

　2. This volume has been prepared in collaboration with Major Edward L. Keyes, Captains M. L. Boyd, Everard L. Oliver, W. H. Mook and D. M. Davis, and Lieutenants J. E. Moore and William D. Jack.

　3. I wish to acknowledge the assistance of Major Alexander Lambert, Capt. Kenneth Taylor, Dr. James C. Johnston, Dr. D. O. Robinson and Miss Herford, artist, of the American Red Cross.

HUGH H. YOUNG
Major, M.R.C.,
Director of Urology, A.E.F.

First Indorsement
A.E.F., C.S.O., France, January 8, 1918
To Commander-in-Chief, A.E.F.

1. I transmit herewith the manuscript mentioned and earnestly recommend that its publication be authorized as an official document for distribution to the A.E.F.

A. E. BRADLEY
Brigadier General

Approved:
JOHN J. PERSHING
General

The scope of the *Manual of Military Urology* is given in the preface:

This volume has been authorized for use of the Medical Department of the American Expeditionary Forces in the field. It deals with three topics: Venereal Diseases, Dermatology and Surgery of the Urinary and Male Genital Organs which, under Circular No. 2, C.S.O., A.E.F., November 9, 1917, are grouped in one Division entitled Urology. These topics are discussed primarily in their relation to the hygiene of armies, i.e., the diagnosis, prevention and cure of those diseases that affect large bodies of troops, and to the wounds of war. No attempt has been made to discuss any topic exhaustively with which the practitioner of medicine and surgery in civil life might reasonably be assumed to be familiar. . . .

In one of the subjects herein treated, venereal disease, the Medical Corps of the United States Army has for eighteen years had a proud record of achievement in decreasing the ravages of these infections by education and prophylaxis. In the A.E.F. new problems have arisen and the importance of minimizing the loss of effectives from these diseases has led to the development of greatly simplified methods which make it possible generally to provide thorough and consecutive treatment without evacuation of the soldier from his training area, or zone of the advance, thus avoiding the necessity of great base hospitals for venereal diseases.

This volume gives in detail a survey of the situation in Europe, the problems presented, the plan adopted, the therapeutic indications and the systematized methods to be employed.

Skin diseases in the armies are also largely preventable, and much stress has been laid in this manual on methods of sanitation, hygiene and early treatment, by which it is hoped to keep the incidence to a minimum and avoid evacuation for treatment from the zone of operations.

In the surgery of the Genito-Urinary tract (the third subject included in this Division) much that is new and important has been discovered in the literature, records and experiences of army surgeons. A careful study and compilation of these data have been made, and are presented with the hope of standardizing the war surgery in this field.

The existence of a large number of General and Special Orders, Regulations, Acts of Congress, etc., has made it advisable to have an appendix in which these are collected, along with data from French and English sources and brief papers of general interest.

Our special thanks are due General Pershing for his great and intelligent interest in the prevention and cure of disease, and the remarkable series of General Orders and circulars bearing on the subject which he has issued to the A.E.F.

General Bradley, at whose suggestion this manual was compiled, has ever been the mainspring of the activities and accomplishments of this Division.

HUGH H. YOUNG
Director, Division of Urology, A.E.F.

February 16, 1918

CONTENTS

PART I. VENEREAL DISEASES IN THE ARMY

PART 2. DERMATOLOGY

17. Seborrhea
18. Psoriasis; Pityriasis Rosea
19. Eczema

PART 3. SURGERY OF THE URINARY AND MALE GENITAL ORGANS

20. The Principles of Urinary Antisepsis
21. Wounds of the Kidney and Ureter
22. Wounds of the Bladder
23. Paralysis of the Bladder
24. Wounds of the Posterior Urethra and Prostate; Wounds of the Bulbous Urethra
25. Fistulae of the Urethra
26. Wounds of the Scrotum, Testicles, Penis and Anterior Urethra
27. Testicular Transplantation
28. Rupture and Traumatic Stricture of the Urethra

PART 4. APPENDICES

Appendix 1. Citations of the War Department on Venereal Disease
Appendix 2. General Orders and Bulletins Issued by the A.E.F. concerning Venereal Disease
Appendix 3. Regulations concerning Prostitution in France
Appendix 4. Regulations concerning Sale or Gift of Alcoholic Beverages to Soldiers
Appendix 5. Documents concerning Trench Feet and Scabies
Appendix 6. Pharmacy for Dermatological Cases in the Army
Appendix 7. Wounds and Injuries of Genito-urinary Tract as seen at a British Casualty Clearing Station
Appendix 8. Specimen Orders on Prevalence of Veneral Disease and on Prompt Establishment of Proper Prophylactic Stations by Chief Surgeon of a Division
Appendix 9. Suggestions Approved by Gen. Pershing

The American Red Cross was charged with the publication of the work, which appeared from the presses of the Imprimerie La Hute in four weeks. We expected that the proofreading would be made difficult on account of typographical errors, inasmuch as the printers were ignorant of the English language, but the work was done with amazing accuracy. A thousand copies were distributed to the Medical Corps, and a second edition was necessary in a few months.

In order to make it easy for the busy medical officer to comprehend the subject matter of the book, a digest of the contents of each page was printed as a running commentary along the margin, as shown in the photographic reproduction of one of the pages.

ganate or oxycyanide.

of potassium or 1 : 8000 oxycyanide of mercury at this stage. (Not before the tenth day). Following this treatment the discharge should either stop or become nonpurulent and examination of the prostate and seminal vesicles should be made.

Prostatic massage if the disease tends to chronicity. Also sounds.

By massage obtain a specimen of the prostatic secretion. This should be microscopically examined for pus and gonococci. No case is cured that has a purulent prostatic secretion, even though gonococci are not present, and such cases should be given a course of weekly prostatic massage and bladder irrigations, after consultation with the Division Urologist.

Posterior urethra involved in third of cases.

Complications of Acute Gonorrhoea. — In at least one-third of the cases the gonococcus passes through the external sphincter and invades the posterior urethra. This posterior urethritis is generally, though not always,

Complicated frequently with prostatitis, vesiculitis and occasionally epididymitis.

complicated by involvement of the prostate and seminal vesicles and occasionally a localized inflammation of the vesical trigone occurs. The infection may also travel up the vas deferens, producing deferentitis and epididymitis which may be complicated by an acute hydrocele. In most cases the prostatic inflammation is of a follicular type but occasionally there is a widespread parenchymatous and interstitial prostatitis which may lead to abscess formation

Involvement of bladder and kidney rare.

or even to marked peri-prostatic infiltration. In very rare instances gonococcal involvement of the kidney occurs. General complications due to the gonococcus — arthritis, endocarditis, and septicaemia — also occur and are much to be feared under the physical strain of war conditions.

Extension to posterior urethra indicated by dysuria, frequency, cloudy second urine.

Acute Posterior Urethritis. — The signs of extension of an acute anterior urethritis to the posterior urethra are frequent and painful urination and the appearance of pus in the second glass of urine. The patient should be promptly put to bed, placed on a light diet, his fluids increased and if the pain on urination is severe injections suspended. However, if tenesmus is not marked and the patient tolerates his injections they should be continued.

Treatment

When an infection of the posterior urethra becomes

AFTER the Chief Surgeon accepted our plan to place in each division a urologist in charge of venereal diseases and urological surgery, the next problem was to find suitable medical officers. In the Chief Surgeon's office complete information concerning every officer arriving in France was to be found. Most of these were with organizations; some came over as casuals. By carefully studying these lists I was able to determine what men had had experience in the treatment of venereal disease, and also those who were accomplished urological surgeons.

In order to prepare these men for the special methods we had adopted for the A.E.F. they were ordered to take a special course in the treatment of syphilis at the Hôpital Broca in Paris, where Professor Hudelo gave them lectures and actual experience in intravenous injections and other methods used in the treatment of syphilis. We had also arranged for similar work at the French Army venereal hospital at Bar-le-Duc, where more particular experience was given in gonorrhea and genitourinary surgery.

The men chosen to be division urologists then came to our headquarters at Neufchâteau, where we acquainted them with our special work. They were given an opportunity to study the records we had amassed concerning venereal disease in the British and French armies and also in American divisions that had been in France for sometime. After this initiation I conducted the urologist to the headquarters of his division and discussed the program adopted by the Division of Urology with the division surgeon, and sometimes with the commanding general, who always said he was greatly interested.

About this time Major Edward L. Keyes asked to be transferred to Neufchâteau. When he arrived, we took steps to reorganize the office of the headquarters of the Division of Urology so as to take care of our rapidly increasing work. In casting about for a medical officer of considerable experience with fighting forces, I decided to ask for the transfer of Lieutenant E. W. Bertner from the B.E.F. I had met him in Paris while working on the *Manual of Military Urology*. He would have received the Victoria Cross had the United States Army regulations permitted foreign decorations. He still suffered from severe gassing. In a short time Major Keyes and Captain Bertner had systematized the work of the Division of Urology. Much of the smooth operation and splendid accomplishments of the organization were due to their efforts.

One of the duties of the division urologist was to give special instruction to the battalion surgeons who were delegated to carry out the treatment of venereal cases with their own organizations on a duty status. Some of these battalion surgeons were sent to the French hospital at Bar-le-Duc for additional experience. No difficulty was encountered in securing excellent treatment of both syphilis and gonorrhea not only in the divisions, but also in other organizations in France and England, where the same regulations and program had been put in force. Special orders had been issued by the Chief Surgeon to the division urologists directing that they give lectures to the medical officers and personnel of prophylactic stations, which were to be carefully inspected and supervised. He also was required to co-operate with the military police in investigating local conditions concerning prostitution, regulated and clandestine, and alcoholism. The division surgeon was ordered to place the urologist during combat in one of the field hospitals of the division for surgical work, where he was to supervise genito-urinary treatment and operations.

The daily venereal report of the A.E.F. showed a steady decline in the venereal rate. After the marked increase as a result of the disgraceful conditions at Saint-Nazaire the rate dropped rapidly and finally fell to sixteen new cases per thousand men per year. The venereal rate in the United States Army during the same period in America grew steadily higher as the draft brought in more and more men from the civil population, and venereals were not excluded. These facts furnish an appalling demonstration of the amount of venereal disease in the civil population and the wonderful effect of army discipline and prophylaxis in cutting down the incidence of venereal disease in the troops of the A.E.F.

A problem of importance arose among the Negro troops in work battalions, principally at the seaports, where they unloaded ships and performed other duties. They usually were encamped at or near their place of work, which was in close contact with the large French population. The French women apparently had no aversion to colored troops, and the contacts of each Negro soldier were frequent. It was difficult to enforce regulations in regard to prophylaxis. Many would not take it, or came too late. The venereal rate among these Negro troops steadily grew to alarming proportions. Something had to be done. It was decided to put a barbed-wire fence around the encampments, and whenever a Negro soldier went out, no matter for what purpose, to require a prophylactic treatment on his return. The effect was instantaneous. The venereal rate rapidly dropped until it was as good as or better than that of the white troops.

The colonel commanding one of these camps was approached by his Negro orderly, a regular who had been with him for some years. The orderly calmly announced that he wanted a change of station. Whereupon the colonel said: "Corporal, you've never had an easier job. I simply send you on errands, ten or fifteen within the camp, and perhaps fifteen or twenty outside the camp every day. You certainly can't object to such an easy job as this." "No, Colonel, the work ain't hard, and I don't mind how often you send me on errands inside the camp. It's them errands outside, because every time I comes back they takes me to the prophylactic station, and I'm getting awful sore."

The treatment of venereal-disease patients with their organizations resulted in abandoning the plan adopted in the United States to transport to France one special base hospital of a thousand beds, fully equipped to treat only venereal diseases, for every hundred thousand men. This program had been evolved from advice obtained from both French and British sources. I am told that when it was announced in Washington that base hospitals especially for venereal diseases would not be needed by the A.E.F., so little credence was given to the report that four new base hospitals, equipped entirely for the treatment of venereal diseases, of a thousand beds each, were sent to France. As we had no need for them in the treatment of venereal disease, they were put to various other uses. It was not until two more venereal-disease hospitals had been dispatched that it was realized in Washington that the plan of treating venereal diseases with the organizations adopted in the A.E.F. was a working success and that the venereal hospitals were really not desired.

It was with some pride that I was able to point out at the end of the war, when two million American men had arrived in France, who according to tables of organization would have been accompanied by twenty hospitals for venereal disease, with a thousand beds each, that this number of beds had been saved for the sick and wounded. We had twenty thousand beds for the supreme crisis of 1918, when every hospital bed was needed to care for the deluge of wounded and sick that swamped the Medical Corps.

My headquarters had been located for several months at Neufchâteau when Major Finney and Colonel Siler came there for a conference. As the rooms we occupied were inadequate, a larger building was secured as headquarters for the newly appointed directors of the different branches of medicine and surgery. In a short time assistant directors and other medical officers were added to the staff, and it was necessary to have more room. It was decided to construct a special building for this purpose on the grounds of the hospital that I had had constructed for the American Medical Service for the Civil Population. A rambling frame building was erected, with adequate meeting-rooms and offices. Oiled paper was used in place of glass in the windows. There was no central heating system, and not even fireplaces. The partitions between the various rooms were of paperboard, and for heat and artificial light we had to depend entirely on kerosene stoves and lamps. By the time the building was finished in December we were in the midst of a hard winter. The thermometer fell to a few degrees above zero. In the coldest weather we had to wear our overcoats in our offices and huddled around the tiny kerosene stoves. It was with difficulty that our typists could use their fingers. As automobiles were very difficult to secure, for a time only the directors of the various divisions had transportation; the staff had to make their way back and forth on foot through heavy snows to their billets in the city.

As the members of my staff had grown we had secured an attractive château on the outskirts of the city, where we organized a splendid mess. One entered a large stone-flagged hall with a winding staircase. To the right was a salon with fine old paneling. Immediately back of this was a dining-room that we used as our mess, and adjacent to it, immediately back of the entrance hall, a very large kitchen with fine ovens of antique pattern.   We secured an excellent cook and a pretty young waitress. The first name of both these women was Marie and their second names were long and unpronounceable, so we dubbed them Marie Antoinette and Marie Louise.

As the professional services grew we took in officers from other divisions, and before long our mess had grown to twelve. Much of the food came from the A.E.F. commissary, but there were excellent stores in Neufchâteau, and we had no difficulty in running a very fine cuisine. Vintage wines and liquors were very cheap, so that the top of our old oak sideboard eventually became covered with bottles. Major Keyes occupied a bedroom immediately behind the dining-room, and I had one on the floor above. Adjacent to me was a huge room in which someone had placed a very small basin with running cold water, and near by was an old narrow tub of cast iron painted white inside, with a spigot for cold water and another that connected with a large brass contraption which looked like a huge samovar. This turned out to be an apparatus for hot water, which was fired by small twigs.

On the morning after our arrival I decided to luxuriate in my first complete bath for months. I ordered Marie "Antoinette" to prepare it. I could hear her and Marie "Louise" walking around the room engaged in serious conversation for over half an hour before I went in to see what was delaying my bath. The room was full of smoke; the small faggots were burning bravely in the base of the "samovar." Above were coils of small copper tubing, which finally emerged from the top and ran to the tub, into which a tiny stream of warm water fell. There were about six inches of water in the tub, and only lukewarm. The maids added more fuel to the flames, but without much effect. Finally I dismissed them and, disrobing, got into the tub. The amount of water was very little, and the heat so slight that I stood up in the tub and tinkered with the apparatus to see if I could not increase the flow of hot water. In so doing I evidently committed a violent offense to the ancient apparatus, which soon began to sputter and finally exploded. All the scalding water seemed to come in my direction and, howling with pain, I jumped out of the tub. This so startled the two Maries that they came rushing in while I stood there looking like a broiled lobster. Nothing abashed, these two began to collect the remains of the "samovar" while I beat a hasty retreat to my room to nurse my burns.

Two other messes were organized, one ruled over by Colonel Finney and one by Colonel Goldthwait. The orthopedic mess, as it was called, was highly respected, as Dr. Goldthwait was said to open and close the meals with prayer. Some of the young bloods who happened to be in that mess used to beg to be allowed to come to ours, which had become known as one of the most rollicking in that part of the A.E.F. We were joined occasionally by itinerant officers and sometimes by members of the press who had their headquarters at Neufchâteau. Very vivid in my memory is one evening in which we were honored by the presence of F.P.A., the celebrated columnist whose humor and inexhaustible fund of ribald poetry by Eugene Field and others kept us in stitches of laughter until midnight.

Sometime during the winter, after a delightful meal, we were having a gay time around a great fire. A lieutenant from Division Headquarters arrived and begged to announce that Bishop Cannon had been sent by General Pershing to interview us on the prevalence of inebriety and venereal disease in the A.E.F. I turned to Major Keyes and said, "If the Bishop is coming here to talk to us about drinking, don't you think we had better remove those thirty bottles on the sideboard?" Not knowing where to put them, we finally set them on the kitchen floor, and closed the door. We were then prepared to receive the Bishop appropriately, and sat down by the fire to await the jangle of the bell on the front door.

The first thing we heard was a crash of bottles in the kitchen. When we opened the kitchen door, a flood of light from our mess fell upon the gaunt form of the Bishop, who stood there among the bottles, not knowing which way to turn. We led him quickly into the mess and closed the door. Somehow the Bishop had failed to see the ancient handle of our doorbell high up on the frame and had walked into the entrance hall and from there into the kitchen, where he encountered the forest of liquor. He said nothing about the bottles, but at once plunged into the questions uppermost in his mind. "It has been reported in the United States," he said, "that there is no prohibition in the A.E.F., that the soldiers are very dissolute, drunkenness is general, and the forces are riddled with venereal disease." Fortunately, we had tabulations on hand to disprove his statements. We were able to show that since General Pershing had put all places selling hard liquors out of bounds and had restricted the troops to light wines and beer, drunkenness was comparatively rare; in fact, the American army was one of the soberest in the world. As a result of the great crusade against venereal disease, the insistence on prophylaxis, and the regulations depriving men of pay when they acquired venereal infections, the venereal rate in the forces had steadily dropped until there were now only sixteen new cases per thousand men per year, less than one-fifth the venereal rate in the standing army of the United States before the war. After we had showed chart after chart to back up our assertions, the Bishop was convinced, and even congratulated us on the great work that had been done. Thanking us, he started to go, and we led him out through the paneled salon into the paved court and then out the front door. As he passed out of the gate in the moonlight he said to me, "Major, what were those bottles that I ran into?" I said, "Bishop, I can't say just what all those bottles were, but members of the mess drink a great deal of ginger ale, coca cola, and soda." (Quite true—soda and whisky.)

A report on the work of the Division of Urology would be incomplete without reference to our debt of gratitude to superior officers who listened sympathetically to our plans and aided powerfully in putting them across. First comes General Merritte W. Ireland, who on the *Baltic* had brought me to the attention of General Pershing when he asked me to lecture on the venereal problem in the army; then General Alfred E. Bradley, Chief Surgeon, who was never too busy to confer at length on our problems, and even read the entire manuscript of our *Manual of Military Urology* before presenting it, with me, to General Pershing. Later, when a bureau was organized at headquarters to systematize the work of the medical consultants, Colonel S. H. Wadhams proved an ever helpful and resourceful director. He was followed by Colonel W. L. Keller, who in the turbulent days of the last half of the war managed the increasing work of the consultants with great skill. To General

J. M. T. Finney as Chief Consultant in Surgery, and Colonel William A. Fisher, his next in command, we owe a debt of gratitude for their fine spirit of co-operation.

Sending our papers properly through "channels" was always difficult for us untrained soldiers. Finally, on the pretext of systematizing the paper work in my department, I issued "G. U. No. 1: 'Hereafter all communications will pass up through the proper urinary channels.'" It was accompanied by an anatomical chart of the urinary tract in which certain officers of our force were placed at strategic points according to their rank. Lieutenant Bertner insisted that his place was at the point of arrival at the lower end. His position was indicated by a wart on the penile head. Major Walker, of the seaport bases, was stationed in the bladder, Colonel Keyes at the great functional center, the kidney. I, as superintendent, occupied the adrenals, from which point, through the sympathetic nervous system, we reached General Finney in the spine, and the other consultants through branching nerves, finally down to Major Dexter, head of the gas service, in the rectum.

We decided that our department needed a coat of arms. It was in the shape of a shield with a blue background—very blue, like our patients. In the upper left-hand corner was the gonococcus, and in the lower right, the cootie. Separating them was a group of spirochetes, and the whole was dependant on 606 (salvarsan). Below was the motto "Continent or Careful."

Bertner's "News Letter" went out monthly to all officers in the Division of Urology. It consisted of four mimeographed pages, the first two devoted to the records of various organizations in the prevention of venereal and skin diseases; comments on new plans and procedures; and a pep talk to cheer up the urologists with the fighting forces. The last two pages were in a lighter vein. Bertner showed great skill in assembling a variety of literature that would appeal to officers in the division with our far-flung forces. James Whitcomb Riley's "Diabetic Dog" was the poetic offering in the first number. Eugene Fields' pornographic poems had a prominent place in other issues. A collection of gay stories completed the sheet, which became famous in the A.E.F.

AFTER our report of the horrid conditions present in the houses of prostitution at Saint-Nazaire, and General Pershing's General Order No. 77, which put these houses out of bounds, criticism of our attitude grew steadily, and culminated in a letter of protest from M. Clemenceau to the Commander in Chief:

Paris, February 17, 1918.

From: The Président du Conseil, Minister of War
To: General, Chief of the French Mission, A.E.F.
Subject: Prostitution and Venereal Diseases

The presence on French territory, specially in certain important centers, of American troop agglomerations brings up questions of social hygiene which it is of great importance to solve to the best interest of the health of the Allied troops and of the civilian population.

Regarding more specially the propagation of venereal diseases, the methods followed so far by the American Commandant do not seem to have given good results. In fact, total prohibition of all regulated prostitution in the vicinity of American troops has had for result, in spite of the measures of prophylaxis and discipline taken by the American authorities, the increase of propagation of venereal diseases among the civilian population of the neighborhood.

Consequently, I would be very much obliged to you for calling again the attention of the American High Command to this serious question.

In this respect it is certain that clandestine prostitution offers to men more numerous and, above all, more dangerous temptations than regulated prostitution. The latter, under its strictest form, that is, the house of prostitution, if it does not exclude completely, at least reduces very sensibly, the dangers of unrestrained prostitution. Owing to the administrative and sanitary control by the public authorities it offers the maximum of security, reducing the risk of contagion to the minimum.

Should the American High Command see this question in the same light, I would put my services at its disposal for providing if necessary, in concert with the Minister of the Interior, the creation of special houses of this kind.

I beg of you to let me know as soon as possible the reply of the American Commandant.

G. CLEMENCEAU

General Pershing's reply:

France, 23 February, 1918

From: Commander-in-Chief, G.H.Q., A.E.F.
To: Chief of the French Mission, G.H.Q., A.E.F.
Subject: Hygiene of the Allied Troops.

1. Referring to your communication of February 19th, No. 5700/SS, on the subject of Hygiene of the Allied Troops in which was forwarded a letter signed by Clemenceau, No. 1168 C, dated February 17, 1918, I have to reply as follows: It is believed the statement made in the letter from M. Clemenceau, that the methods followed by Americans have not given good results in the prevention of venereal disease, is without foundation. As a matter of fact it is thought that the records of the American troops for non-effectiveness and for admissions because of venereal disease is better than any other Army of which we have knowledge.

2. It is proposed that a conference take place in which it is desired that three officers of the Medical Department be present and any number which may be determined upon by the French authorities. If it meets with your approval, it is suggested that this conference meet in Paris on or about March 5th for the consideration of the questions involved.

3. While thanking you for bringing this matter to our attention, I beg to express also my appreciation.

By direction:

A. E. BRADLEY
Brig. Gen., N.A.

The conference was held in Paris in March, 1918. Colonels Ireland, Keyes, and Young represented the A.E.F. We found a great assemblage of high-ranking officers of the French Army and also members of the Government, in frock coats. The conference continued off and on for weeks, and vigorous efforts were made to prove that the regulatory methods adopted by the French were ideal, and that with the A.E.F. co-operating with them, could not be improved upon. The conference afforded us an opportunity to present statistics which showed that many venereal infections among the American troops had been acquired at French houses of prostitution, which were inspected regularly twice a week; that there were cases of syphilis acquired in houses in which it was acknowledged by our medical officers participating with the French in the examination that the women themselves showed no evidence of primary or secondary syphilis; that, using no lavage or prophylaxis, they transmitted one soldier's infection to another. We presented positive evidence that the methods of examination carried out upon these registered prostitutes was often most casual and unscientific. As the examining finger passed from one patient to another without any attempt at sterilization, it surely acted more as a spreader of filth than as a detector of disease. We finally obtained from the French a complete acknowledgment that the methods in the A.E.F. rested on a scientific basis, that the French *réglementation de prostitution* was far from satisfactory, that it was safer to place these houses out of bounds to soldiers, and that American methods of prophylaxis should be adopted.

It seems strange that our methods, which had their inception in the great experiments of Metchnikov at the Institut Pasteur, had never been adopted in France itself—further proof that a prophet is not without honor except in his own country. Another who played a heroic part in this discovery was Maisonneuve, a young assistant of Metchnikov, who offered himself as an experiment to prove that the mercurial paste was as effective in human beings as it had been shown to be on monkeys in destroying the germs of syphilis and preventing infections. Maisonneuve, after scarifying his genitals, sat for an hour with the wound filled with the germs of syphilis. At the end of that time Metchnikov's paste was applied and Maisonneuve began the long wait through days and weeks to see whether he would become syphilitic. He did not.

The publication of this remarkable scientific work had greatly impressed the officers of the Medical Corps of the United States Army, and in 1912, after confirmatory experimentation, prophylaxis with Metchnikov's paste to prevent syphilis, and a urethral injection to prevent gonorrhea, had been adopted in the army, with extraordinary results.

The ravages of venereal disease in the B.E.F. and in Great Britain generally eventually led to a royal order from King George V on the subject on March 22, 1918:

His Majesty is pleased, with the advice of his Privy Council, to order that the following regulations be promulgated: No woman who is suffering from venereal disease shall have intercourse with any member of His Majesty's forces or invite any member of His Majesty's forces to have sexual intercourse with her. If any woman acts in contravention of this regulation she shall be guilty of a summary offense.

On May 10, 1918, at the War Office in London, a conference on venereal disease was held. Those present included I. N. MacPherson, Undersecretary for the State of War, the Lord Archbishop of Canterbury, Lord Sydenham, Sir T. MacKenzie, High Commissioner for New Zealand, General Sir Neville Howse, of the Australian Expeditionary Forces, Sir G. H. Perley of the Canadian Expeditionary Forces, three generals from the War Office, Chaplain General Bishop Smith and Bishop Bidwell, and two officers from the Admiralty. Representing the A.E.F. were General Bethel, Colonel Ireland, and Bishop Brent, our Chaplain General, who acted as chairman.

The Archbishop of Canterbury said:

When this matter was raised in the House of Lords it was in answer to words I had spoken about our working with the forces from America, when I rather referred to measures of a preventive measure. It is with regard to these measures that I gather the Chairman is now going to deal.

Bishop Brent spoke:

This is the moment of the ages when we can take hold of this horrible thing in such a way as to make a cleaner and better world. Soon after the A.E.F. had arrived in France General Pershing issued a general order . . . to the end that venereal disease may be minimized, prophylactic stations will be established. . . . All the members of the A.E.F. were directed to report for treatment. In a subsequent order General Pershing said: "Should men return to camp in an intoxicated condition they will be seized and . . . prophylactic treatment administered."

General Bethel read a letter from General Pershing to Lord Milner, which said, in part:

I am glad to respond to your call for the conference aimed at joint action by the British and American authorities to handle the venereal situation. I have heard with great satisfaction the recent decision of the British War Office that licensed houses of prostitution are to be put out of bounds in the B.E.F. Many of us who have experimented with licensed prostitution have been forced to the conclusion that they are really ineffective. The question long since was an international one. . . . The gravest responsibility rests on those to whom the parents of our soldiers have entrusted their sons for the battle, and we fail if we neglect to safeguard them. We have the common ground of humanity; we have the well-considered conclusions of the best scientific minds on our side, and in this War of nations in arms . . . we have all the elements with which to force cooperation between military and civil authorities. With our nations cooperating we have the brightest prospects of winning the victory.

Colonel Ireland told of the remarkable reduction in venereal rates in the A.E.F. as a result of prophylaxis, and then said: "But we all feel we can go no further without active help from the British and the French."

The British were against the use of prophylactic tubes to be carried by officers and men, because they thought they were incentive devices, but finally agreed that they would not object to prophylaxis after the act.

Surgeon General Howse, Chief Surgeon of the Australian forces, said that they issued outfits of mercury and French letters, in addition to treatment at prophylactic stations, and had thus greatly reduced the percentage of venereal disease.

Your men have no necessity to expose themselves as ours have; they have their womenfolk here; they have their own homes; they know the dangers of London, but our men have none of those things. They have more money and more virility, and to say it is an incentive to men to issue prophylaxis—well, as far as this is concerned we think it is ridiculous. You need not regulate for the man who is chaste; he hardly exists and you can wipe out chastity as far as the younger men of the Service are concerned.

Sir T. MacKenzie, High Commissioner for New Zealand, spoke:

It seems to me the great evil in this communication is that you have not the courage to face the problem of treating this disease properly and dealing with loose women who everywhere lie in wait for the soldiers, who before they leave the railroad station are seized and accosted by young girls and insulted if they do not go with them. I endorse what Bishop Brent has said; this is the opportunity for dealing with this awful evil.

Bishop Bidwell stated that he was greatly impressed with the account of the success the Americans had had in dealing with venereal diseases, and with their methods. General Richardson, officer commanding the New Zealand forces, said:

I came here in 1916 and found the large percentage of our men had contracted venereal disease. I called all the chaplains together and asked them to carry out a purity campaign. Still the percentage went up. I got the medical officers together and asked them to have lecturers point out to the men the evil of the thing. Still the percentage went up. I discussed the matter with General Howse. Then after experimenting with early treatment I decided to issue prophylaxis tubes. From that time on the percentage of venereal disease went down.

Bishop Brent thanked the British officers and the Archbishop of Canterbury and closed the meeting.

CHAPTER 20. SKIN DISEASES

AND THEIR PREVENTION

IN THE A.E.F.

IN CIRCULAR No. 2 the responsibility of skin diseases was placed upon the Division of Urology, which previously comprised only surgery of the genitourinary tract and venereal disease. Our studies disclosed that most diseases of the skin were due to infestations with lice and scabies (itch), pus-producing bacteria, and other infections, and that they were largely preventable by hygienic measures. I told the Chief Surgeon that as he had placed upon us the responsibility of skin diseases, about which I knew nothing, I was going to try to prevent them.

An exhaustive study was made of methods that had been developed in the French and British armies. Infestation with lice or scabies was responsible, in the British Army, for over 50 per cent of the evacuations from the front lines for disease. We found splendid arrangements for bathing in the French Army back of the Chemin-des-Dames. Shower baths had been provided for battalions in support at the front, and farther back there were extensive mobile bathing and disinfesting establishments accompanied by mobile laundries. The British had developed a wonderful steam automobile disinfestor that traveled under its own power and was capable of dragging trucks containing entire bathing establishments, extensive equipment, and personnel as it moved from place to place along the front or back with the divisions at rest.

In the United States the army had excellent facilities for bathing

334

in the great army posts, but little preparation had been made for sending apparatus for these purposes to France. Every bit of space available in the ships was required for the transportation of troops, munitions, and the thousand other things urgently required by a great expeditionary force.

Few orders had been issued on bathing and disinfestation. General Order No. 8 (September 17, 1917) stated: "A bath house approximately 26 x 22 feet with a concrete floor and eight to twelve shower heads is authorized . . . with arrangements for heating the same for each battalion arriving." General Order No. 13 stated: "The Quartermaster Corps will provide and operate laundries. . . . All garments laundered will be sterilized, washed and repaired, no attempt being made to return to the soldier his identical garments. Complete outfits of clean clothing will be issued to front line troops after leaving the trenches and using the bathing facilities authorized by General Order No. 8. Organizations moving into the zone of advance will take with them their portable shower baths . . . to be installed in suitable shelters with the least possible delay after arrival. Engineer troops, when available, should make the necessary installation." General Order No. 18 said: "The Quartermaster is responsible for the location and maintenance of suitable . . . baths."

The responsibility of bathing, disinfesting, furnishing clean underclothing, laundering, and treatment of skin cases was placed on no one corps, but divided between the Commissary, Engineer, and Medical corps.

In a series of reports I made to the Chief Surgeon statistics were presented from both the French and British armies, a description of what they had done, details of the apparatus developed, and recommendations for the purchase of supplies we needed in France. If it were possible to obtain this equipment, we probably would be able to keep down the incidence of skin disease to such a point that few men would have to be evacuated from their divisions; like the venereals, they could be kept with their organizations on a duty status. It was particularly urged that as many as possible of the British Foden-Thresh steam automobile disinfestors be purchased, and that French bathing establishments, capable of bathing and delousing a thousand men a day, be acquired. It was recommended that each bathing establishment be accompanied by one of the French mobile laundries, which were models of compactness and efficiency. In addition, individual shower heads with heating apparatus for minor organizations should be obtained. It was hoped that skin diseases would be so rare that they could be cared for, like the venereals, with the divisions.

A little later, when I returned from an inspection trip among the divisions holding sectors along the front, Major Keyes told me that Majors Hans Zinsser and Haven Emerson had called to see me "mad as the devil because the Chief Surgeon had ordered them to report to a damned urologist." This distinguished bacteriologist and this great public health official had been commissioned majors in the Medical Corps and sent by the Surgeon General to the British Army to study hygiene, infestation of troops, and resultant diseases. They had prepared a voluminous report, which they submitted to the Chief Surgeon. He glanced through their lengthy document, called for the files pertaining to the subject, then ordered them to make their report to the Director of the Division of Urology. On their inquiry as to why they were being sent to me, the Chief Surgeon replied that he found most of the reports on skin diseases had come from me. Keyes told me that after reporting they had gone on a motor trip and had left an address where they might be found.

I hurried after them and admitted that I had been almost as disgruntled as they were when I discovered that skin diseases had been assigned to the Division of Urology. Somewhat mollified, they turned over their report, and we sat down to prepare recommendations on the subject. It did not take long to formulate a joint report, which we three signed and sent to the Chief Surgeon. We presented exhaustive statistics from studies made by Zinsser and Emerson

with the British Army, reiterated the importance of bathing, disinfestation, and clean underclothes in the prevention of skin diseases,
and offered an extensive program. Unfortunately, no one corps in
our army was completely responsible for carrying out these procedures, and no concerted action was possible. Our report brought
forth favorable replies but no immediate results.

It was necessary for the Director of the Division of Urology to
send another urgent communication to the Chief Surgeon, in which
it was pointed out that the skin-disease situation was bad and would
soon lead to serious conditions unless immediate action was taken.
It was recommended that commanding officers of battalions be
ordered to set up portable bath apparatus in all rest and support
camps and if possible in the zone of the advance; that commanders
be ordered to see that men bathed and changed underclothing at
least once a week while in rest and support camps if not absolutely
precluded by military exigencies; that commanding officers be
notified that if lousiness and skin infections became prevalent among
their troops, it would be considered an evidence of inefficiency in
determining their fitness for command and for promotion (adopting
the same stringent orders issued by General Pershing for venereal
diseases in General Order No. 77). The communication closed with
the statement that unless immediate steps were taken to do away
with the fearfully infested conditions of our troops, skin diseases
would rapidly increase and complicate the surgery on wounded men,
and that the danger of trench fever and typhus, transmitted by the
louse, was ever present.

Following this report, the Chief Surgeon announced that important action had been taken, and another report came from the Chief
Quatermaster. Finally a plan was adopted for the prophylaxis
(prevention) and treatment of skin diseases, but still there was no
centralization of authority. We got nowhere.

Circular No. 22 from the Chief Surgeon's office reinforced the
recommendations and orders previously made, and stated that every
medical officer in the A.E.F. would be expected to give his personal

attention to the prevention and treatment of scabies and infestation in the command for which he was responsible. In the meantime we had notified the division urologists that the prevention and treatment of skin diseases had been added to their duties and, without orders from the Chief Surgeon A.E.F., we had finally secured orders from generals commanding divisions to place bathing, disinfesting, and issue of underclothing in the hands of the urologists. Major MacGruer, the dermatologist attached to our headquarters, did fine work in the divisions in inaugurating our program.

From Captain H. L. Sanford, urologist of the Forty-second Division, came a report which showed that from 25 to 75 per cent of the various commands were heavily infested with lice. Scabies had become so prevalent that in May one of the field hospitals was delegated for its treatment. This hospital, placed along the river Meurthe, just out of Baccarat, was dubbed "Scratchville-by-the-Sea" by the doughboys. On May 22 the cases of scabies reached four hundred and twenty-five, but as a result of active treatment and hygienic measures the number fell rapidly until by June 20 there were only seventeen cases in the hospital. The men who had been so miserable from the universal infestation of vermin were practically free from them, and skin diseases had virtually disappeared. The splendid results obtained in the Forty-second Division were transmitted by us in a communication to other divisions and were a great incentive to an intensified clean-up campaign throughout the army.

Throughout the rest of the war the Forty-second Division maintained a remarkable record in the prevention of skin disease. This magnificent division left the quiet sector of Baccarat during the latter part of June and was thrown successively into the battles in the Champagne, north of Château-Thierry, against the Saint-Mihiel salient and the Argonne, finally ending up at Sedan and then going with the Army of Occupation to the Rhine. During these wanderings they took with them their two Foden-Thresh disinfestors that dragged the baths and the laundries. Colonel Fairchild, division surgeon, kept this equipment with his division against orders from corps and army headquarters that it be left behind. In my last visit to the Forty-second Division, in Germany, I found these huge machines busily engaged keeping the doughboys clean under the active direction of the division urologist, Captain Rolnick. Throughout the terrible fighting in which this division had been engaged the men were virtually free from skin disease, a lasting tribute to the wisdom of putting the bathing and disinfesting of the troops under the division urologist.

The record of the Third Division is equally praiseworthy. Lieutenant Colonel McCague reported that he had been able to keep the baths going during the Marne offensive. As the men came out of the line they were given baths and clean clothing, and were deloused. The skin and scabies cases were sent to one of the field hospitals, but had to work as stretcher-bearers during the offensive. As the Third Division moved into the Saint-Mihiel offensive, two Foden-Thresh disinfestors drew wagons containing coal and tentage as well as trucks with other equipment and traveled a hundred and thirty-five kilometers in four days. There had been only thirty-five cases of scabies in the division, and they remained for treatment only four days each. During the intense activity of the Meuse-Argonne offensive the same fine record for cleanliness and absence of skin diseases was maintained.

It is impossible to describe adequately the equally fine record of other divisions or even mention the splendid work and remarkable ingenuity of certain division urologists who improvised apparatus for bathing and disinfesting their troops under great difficulties. These men struggled with two vast problems of preventive medicine, and obtained results in the prevention of skin and venereal diseases that were indeed remarkable.

In October, 1918, Major F. C. Knowles, assistant consultant in dermatology, showed that not more than a hundred cases of pyodermia (supparative skin disease), which had been so common in the British Army, had occurred in the entire A.E.F. Much credit is due the three consultants in dermatology—Majors MacGruer, Knowles, and Mook.

CHAPTER. 21. THE TROOPS LEAVE FOR
GERMANY AND HOME

After the Armistice the Third Army was formed, and marched to the Rhine. Lieutenant Colonel McCague, who had been so efficient as division and corps urologist, was made urologist to the Army of Occupation. The venereal problem here was recognized as one of extreme importance. Houses of prostitution were put out of bounds, and fraternization with the civil population prohibited, but the women looked upon our soldiers as anything but enemies, and it was difficult to keep them apart.

The soldiers reported that on the march to the Rhine they were put in billets that were much better than they had in France, with eiderdown pillows and clean white sheets. Often the landlady would take no money for accommodations. One sergeant remarked that for a stick of chocolate or a piece of soap he could get anything he wanted.

McCague and I made the rounds of Coblenz to study the social problems. A good many Germans were still in uniform, but wore an army band with an American Army stamp. In the music halls and cafés we saw our soldiers and the *Mädchen* in close harmony. Prostitution in Coblenz was confined to a segregated district that consisted of small blocks with narrow streets, little two-room houses right on the sidewalk. The women sat at the windows with almost no clothes on, giving their clients a chance to appraise their charms before entering. Our M.P. had the district well guarded, and no Americans got inside.

The venereal rate of the Army of Occupation during the winter of 1918–19 averaged thirteen new cases per thousand men per annum— a very low rate. During this period no leaves were allowed. With the coming of spring and the departure of the men on leave to areas more difficult to supervise, the rate rose, and by June, 1919, had reached 44 per thousand per annum. Even this was less than half the rate of the regular United States Army before we entered the war, and only a small fraction of the rate that was present in the armies of our Allies.

The Troops Return Home

American organizations were returned from Europe as quickly as possible. At our suggestion a general order was issued that a careful inspection for venereal disease be made at all camps through which the troops passed, especially at ports of debarkation. If any were found with active disease, they were to be held for treatment until pronounced well. The ruling applied also to officers. The number of men detained in France was not large, but some were kept for several months. On board the transports and also at ports of debarkation in America another thorough examination was made.

As I stood in line at the examining office at Hoboken a major general, evidently well beyond retirement age, was in front of me. The young lieutenant of the Medical Corps looked up and realized that he had before him a high-ranking officer. He apologized for the indignity, to which the major general replied: "Don't worry. I'm not insulted, I'm flattered."

What was the effect of education, intensive effort at prophylaxis, upon our troops? The use of protective measures and early treatment became much more general, and venereal diseases less prevalent, in this country after the war. The simple methods that we inaugurated for the treatment of syphilis in the A.E.F. have been largely adopted in the United States. Dr. J. Earle Moore, the Johns

Hopkins consultant in syphilis, reports that the methods used were efficacious in curing the disease, and that relatively few cases of chronic or cerebrospinal syphilis have been found among the troops who returned to America. The crusade against venereal disease and bodily uncleanliness, infestations, and infections has been of lasting benefit to our population. General Harbord in his book *The American Army in France* says: "Generations to come owe a great debt to the wisdom and courage of General John J. Pershing. No such record has ever before been made with a returning army."

AND EXCURSIONS

IN ADDITION to planning, organizing, and directing the Division of Urology, A.E.F., much of my time was taken up with inspection trips and surveys. These occurred from time to time as our work progressed. It seems desirable to group these here, although some of them in point of time came before occurrences that have been described in foregoing chapters.

A Visit to the Twenty-sixth Division

On February 20, 1918, I left our headquarters with Lieutenant Bertner, and reached Châlons late at night. We went to bed in the dining-room of the principal hotel. Leaving about eight o'clock the next morning, we went towards Reims and saw tremendous preparations for defense in the second, third, and fourth lines that had been recently constructed. Thousands of men were still engaged in digging trenches and placing wire entanglements many kilometers back of the present line. Entering Reims, we took a look at the cathedral. It had changed little since the summer of 1917, but the city was almost completely destroyed and few people were left.

We turned off to Couvrelles, where the Twenty-sixth Division A.E.F. had their headquarters in a château. Colonel Bevans, division surgeon, was greatly disturbed because the medical corps was scattered and the care of the sick and wounded was entirely in the charge of the French. Colonel Bevans said that discipline "had gone to the dogs."

At Soissons we met several consultants—Boyd, division urologist; Besley, surgeon; and Dickson, orthopedist—and spent the night there. The planes dropped no bombs and I slept well. The next morning I went to headquarters to see Major General Edwards, commander of the division. He was proud of the record his troops had made. He said they had already brought out new methods of handling the enemy when they came across in raids. The Americans did not remain hidden in the trenches until the Germans reached them, but while the barrage was still going on got out and fired at Germans, and before the Germans reached the trenches, mounted the top and had it out with them on the surface. Several raids had been completely repulsed. The French were astonished at the daring of the Americans. He talked at length on the desirability of our having our own front, and was confident that the Americans would make a fine showing and would develop a more effective system of warfare. General Edwards thought, from the massing of German troops, that there was soon to be a great attack near the junction of the French and British lines—a remarkably accurate forecast!

In the afternoon I joined Boyd and went to the dermatological and venereal-disease hospital, and later to the Hôpital Mixte at Soissons, where I found an old friend Professor Nogués, consulting urologist for the Sixth French Army, and got from him a record of the operations he had performed. Most of the kidney work had been done in advance surgical units.

Leaving Soissons across one of the ruined bridges of the Aisne, we passed through Crouy, in which the Germans had lived so long, and then through Régny, where we picked up Captain Glass, the medical officer of our 101st Infantry. He lived in a dugout in the destroyed village, but he had a very good infirmary, with about twenty beds for his lightly wounded and venereal cases.

We crossed the field of battle of October, 1917, in which the Chemindes-Dames ridge was taken by the French. Passing through the deep valley on the north of the Chemin-des-Dames, we entered the communicating trenches and stopped at the regimental aid station, located in an old limestone quarry in the hill. The aid station contained quarters for officers and men, beds, a dispensary, a drug room, a mess, and places for treating newly gassed cases and for dressing the wounded. It was beautifully clean, well lighted by acetylene lamps, and only a mile from the lines. We followed the communicating trenches toward the front lines, but at the bottom of the hill the ground was marshy and the communication trench disappeared. A French officer explained that trenches were not necessary because of the forest ahead. The battalion dressing-station was located in three dugouts, and was well equipped for dressing wounds, applying first aid, and handling a dozen or more patients for a short time. The doctors were quartered in one dugout adjacent, and the men in another. Returning laboriously over the hill and up the communication trenches to the regimental aid station on the hill, we sat down to a good meal underground with a Captain Pellissier.

A little farther back we found a model gas station consisting of three barracks, a waiting-room, a depot of clothes, and a bathing establishment, each about 25 by 80 feet in size, and beautifully equipped for taking care of the great number of gassed cases that were constantly coming in. These patients were brought first to a room where they were undressed; their clothes were taken by attendants who wore rubber suits, long gloves, and masks in order to keep themselves from being gassed by the chemicals in the clothes, which were thrown out of the window. The men then passed into showers, where carbonated soda water was douched upon them, and then were carefully dried and covered with dusting powder or sometimes with ointments. From there they passed into the next room, where their eyes, noses, and throats were treated with bicarbonate of soda, some of which was swallowed as an antidote for gas that might be in the stomach. Those who had breathed the gas were given small rubber bags filled with oxygen, which they took into their lungs to combat the fearful irritation produced by these gases. This was merely a first-aid station. The patients were then conducted to hospitals in the rear.

Farther along we came to a wonderfully arranged Hôpital de Triage (Sorting-out Hospital) located entirely underground in an old quarry. There were rooms for reception, examination, X-ray, sterilization, operations, recovery, a ward for sixteen patients, a pharmacy, a kitchen, a dining-room, and a beautiful system of electric lights. The walls of soft limestone had been sculptured here and there by the pharmacist, who was an artist of note in civil life. The operating-room was covered with white oilcloth. In this hospital cases were sorted out and desperate abdominal and lung cases were operated on. From here the cases were sent to the different hospitals according to the gravity of the condition. These *postes de triage* of the French, entirely unknown to the English and American armies, were valuable adjuncts in the medical work.

On February 24 I went to the Hôpital Mixte, where I met Major Gross, chief surgeon of the Sixth French Army. Before the war he had been a prominent surgeon at Nancy. He had made a great reputation as the principal exponent of immediate closure (suture) in wounds of war. He explained to me the methods he had employed for over a year with brilliant results. Almost all wounds were closed after first carrying out debridement, that is, excision of the lacerated and injured skin, fascia, muscle, and so on.   Before closing, however, cultures were carefully taken from the wound. Six hours later an examination was made, and if the microscopic examination showed that streptococci were present, the wound was then opened and drained, because experience had shown that in these cases the wounds almost always broke down and often blood poisoning resulted if the wounds were not opened early. Other wounds were allowed to remain closed even though staphylococci and bacilli of considerable virulence, sometimes even the gas bacillus, were present. I talked to numerous French surgeons. They claimed to have by this method about 90 per cent successful closures, that is, primary unions without breakdown. The saving in doctors' and nurses' time by the elimination of frequent dressings made this one of the greatest advances in surgery.

At ten o'clock I started off with Boyd and Bertner and later picked up Captain Martin, who conducted us through Ostel to the well-arranged battalion dressing-station in an extensive quarry under the Chemin-des-Dames. It housed three thousand soldiers, and extended entirely through the hill. The whole medical detachment was excited over the raid pulled off the day before by our men, in which they brought back twenty-five German officers and men. We crossed to the other side of the underground quarry, passing hundreds of French and Americans who were billeted there, and a stable of artillery horses.

On our way home we came upon an interesting presentation of medals to two American officers and two noncommissioned officers, and eight Frenchmen, who had been selected for the Croix de Guerre by the French general on account of their gallant services in the raid the day before. The American doughboys winced as he kissed them.

We then visited a wonderful French bathing establishment. It consisted of a quickly demountable building of canvas and wood panels with rooms for undressing, bathing, and dressing, and a large steam sterilizing plant on one side, through which the infested clothes of the men passed. The entire establishment cost 40,000 francs, and similar ones were supplied at the rate of one to every two divisions. Such an establishment is about 30 by 60 feet in size, and is able to take care of about a thousand men a day, the clothes being sterilized for fifteen minutes at a temperature of 115°C., with five minutes' dry sterilization for drying. We passed the ruins of a large factory that the Germans had destroyed and on which they had left their sign "*Gott Strafe England.*"

On February 25, 1918, with Major Gross, I visited a number of the French hospitals. They were models of organization, the barracks being connected with corridors, often steam-heated throughout. The wards were painted and decorated with interesting posters, the beds covered with attractive coverlets, and each had X-ray plants and splendid laboratories—altogether far superior to anything I have ever seen with the British. We ended up at a great "H.O.E." (evacuative hospital) containing about twenty-five hundred beds, and a whole series of operating-rooms, in which thousands of cases were handled at times of great stress by numerous teams of expert surgeons and nurses.

After luncheon I visited one of the French divisions and obtained ideas about bathing and disinfesting troops. The French had small portable shower-bath systems that they sent to the regiments in support camps within a mile or two of the lines. Here they were able to give their men baths and changes of clothes once or twice weekly. In the rest camps some twelve to fourteen kilometers back, the same things were provided and very largely took the place of extensive bathing establishments. The French tactical organization was as follows: The men remained in the trenches nine days, the three companies composing the battalion changing back and forth from the immediate front lines to those a hundred yards or so behind. A mile or two behind these was the second battalion in support, provided with shower-bath apparatus. In nine days they relieved the battalion in the front line. About ten kilometers behind these came the battalion at rest, again provided with shower-bath arrangements, and remaining as a rule nine days in this camp. Attached to this was the regimental infirmary at which mild ailments were treated, the men being kept there instead of going back to the front when the battalions changed. Simple cases of scabies were treated at the regimental infirmary, 20 per cent sulphur ointment being used, and the clothes being disinfested by sulphur smoke produced by a small alcohol lamp or a charcoal fire over which a pan containing a pound of sulphur was placed.

On February 26 I left to visit the English division that joined the French north of Coucy-le-Château. I saw several field and evacuation hospitals, and then went to Noyon, where I took the train for Paris. As we passed across this level country back of the British lines, we did not see the many men working on protective devices as we did behind the French lines, and the country seemed far easier to advance across.

Three weeks after my trip, the Germans made their great attack against this part of the line and drove the British back many kilometers.

A Visit to the Second Division

About the middle of May the Second Division, which had been in trenches south of Verdun for several weeks, came back to Nancy for rest. I went up to confer with the division urologist, because I knew that he would have his hands full with the venereal problem. Syphilis was said to be six times as prevalent as before the war among the many thousand women who remained there. The organization of the urological work had been excellent. Commanding officers had co-operated well, and the importance of going to prophylactic stations promptly had been so impressed upon the division that the venereal rate did not materially increase in Nancy. The necessity for bathing and delousing kept the division urologist very busy.

On my return to headquarters, Miss Robbins, a writer for the A.R.C. magazine, called and asked for information concerning the venereal problem in the A.E.F. After looking over the orders issued by General Pershing urging continence upon his troops, Miss Robbins said: "That's all very well, but do you think men who have spent weeks in the trenches will heed these moralizing injunctions when they get back to rest areas?" I admitted that our experience with the Second Division showed otherwise; in fact I cited the case of an officer, who had picked up a *fille de joie* and taken her to his room on the top floor of a hotel. At an interesting moment a German aviator had dropped a bomb that came through the ceiling and killed the officer, but didn't kill the girl. "That was terrible," said Miss Robbins, "but he died happy."

A Visit to Paris While the Great Gun Was Shelling It

On Sunday morning, May 26, as I was traveling by train to Paris I read with astonishment in a newspaper that the Germans had attacked and overrun the Chemin-des-Dames and were firing on Paris. The wildest rumors were rampant that the French Army had been routed, and that the big gun which was shelling Paris was much closer than previous German lines. When I arrived at the station, I saw a large crowd around a big hole where a shell had fallen. An extra announced that the shells were coming at twenty-minute intervals. Just as I arrived at the Hôtel Continental one landed in the Tuileries garden close by, and during the day, at regular intervals, these shells fell in various portions of Paris. During the next few days these shell bursts came closer and closer to the Arc de Triomphe. What joy it would have given the Germans had they demolished this noble monument celebrating Napoleon's victories over them!

Subsequently Captain John R. Edie, stationed in Paris at the head of naval intelligence, informed me that the Germans knew ten minutes after each shot exactly where it had struck. Edie had discovered that in one of the foreign embassies the Germans had planted a spy who telephoned to the Spanish border the exact location of each hit, and from there it was reported by wireless directly to the gun crew of the Big Bertha.

After the war I went to the forest north of Laon and saw the concrete emplacement in the depths of the forest from which shells from this gun had reached Paris, sixty-seven miles away. The cannon apparently had been directed high into the air through a small opening among the trees. The shell reached a height of about twenty-two miles, it was said, before it leveled out and traveled in the stratosphere, with little resistance against it, many miles before it began to descend. The shell, being very heavy and pointed, had thus traveled the unbelievable distance to the French capital.

I had gone to Paris for consultations with officers of the French

Medical Corps, but everything was in a turmoil as a result of the widespread terror that gripped the city. News of the headlong flight of the French Army before the onrushing Germans created consternation. The French Government was rapidly preparing to leave the city, and the local American command had to do likewise. The roads became jammed with traffic, and citizens were prohibited from leaving until the Government could be evacuated. At our medical headquarters Harry Lehr, brother of Louis, urologist to the First Division, arrived in great excitement. One of the shells had fallen at the entrance to his home and killed the gatekeeper. With his automobile filled with baggage, he had been refused permission to leave. He begged me to secure authorization from the American command. I told him that only those connected with the army could be given this permission. Whereupon he said, "Hugh, I have been working for a long time with the American forces." "What have you been doing?" I asked. He replied that he had been going to the Red Cross Hospital every afternoon and pouring tea for the wounded Americans. Numerous others of the aristocracy were also working at this hospital. In order not to be conscripted, quite a few counts carried bedpans, but it is said that some had a servant waiting outside the ward to take care of the pans.

Then came the glad tidings that the onrush of the Germans had been stopped by the Second and Third Divisions A.E.F. After a while the turmoil in Paris subsided, but not until a million had left.

A Visit to Other Divisions at the Front

A few days later I got a traveling order to visit the headquarters of the First, Second, Fourth, Twenty-sixth, and Third American divisions. Traveling through Beauvais, I stopped to see my friend Natalie Vivian Scott, who had just been decorated with a Croix de Guerre for her bravery in attending the wounded in the hospital, which had recently been bombed. The French staff had taken to the cellars, but Natalie had stuck to her work in the ward, the roof of which had been blown off. At Amiens I visited en passant the great cathedral. It stood almost unhurt amid a scene of wide destruction of the city. The German artillery had carefully avoided the cathedral, and only one shell had entered it. A little farther on I reached Captain Lehr, urologist of the First Division, then holding the lines opposite Cantigny that they afterwards captured with consummate dash. This was the first demonstration of the wonderful fighting powers of our troops. Lehr reported that the venereal and skin patients were at work in divisional labor camps and that troops at rest were being bathed.

Hurrying south, at Lizy-sur-Ourcq I asked a sergeant of military police, who was directing traffic, the location of the headquarters of the various divisions I wished to visit. To each request he politely said, "I cannot tell you." I continued into La Ferté-sous-Jouarre, where I was accosted by military police, who looked at my car and said: "This is the automobile I've been asked to take up. Please come with me to police headquarters." A lieutenant came out and remarked; "Yes, this is the car. Let me see your papers." I did so, and he said they looked all right, but that he had been ordered to hold my car. When I asked him why, he said he couldn't tell me. I would have to see the captain, who was away. After a time the captain approached and said it was the car they wanted, but he was sorry he could not tell me why. I would have to see the major. After a considerable time the latter appeared. "Yes, this is the car, but I can't tell you why we are holding it. You will have to see the colonel, who is off on an inspection trip." It was now about nine o'clock, and I demanded to be allowed to find a place to sleep, suggesting that he could put a guard around me and my machine. This he did.

The next morning the major was there to apologize. He said that a big mistake had been made, but I would have to see the colonel at corps headquarters to get the details. When I arrived there, the corps surgeon burst out laughing. "So you're the German spy they've picked up!" It turned out that a lieutenant colonel had appeared about a week before at one of the artillery positions, inspected the guns, and then departed. Several hours later German artillery had concentrated on this position and killed and wounded many. A few days later the lieutenant colonel appeared at corps headquarters, and shortly after his departure a squadron of German planes had bombed it. The immediate deduction was that the lieutenant colonel was a German spy, and probably still operating within our lines. Orders were issued to look out for a man dressed in the uniform of an American lieutenant colonel, and when I asked the sergeant of military police the location of many divisions, he concluded that I was the spy and telephoned La Ferté, where I was "apprehended."

A Night Trip to Outpost Sentries

The question arose as to whether men recently under treatment should be sent back into the most active part of the front, and it seemed desirable for us to make a personal investigation. While visiting the Twenty-sixth Division on June 3, 1918, I discussed the matter with Colonel Bevans, the division surgeon, who said that the region of Seicheprey was too active for comfort, and suggested a portion of the line west of that. But Seicheprey had recently been the scene of an important action, and I was eager to see it. After much persuasion the general issued a pass. He told us that the front was now largely a matter of separate outposts well advanced beyond the main-line trenches into so-called no-man's land, which was about a mile wide, and that both sides almost every night sent out scouting parties on raids. In one of these the Germans got so far behind the American lines that they were able to capture a provision wagon with its personnel, and took back a quarter of beef.

We drove out to Mandres, where we were stopped by a sentry who informed us that automobiles were allowed to go no farther. Arranging for the machine to meet us here at six o'clock the next morning, we walked out toward Beaumont, passing along the road by "Hell Fire Corner." Beaumont was about half a kilometer behind the lines, utterly in ruins and occupied by soldiers, who lived in underground cellars and dugouts. We called on the commanding officer, Colonel "Gatling Gun" Parker, and told him of our desire to visit outposts. He questioned the wisdom of the trip, because he would have one large scouting party out that evening, and the Germans surely would retaliate at least with a barrage. He finally agreed to send a runner with Lieutenant Boyd and me, and another with Comfort and Dickson, but required that we go to separate places.

We entered the communication trenches, and came out upon the road that led over the hill to Seicheprey, the scene of the first American engagement. The darkness was relieved from time to time by flashes of German guns and occasional replies from the Americans behind us.

We then went on toward one of the outposts. After going a short distance, out of the darkness came the call "Halt!" After the countersign had been given, we advanced to find a soldier in a small trench only a few feet deep. While gazing toward the German lines, suddenly we saw something moving on the left. The call "Halt!" came promptly. "Advance and give the countersign." The answer was correct, and three men, who had been sent over from another outpost, entered the trench. In this way these isolated outposts kept in touch.

I persuaded these men to take me to their outpost. There I found a lieutenant and a small squad holding a trench. The Americans behind and to the left were sending up star shells, and in the distance machine guns rang out, suggesting that some scouting party had been detected. A few minutes later the same thing happened on the German side, and I wondered whether the American party had been caught.

The lieutenant mentioned a listening-post out in front, and finally consented to let me go to it. Mounting the parapet, a corporal and I picked up a delicate wire, which led us across the marshy lowland; suddenly my guide clapped his gas mask softly three times, and a similar reply came back. One man occupied the listening-post, a small trench just deep enough to hide him lying down. You could hear conversation in German just ahead in their deep trench.

On our way back the Germans sent up several star shells; the guide fell flat on the ground, and so did I. It seemed interminably long before the glare went out.   We finally reached the trench, then crossed over to where I had left Lieutenant Boyd, and we went back through Seicheprey. Although dawn was beginning to break, we did not take the communication trench, but kept on the road. Suddenly we heard a shell coming, and dived into near-by shell holes just in time. The Germans had spotted our small party on the white road. Other shells followed in quick succession, and it seemed wise to dash for the communication trench a few yards away. The Germans sent over fifteen shells and then stopped. Wishing to see the extent of the damage, I crawled out on to the road; the shelling started up again, and in my haste to get back into the trench, I lost my glasses. Now content to finish the journey in the tiresome zigzag communication trench, we finally reached Beaumont, where we ate breakfast with some soldiers.

This night was considered a very quiet one, but the men I had seen in these advanced posts were under strain, and it was apparent that unless men were physically very fit, it would be unwise to place them in these posts.

A Visit to the Thirty-second Division in Alsace

In pursuance of my duty to send well-trained men to be division urologists, on one occasion I took Lieutenants Pius A. Rohrer and Alexander Reichelderfer through the rugged mountains and beautiful valleys of Alsace to the interesting old city of Belfort, with its mountainous rock upon which Bartholdi had sculptured the huge lion that gazed defiantly at Germany across the way. During the preceding four years the war had been very peaceful in Alsace. The French and the Germans had sat there looking at each other, and had long since ceased attempting any military action. They were almost comrades as they gazed at each other across no man's land. There was a mutual understanding not to molest or interfere with each other, and so free had they become that in the morning the officers would climb out of the trenches, stroll across the surface of the ground, take a bath in the creek, or attend to the requirements of nature in full view of their enemies.

The Thirty-second Division was brigaded with the French in this lower end of the lines where they butted into Switzerland. The American troops had arrived at night. The next morning they were shocked to see the hated Germans calmly walking through the woods and carrying out their matutinal toilets. The commander of this Yankee company immediately ordered the privates to shoot the "damn Germans." A French captain rushed up and told them not to fire. "These men are our friends. We have been living here now for four years; if you shoot, they will fire back at us and our peaceful lives here in Alsace will be ruined." The Americans stood it for awhile, but when a large German officer boldly walked out in front of the trenches and took his breeches down, it was more than the Americans could bear. One of the sharpshooters took a potshot at him, hit the exposed region, and created much consternation among the Germans.

We called on the division surgeon, but found him away from his headquarters. As we had several hours on our hands, one of the urologists said he would like to get an idea of things nearer the front. Down the road, which ran from Belfort to Altkirch, a little Alsatian village within the German lines, we started in my big Delaunay-Belleville, which weighed about three tons, easily carried nine passengers, and had around the roof a small balustrade, within which we had piled three large bedding rolls. The motorcar looked very much like an omnibus or a truck. We passed a sentry, who paid no attention to us. A little farther on we saw a well-camouflaged battery of seventy-fives that was occasionally firing, but no one interfered, so we went on, and soon came to trenches filled with troops. Our road paralleled these trenches along the crest of a wooded hill.

Suddenly the car stopped, and we saw barbed wire across the road. Sticking my head out of the window, I asked one of the men in the trenches, "Why is that wire across the road?" "Because, sir, this is the front line. How did you get here in that bus? You wouldn't have if it hadn't been a cloudy day. You better go quick, because yesterday we shot one of their officers who showed his insolence by squatting before us. The Germans then came across and captured four of our company. We are getting ready to pull off a raid of our own in retaliation." We needed no urging, and were soon off.

A Visit to the Eighty-second, Fifth, and Thirty-fifth Divisions

On July 12, accompanied by Captains Alexander Randall and Roy H. Cox and Lieutenant Royal G. Tharp, I went to Toul to visit the hospital for skin and venereal diseases of the Eighty-second Division, and showed the new urologists who were with me the problems presented there, the methods of handling them in a field hospital that was organized in one of the large French military barracks—*casernes*.

After lunch we hurried through Nancy, giving my fellow travelers a brief view of the beautiful royal buildings and the gardens around them. In the little village of Saint-Nicolas, about fifteen kilometers southeast of Nancy, we stopped to see the Gothic cathedral, whose towers, like Turkish minarets, can be seen for miles around. As we entered the cathedral a flood of music burst from a great organ, high up on the north wall. Randall immediately remarked, "By jove, that's an American song—'I Love Thee Truly, Truly Dear.' " An American soldier was perched on the organ bench forty feet above us. At his invitation we climbed the winding staircase built in the massive walls of the cathedral, and found a young private from an engineer company that was in training with the French.

We asked him how he came to be in the cathedral. "I was a Cornell student before I enlisted, and fond of the pipe organ. I spent my summers in the Estey factory with my pal, who is also an expert on pipe organs. When our company of engineers were sent here to train with the French, we found this magnificent old organ, which was built a hundred years ago and which is said to be one of the finest in France. But it had been so out of repair that it had not been played for fifteen years. Experts, sent here to restore it, said it was beyond repair. It seemed an awful crime for it to remain here idle in this wonderful church, so as my pal and I had nothing to do after five in the afternoon, we asked the old padre if he minded if we tried to see if we could get it going, but he refused. We continued to hang around and frequently importuned him, until he finally gave his consent, and we set to work on it. It soon became evident that to do any good we would have to remove and clean its thousand pipes. It took us six weeks to do it. As we had none of the ordinary trestles, windlasses, and so on, we had quite a sporty time pulling out pipes with a rope slung over the rafters, but we finally succeeded in getting them all out. In the course of the cleaning we removed fourteen barrels of dirt and bird's nests, collections of the preceding century. The reeds had to be cleaned with sulphuric acid, the bellows repaired with canvas. Now after six weeks we have the old thing going well. Last Sunday we played at services. The whole country is so excited over the restoration of their adored organ that the Arch-bishop visited us and arranged a triumphal mass, at which my pal and I gave them the best church music we could. It has been arranged to have a grand celebration on July 14." Randall and I took turns pumping for him while he played ragtime on the ancient masterpiece.

We arrived at Baccarat just in time to reach "Scratchville-by-the-sea" before dinner. This little tented hospital on the banks of the Meurthe put an end to the scratches of those of the Seventy-seventh Division with scabies.

I spent the night in billets and left early with the division urologist to visit the venereal-disease labor camp north of Merville. This camp was doing fine work, the patients being engaged in useful labor, building roads and working in various and sundry details. They were carried to work in trucks, doing their bit for their division while still under treatment. Their labor was conserved for the use of the A.E.F. at the front instead of being lost by their transfer to base hospitals far in the rear, as was the case with the French and the British. My plan was working well.

We also visited the divisional baths, not far distant. These were in full operation, with their twenty shower heads busy, and disinfesting clothes and blankets at the rate of eighty men an hour, about eight hundred a day passing through renovated and rejuvenated in spirit and health. The Germans had recently dropped a few shells in the lot around there, and yesterday the barber who had clipped off half the hair from his soldier client took refuge in a field and did not show up until the next day, while the victim went around half-shorn for twenty-four hours.

Passing through Saint-Dié, we took time to visit the old house where America got its name.   (The monks who ran a printing establishment there in the sixteenth century were publishing the geography of Amerigo Vespucci, and decided to call the unnamed continent America.)   We reached Gérardmer for lunch, and I introduced Cox to the division surgeon, started him off on his work as urologist to the Fifth Division, and arranged for him to have charge of the bathing and disinfesting of the troops as well. The division surgeon suggested that Randall and I should accompany him to the mountaintop of Tête-de-Vaux, four thousand feet high, over the summit of which ran the French and German lines, only a few yards apart. The munitions were carried up on the backs of donkeys, numbers of which we passed. In places we had to go very slowly in order that no dust would be raised by the limousine. The last mile was made on foot, through a wood in which the regimental kitchen was situated, surrounded by barbed wire. This seemed strange, but it was explained that a few weeks before a German scouting party had slipped through the French lines and captured the cooks and much provender. The precious cooks were now surrounded by many rows of barbed wire and prepared their feasts in safety. The last stretch or the journey was over precipitous paths on smooth rock from which fine views of the surrounding country, looking far into Germany and the Rhine Valley, could be had. Our French conductor urged that we hurry. We had hardly reached the trenches in the rocky mass at the top when a little spell of shelling ensued. At the summit a thick steel plate, with a two-inch opening for observation, had been let into two boulders. I asked the *poilu* sentinel why the hole was stopped with a rag, and he explained that it was because the Germans had a similar observation post just opposite with the same sort of a steel plate with a central hole, in which a rifle was aimed constantly upon this French hole, and that a short time ago when a French colonel had insisted on gazing too long through the aperture, a German opposite had shot him in the face. He was therefore willing to give me only a short look through when he removed the cloth stopper. It was easy to see the German steel plate only thirty yards away, but I could not make out the rifle in the fleeting glance I took. It seemed ridiculous that the two enemies should hold this peak, and when I teased our French officer about it, he said, "We thought so at first, but we have had several hundred men killed trying to run the Germans out." Over toward the northwest we saw a peaceful German farm with women calmly raking hay just behind the German lines. In the distance the cities of the Rhine could be seen. During our descent from the peak a stray shell fragment happened to strike my heavy boot. I picked it up and was amazed to find it very hot. It seemed evident that such a fragment could cause considerable tissue destruction from the heat alone.

On July 14, Randall and I proceeded over the mountain into the valleys of northern Alsace. At Wesserling in front of the Hôtel de Ville we came upon two hundred huskies. They were magnificent dogs, and the major in charge told us that he was an Alaskan trader. At the command of the French Government, he had collected these dogs and brought them from Alaska. At one time he had had six hundred, but many had died. They did wonderful work during the winters carrying food and ammunition up the precipitous slopes to the French trenches.

This being the Fourteenth of July, there were many French flags decorating the cottages along the road and the peasants were out in holiday attire in their native Alsatian costume, the women wearing large black ribbon bows on their hair. The Americans were in high favor, and many were out for a lark with their Alsatian girls. I reported to headquarters of the Thirty-fifth Division, and introduced Randall to the division surgeon, Colonel Turck.

The evacuation of the wounded from this front line was effected with great difficulty: litter carries down the mountain for half a kilometer, wheel stretchers for one kilometer, Ford ambulances for two kilometers, four-mule army ambulances down the winding road of the mountain to the base, five kilometers (automobiles were not used, as the brakes wore out too quickly), motor ambulances to the field hospital ten kilometers away, where wounds were redressed, then train to evacuation hospital through a mountain pass twenty kilometers back. Some were badly shocked by the long trip and frequent changes.

A Visit to a Negro Division

On July 15, 1918, I went to Bourbonne-les-Bains, where I found the headquarters of the Ninety-second Division (American Negroes). I discussed with Colonel Boyer the venereal problem. He was having considerable trouble with the Negro troops on account of the enthusiastic hospitality accorded them by French women. The lieutenants and captains were admitted to the very best French homes. A major of the medical corps told me that he had been much taken with a French girl until, one evening, the doorbell rang and the servant admitted a Negro lieutenant. Being a Southerner, the major risked court-martial by ordering the Negro out, and "then said good-by for good and all." Many of the Negro officers became engaged to French girls, whose parents could not understand why General Headquarters denied them the privilege of getting married. Protests were sent to Washington.

It seems to me that it was a mistake to allow a Negro to become an officer in the army. Experience has shown that the average Negro soldier does not respect a Negro officer. We were certain that this division would make a poor showing when it got to the front, and it did—it ran. It is said that a colonel from another division halted a Negro captain, and demanded the cause of this disgraceful retreat. The captain replied, "We lost our morale."

The division surgeon invited me to attend a weekly meeting of his medical officers from various regiments and to address them. To my surprise I found them all Negro doctors, lieutenants and captains. I talked very frankly about the unsurmountable barrier between the two races, the necessity of leaving white women alone, and their duty as officers to impress these facts upon their men. I heard afterwards that my remarks did little good and that most of these Negro doctors became engaged to French girls.

The Soissons Offensive

On July 18, at the headquarters of the medical consultants, we were thrilled by the report that Marshal Foch had hurled the First and Second American divisions and one Moroccan division at the base of the German salient west of Soissons, and that they had broken through and penetrated about four miles that day. The next afternoon, with my motorcar loaded with surgical teams and their bedding rolls, I started for the scene of battle.

At Artonges, headquarters of the Twenty-eighth Division, I met Captain Hibbs, the division urologist, at a field hospital. He had done fine work as a surgeon during the two days of terrific fighting. His division was brigaded with the French along a great bend of the Marne.

The Third American Division was to the left of the Twenty-eighth. A regiment of French infantry was interposed between the

Third Division and a regiment of the American Twenty-eighth Division. Hibbs told me that the Germans, using a smoke screen, had crossed the river at this point, that the French had recoiled, thus exposing the Americans on each side. They were therefore forced to retire for a short distance after considerable losses. West of the bend in the river, east of Château-Thierry, the Third Division had prevented the Germans from crossing the river. On the following morning, by a magnificent counterattack, the Third Division cleared the bend in front of them, forced the Germans back across the river, regaining the territory they had lost, exposed the Germans to the east to the danger of a flank attack, and prevented their further progress to the south.

At Vieille-Maison I met Captain McCague, urologist to the Third Division, who had been put in charge of all bathing and disinfestation of troops by order of the general commanding the division. I went with him to see the bathing arrangements, which were functioning even during battle. As it had been impossible for him to secure from the army apparatus for bathing, disinfesting, and laundering for his division, McCague got the Red Cross to rush equipment from Paris. I saw men who had driven the Germans back across the Marne arrive in motor trucks by the hundred, dirty and bedraggled. Stacking their guns and doffing their clothes, they were soon under hot showers, and a bedlam of yells and songs attested to the effects of such measures in restoring the spirit of fighting men.

At Third Division headquarters the chief of staff showed me a German artillery map on which, in great detail, was given the location of all our battalion and regimental aid stations, along with other important points that were laid down as military positions against which artillery fire was to be concentrated. Colonel Moore remarked that the location of the American positions was almost as accurate and perfect in detail as our own maps, another evidence of the marvelous efficiency of the German spy system and their intelligence corps. As a result of their accurate knowledge of our positions, the losses in our Medical Corps were heavy. It was remarkable that our troops had withstood such terrific artillery fire and had not wavered when the Germans attacked.

A trip to the front, along the river Marne, was proposed by McCague. We went on to Coubon, the regimental aid station. One of the battalion surgeons there was almost hysterical from what he had gone through. Proceeding farther, we reached the battalion aid station at Crézancy, not far from the Marne. It was located in an old stone house, and imbedded in the wall was a six-inch German shell that had failed to explode. It was here that Captain O. D. Daniels, regimental surgeon of the 30th Infantry, had discovered with his field glasses a group of American wounded in the hands of a few German soldiers who had been left to guard them in the bend of the river beyond the point recaptured by the Third Division. Calling for volunteers, he took with him a corporal and six men of the Medical Corps, stripped them of their Red Cross brassards, armed them with grenades and rifles, and started off. After a dash of over a kilometer he brought back forty wounded Americans. The next day the gallant Captain was killed by a sniper's bullet.

My next objective was to visit Captain Boyd, urologist to the Twenty-sixth Division, which held the lines north of the Marne. Starting early, I reached La Ferté-sous-Jouarre by 8 : 30 A.M. I found Boyd in the midst of an abdominal operation at the 103rd field hospital. He had to abandon his other duties and pitch in at this makeshift hospital, where a number of surgical teams were endeavoring to care for the nontransportable desperately wounded. These cases usually were taken to evacuation hospitals. Field hospitals are not equipped for such major surgery, but owing to the emergency and the absence of evacuation, the field hospitals did the best they could. These medical officers had worked five days almost continuously on the hundreds of wounded brought in. It was a hopeless and a demoralizing experience. The casualties of the Twenty-sixth Division, which held firm against violent attacks by many German divisions, were heavy.

In the afternoon I replaced Boyd at an operating-table. My first case was an abdominal one. The intestines had been cut across in eight places, and it was possible only to carry out hasty closures. The next was a kidney case.

Traveling by moonlight, without automobile lights, I reached Château-Thierry, which the Germans had left a few hours before. The American Third Division had just crossed the Marne on pontoon bridges. The Germans were evidently retreating rapidly, as only one shell arrived while I was there. On all sides was evidence of the haste with which the enemy had left. Clothing, loaves of bread, and other provender were scattered about the houses, which showed furniture smashed in wanton destruction. We were soon stopped by an immense shell hole into which an American truck had fallen.

Taking another road, we arrived at the top of a hill north of Château-Thierry, where we beheld a most enthralling picture. The horizon was aflame with burning villages and exploding German dumps. The sky was brilliant with rockets thrown up by the retreating Germans to light the way for their precipitate retreat. On this hill confusion was everywhere, with artillery and infantry converging from the south and west. In this struggling mass some doughboys were pushing a handcart in which peacefully lay a nanny goat. They explained that the goat was the pet of the company, and besides furnished a lot of fresh milk. They had a hard time to keep her from being stolen and therefore kept her in the cart. At this moment, out of the dark, an officer asked me a question. I was surprised to see Captain Bayne-Jones, now professor of bacteriology at Yale, but then a medical officer who had distinguished himself by his daring.

I found a bunk that had been left by a German officer. It was in the château of a wonderful stock farm. The beautiful rooms were in fearful disorder, with mutilation and vandalism everywhere. The German evidently was literary, as he had selected a number of lovely volumes from the library. One I noticed was the history of Château-Thierry, into which a saber had stabbed deeply. I have the volume at home. Our artillery stationed around the château kept up an incessant fire, and I was also kept awake by a lot of German fleas. The next morning I looked as if I had smallpox.

I turned north in search of the First and Second division urologists, passing through Vaux and Belleau Wood, where a month before the Germans had been stopped in their tracks by the Second Division. At this celebrated Bois de Marines, as it is known now, I saw by the roadside eighteen American soldiers whose bodies had just been brought in from the front.

At Villers-Cotterêts I found the headquarters of the Twentieth French Corps, Major General Berdoulat commanding. He was in the yellowish-green uniform of the Chasseurs d'Afrique. In his corps were two American divisions. He showed me the plan of battle that Marshal Foch had organized to break through the German salient west of Soissons. Three divisions formed the "spearhead" of this attack. In the center were the First Moroccans, and on either side the First and Second American divisions. Two other Moroccan divisions were also in the Twentieth Corps. They were to the right and left of the American divisions to prevent flank attacks by the Germans as the Americans advanced. General Berdoulat pointed out with pride that the men picked by Marshal Foch to make this great offensive were all in khaki—all from overseas, not a European among them.

I found the headquarters of the First Division in an old quarry cave that had been occupied by the Germans a few days before. The division surgeon told me that the First Division had suffered five thousand five hundred casualties in six days, and that they had been terribly hampered by a lack of transportation. This division had been thrown into the attack after only five days' rest. They had with them field hospitals and ambulances, but it had been impossible to organize transportation for the wounded to evacuation hospitals. The division surgeon had no idea where they were going or what they were going to do. He had hoped the French would take care of the transportation of their wounded to evacuation hospitals where they would get surgical attention, but he was sadly mistaken.

I next visited the most advanced field hospital, where *triage* (sorting) was done of the thousands of wounded, and then went back to the second field hospital, which was located in a small hotel at the base of the hill on which the great château of Pierrefonds stood. While looking for a place to locate a field hospital, the division surgeon saw this hotel, but was told he could not have it, because the French owners had locked it up. He broke open the door and during the night arranged operating-room, X-ray plant, wards, and when zero hour had come was ready to work with three teams made up from his own scanty divisional staff. One of these teams was headed by the division urologist, Captain Lehr.

At 4:30 A.M. the American barrage was put down. The doughboys attacked and went through the German lines with a rush, but with heavy casualties. By nine o'clock the wounded began to arrive. By noon the two hundred beds in the little hospital were filled. By four o'clock eight hundred wounded had arrived, filling the adjacent yard. As night came on other hundreds came and were placed on the flagstones of the adjacent square, with only their meager blankets and not a rubber sheet to cover them during the night, which was wet and cold. There was no transportation to take them farther back, the field ambulances being completely occupied in bringing the wounded from the battlefield. During the night and the next day the numbers increased steadily. The scene was indescribable. The three surgical teams struggled all night and the next day, picking from the hundreds of wounded cases those they might save, but able to attend only to a few. Many who might have been saved died from exposure and lack of attention. On Friday evening two teams of navy surgeons and nurses arrived, and on the next day three teams from the Maryland base hospital. In five days three thousand and five patients had come to this little field hospital of two hundred beds. One hundred and seventeen had died and one hundred and eighteen had been operated upon.

No blame can be attached to the Medical Corps of this division, which had been hurled forward with no chance to arrange for lines of evacuation or for hospitals in the rear. But the success of this offensive was due largely to its character of surprise, and the commanding general thought it necessary to withhold all information from the division surgeons and other important officers, regardless of the consequences to the wounded.

I found Captain Kraft, urologist to the Second Division, near Crépy, several miles back. He had been with me in my early work with the civil population. To him the division surgeon had entrusted the evacuation of the wounded. Here, again, practically no facilities for transportation to the rear and no hospitals had been provided. A few trucks and automobiles were available, but hundreds of wounded had to walk. With the division ambulances, Kraft had got five hundred wounded back to the railhead and spread them out on the grass, where they waited four hours in the rain before the hospital train arrived from Paris. In the meantime Kraft and other division surgeons hastily improvised operating teams and did their best for cases urgently needing attention. An American mobile hospital arrived and was set up on the fourth day. *"C'est la guerre,"* said Kraft. Perhaps it was for the best, because the surprise attack saved thousands of lives.

After spending another night at Pierrefonds I hurried south. I found the headquarters of the Fourth Division at Bonneville. This division had been brigaded with the French and lost only twelve hundred men. Their wounded had been well taken care of in the French hospitals. I discussed with the division surgeon the importance of beginning at once bathing and disinfesting. His troops were then coming back from the line, and the urologist was set to work on these problems of hygiene.

Going back to La Ferté, I went to the field hospital of the Twenty-sixth Division to see Boyd, and took him forward to consult with the division surgeon on bathing and disinfesting his troops.

The headquarters of the Twenty-sixth Division were in the buildings of a model pig farm—large barns with immaculate tiled stalls for the porcine occupants. These were as elegant as the compartments of an American bank. The division surgeon and other officers were rushing to prepare orders for a great attack to be started that night (July 24). The orders issued at 10:30 P.M. stated that "the 26th Division should push on without cessation during the night in a supreme effort, with the 42nd Division, to break through the German lines and permit a brigade of French cavalry to pass through and break up a retreating and hard-pressed enemy. A complete victory is at hand."

I was greatly excited over these orders, and asked to go forward with the ambulances to study their operation during active combat. The colonel gave his consent, but asked that I first go back with orders to hurry forward the four field hospitals located on hills overlooking the Marne. About eleven o'clock I started back along the great highway leading toward La Ferté. I passed squadron after squadron of French cavalry, each man with his spear resting upright on a stirrup and a small pennon fluttering from its staff. These were the troops which were expected to break through and harass the disorganized Germans.

After delivering the orders I turned again to the east and passing again through Château-Thierry, at two o'clock in the morning arrived at Farsoy Ferme, headquarters of the field ambulances which, an hour later, started northward on the road to the advancing troops. After being held up for a time by shellfire, we reached another farm—Trugny—near Epieds, at five o'clock in the morning. On the way we passed broken-down ambulances and gun carriages. German machine guns were still standing on their tripods in the wheat fields, which formed excellent cover, with a string of American dead before them and occasionally a dead German at his gun, one of whom had in his hand a child's shoe. In the basement of the farmhouse we found many German dead. Our ambulance men cleared away the bodies to make room for an "ambulance dressing station" for our wounded.

A small Ford ambulance filled with wounded arrived from the front line. It was driven by an American college boy still in French uniform—one of those young men who drove the hundreds of Fords sent over by Americans. Mrs. Young had her name attached to one of them. The ambulance-driver started back, and as I was eager to see the work of the stretcher-bearers at the very front, I went with him. After crossing a field pockmarked with shell holes—some had just been made by bombs from a plane that passed over us—we came to a wood in which American machine-gun units were to be seen. We began to pick up some of their wounded. While this was going on, I tried to get a more intimate idea of what was happening, but although this company was closely following the Germans, there was little to be seen or heard except the occasional fire of machine guns and rare replies from the enemy artillery. Instead of the solid phalanxes in gorgeous uniforms and great shakos, as of old, the soldiers of the attack consisted of scattered groups who dashed from one bit of cover to another, attacking machine-gun nests. They had none of the great panoply of war, but were just as intrepid as their forerunners in battle. A French officer said that the Americans attacked like lions but were *"très imprudents."*

The little ambulance, with four lying wounded and one on the seat beside me, returned to the farmhouse. Here first-aid dressings were done, and after the bleeding was stopped the wounded were placed in larger ambulances. I climbed in with them as they started on the road to the rear, wondering what would happen to the men I left. A few hours later they were shelled and several were killed.

I next went to see the work of one of our urological-surgical teams. Passing over a pontoon bridge across the Marne at Château-Thierry, I went on to find Captain Henry L. Sanford, urologist to the celebrated Rainbow (Forty-second) Division, which had gallantly repulsed German attacks east of Reims in their supreme effort to encircle and capture that historic city.

I spent the night at Châlons. German airplanes were flying over the city, but I was so tired that I slept through their bombing, which destroyed many houses and killed quite a few—so I was told.

The following day I reached our headquarters at Neufchâteau. I set to work on recommendations to the Chief Surgeon concerning the varied duties of the division urologists during periods of activity at the front.

The Reduction of the Saint-Mihiel Salient

With the formation of the American army for the reduction of the Saint-Mihiel salient, it was incumbent upon me to visit the urologists whom we had assigned to army and corps positions. The attack had started that morning (September 12) and the urologists of the Twenty-sixth, First, Forty-second, Forty-ninth, Fifth, Ninetieth, and Eighty-second divisions, all of which had gone forward in the attack, were mostly assigned to field hospitals. In order to observe the work, I took the main road north of Flirey and had soon passed through the front lines, from which the divisions had jumped off at daybreak. Before long our car was stuck in the mud. Some American soldiers came along bringing strings of German prisoners to the rear. They soon pulled us out of the bog.

Passing through Essey, I reached Pannes. The advance of the Forty-second division had been so rapid that they were there before the German regimental command could escape, and had captured along with several officers four Frenchwomen, who demanded that these German officers be killed, because for one year they had taken these women with them back and forth along the front. The women had been taken prisoners at their homes near Lille and had been unable to get away from their captors, who used them not only as servants but for their gratification. I have never seen such viragos. They couldn't understand why we would not immediately put an end to the German officers. The Germans were greatly relieved when we sent them off under guard and restrained the women, who were so enraged that they would have killed their captors.

On the way back the road was blocked for a long time by the supply train and ambulances coming north and ambulances filled with wounded. As the jam seemed inextricable, I got out in the mud and, taking command, had some German prisoners carry our wounded across the quagmire to ambulances on the other side.

After the Saint-Mihiel salient had been nipped off, the American divisions continued their rapid advance, and Thiaucourt was captured by the Second Division. On the third day the Germans counterattacked and Thiaucourt was occupied alternately by the Germans and the Americans, who had come to grips in hand-to-hand fighting. The Germans had built sixty feet underground a hospital that had been occupied by them for three years. When captured by the Americans, it was in excellent condition; several surgical teams were immediately placed in it, and began at once to operate on the wounded. Captain Kraft, urologist to the Second Division, removed a spleen to control hemorrhage while overhead the Germans actually occupied the ground for a short time. After that the Germans were pushed back and the American surgical teams were again in the lines of their own army.

That afternoon I entered the tip of the salient in which fourteen thousand Germans had been captured, and took the road leading to the little village of Saint-Mihiel, which had been in the hands of the Germans for over three years. It had not been injured in the attacks of the Americans against the base of the salient on each side. Before the war Saint-Mihiel was a lovely little town of about a thousand, only six hundred of whom remained, and most of these were women. General Pershing and Secretary of War Newton Baker had visited the town only a few hours before. The inhabitants were ecstatic over their deliverance.

One of the old women began to inveigh against some younger women near by. Through her rapid-fire patois I discovered that she was telling me that two hundred of the younger women of the city had traitorously gone over and lived with German officers. As the war went on from year to year and the scarcity of food, clothing, and firewood grew, the younger women had been seduced by the promise of all the good things of life. I was told that two hundred babies had been born to these women, most of whom had been put to death, usually being thrown into wells. A little farther up the road I came to a company of French soldiers who were rounding up these women who had lived with the Germans. As I departed I passed several large trucks filled with these French girls, tightly packed in a standing position in the big camions and looking the picture of desperation. Subsequently they were interned behind barbed-wire fences and treated as traitors and spies.

The Meuse-Argonne Offensive

Immediately after the Saint-Mihiel offensive, General Pershing prepared the First American Army to begin another great offensive —the Meuse-Argonne, which began on September 26. Major Louis C. Lehr became army urologist; Major Sanford was promoted to the First Corps; Captain Boyd, Second Corps; Captain Kraft, Fourth Corps; Captain Randall, Sixth Corps.

At Souilly I found Lehr at Evacuation Hospital No. 6 inspecting the urologically wounded that were coming through this hospital center of seven thousand beds. During four weeks fifty thousand wounded had been brought in by ambulances from the front. There were thirty-seven surgical teams at work, each team consisting of a surgeon, an assistant, an anesthetist, a nurse, and an orderly. Each of these teams was working on eight-hour shifts, so that there were about one hundred and eleven surgical teams at this evacuation hospital. In addition, there were many shock teams engaged in administering stimulants, infusions, and transfusions of blood to men who were gravely shocked, in the hope that they might be sufficiently resuscitated to stand operation. Patients were arriving in such numbers that it was impossible to keep them more than two or three days, when they were placed on trains that rolled up to the hospital doors and carried them back to base hospitals anywhere from thirty to one hundred and fifty miles away.

Lehr had been able to assemble some excellent bathing and delousing centers for the men brought back after a tour at the front and in great need of sanitation. He had displayed such energy and effectiveness in handling these important hygienic measures of the army that he was requested by the Chief Surgeon to take over the duties of sanitary inspector for the army. This would have brought many problems of sanitation not associated with our work, and at my request he politely declined. Consultations over wounds of the genitourinary tract, treatment of venereal cases with their organization, bathing and disinfesting the troops, and issuing clean underclothing made a big enough job.

Going on, I passed Hill No. 304, celebrated in the offensives against Verdun. Malancourt, formerly a large town, was reduced to a mass of dirt. Had there not been a sign to the effect that here was a town, I never would have recognized it as such. At Montfaucon, which had been captured by a Baltimore regiment of the Seventy-ninth Division, I saw the house on the hill, filled with concrete, in the cellar of which the German Crown Prince had lived, with his thirty-foot telescope projecting from the roof through which he watched the fight—brave man!

The road often was blocked by artillery trucks and tanks out of commission. The border of the narrow paved road was a quagmire in which our transports often overturned. The traffic was so heavy that thousands of engineer troops had been put there to widen the roads, and into the trenches that they dug on each side they threw large stone blocks from the ruined houses of adjacent villages. I heard a sergeant of engineers upbraid a corporal for not making the road wider, and not putting in more stones, to which the corporal replied, "I've put a whole God-damn church in there."

At Buzancy I met the surgeon of the Forty-second Division, Colonel Fairchild, who was greatly excited because he had had to evacuate two wounded members of General MacArthur's staff who had been fired upon by a detachment of our own troops of the First Division. One of the most remarkable mix-ups in any war had occurred. As the American armies rushed northward after the rapidly retreating Germans, Sedan was just in front of the Forty-second Division. To their left was the French Fourth Army. Owing to the historic significance of Sedan to every Frenchman, Marshal Foch had issued an order placing Sedan in the battle lines of the

French and turning the American attack well to the right, so that Sedan would not fall to our troops. But the French, who at this stage of the war were always far behind adjacent American divisions, were many miles back when the Forty-second Division had Sedan right in front of it. General Pershing thought he had persuaded General Maistre, Fourth French Army, to offer no objection to American divisions' taking Sedan if the French were not there to do it. General Pershing then let it be known by an order of General Liggett that he was anxious for American troops to capture Sedan, and that all divisional lines could be disregarded.

The First Division was several miles to the right, but liberty to enter the race for the great prize—Sedan—was too much to be resisted. They turned and dashed across through the lines of the Seventy-seventh Division into the lines of the Forty-second, which had been stopped by Marshal Foch just before they entered Sedan. No restraining orders had been issued to the First Division, and on they rushed in the black of the night into the Forty-second. Encountering a group of men whom they supposed to be Germans, the men of the First fired upon this group, captured them, and took them back. These men protested that they were American officers, but as they wore no insignia during battle, and General MacArthur had a peculiar uniform and cap unlike any other American, the soldiers of the First Division laughed at him when he claimed to be the commander of the 84th Brigade. As none of the lieutenants or captains of the front line of the First Division recognized him, it was not until General MacArthur was taken well back that he came across an officer who knew him.

The regulars were said to hate the National Guard more than they did the Germans. There always had been great rivalry between the First Division regulars of the United States Army and the celebrated Forty-second Division of the National Guard, but the capture of the favorite brigade commander of the Forty-second by the hated regulars and the wounding of two of his staff was the last straw.

General Pershing refers briefly to the unfortunate flank attack of the First Division, and intimates that court-martial would have resulted had the war not ended immediately. General Harbord condemns much more strongly this effort of the First Division to "steal a march" on the Forty-second, in whose sector it was a "trespasser"; it even had to be fed by the Forty-second, as it got completely away from its supply trains. But, strange to say, neither General Pershing nor General Harbord mentions the amazing incident of General MacArthur and his staff being fired upon, wounded, and captured by men of the First Division. Some years after the war General MacArthur came to Baltimore to command the Third Corps. He frankly told me that he was still peeved over the wanton behavior of the troops of the First Division.

I found Captain Hissem, urologist of the Eighty-ninth Division, at work in a field hospital in a small town about four kilometers from Stenay on the river Meuse, across which the Germans had retreated. Here I heard that troops of the Eighty-ninth were scheduled to cross the Meuse on pontoons during the night, and as I had long envied the officers with combat troops, I could not resist the temptation to be with the battalion when it crossed the Meuse. I persuaded an ambulance-driver to take me up to the battalion dressing-station. The road to the section of the front that they evacuated had become impassable and it was necessary to take the southerly road to Laneuville, at which point the ambulance passed through the American front line. As we turned north along the river I found to my astonishment that the ambulance was between the American line and the German line, which occupied the opposite high river-bank. The driver explained that it was dark and we probably would not be noticed. We hadn't gone far before an American battery opened up behind us and scared me almost to death. Fortunately, the Germans did not reply. No-man's land at this point was a marsh about half a mile wide, and our road ran on an embankment.

Farther north the river made a big bend, and there the American line crossed our road. Near by were many pontoons lined up in preparation for crossing the river that night. At the battalion dressing-station I could get no information as to the proposed troop movement and went up to the post of command of the battalion with a corporal. When I arrived at this point, which occupied a dugout near the riverbank, I encountered a raiding party coming in with four Germans, who were greatly frightened. As the captain in command spoke no German, I acted as interpreter, and found that they had been told that the Americans invariably killed their prisoners. When I assured them they would receive kind treatment, their relief was great. One wore a beautifully camouflaged helmet, which he gave me, saying he was glad he would have no more use for it. The captain gave me one of the propaganda leaflets that a German airplane had dropped on our lines that afternoon. It will be remembered that President Wilson had sent his famous Fourteen Points to Germany, the Kaiser had abdicated, and this leaflet shows that the popular government that had been formed proposed peace.

I had hoped to see the crossing of the Meuse on pontoons, but as this was deferred, I rejoined my ambulance, which had been filled with wounded, and started back along the road down the marsh between the two lines. The inky darkness protected us. Only an occasional shell fell into Laneuville ahead of us. About this time engine trouble developed, and when we turned west along the pike to the rear, one cylinder after another quit and the muffler fell off. As we went slowly up the long hill the noise of our motor was terrific, and the Germans began to shell in our direction. I was grateful for the huge German helmet, which came down almost to my shoulders. My own tin hat I hugged to my chest. After what seemed an interminable period, the shelling stopped, and we went on to the ambulance dressing-station, where I spent a good night on the floor wrapped up in my blanket.

I then returned to Romagne-sous-Montfaucon—now the site of the great American cemetery—where I had left Captains J. A. C. Colston and Fred C. Colston, operations officers of the 155th Artillery Brigade, both brothers of Mrs. Young. Fred had been through many weeks of nerve-racking work. Upon him and a young French officer had devolved the duty of making the plans for the successive (creeping) barrages that were put down to prepare for the American advance. One day it suddenly occurred to Fred that he had made a mistake in his calculations, that he had not planned to lift the barrage fast enough; he pictured thousands of infantry who would be caught in their own artillery fire. During the fifteen minutes it took to check the figures, he said he lived a century. Fortunately no mistake had been made, and the co-ordination of barrage and infantry attack went along like clockwork. As we left him to return to our headquarters he looked very thin and frail. Returning along the Meuse River through Verdun and Commercy, where we slept on a table in the office of the Military Police, we arrived at Neufchâteau only a few hours before the blast of sirens and the pealing of bells announced that Marshal Foch had granted the armistice which ended the war.

Three days later word reached me that Fred Colston was ill. We found him down with influenza in a château that had been taken over by the artillery command in the little city of Mouzay. He looked emaciated and weak, but his temperature had not been high, and when I returned to headquarters there was every prospect that he would pull through. Two days later I was horrified to receive a telegram saying that he had died at one of our evacuation hospitals. His brother and I reached there just as the army chaplain was holding the funeral.

Influenza had reached our army about the end of the war. As the epidemic was very virulent and it was found dangerous to move men with the disease, a general order had been issued that patients with influenza be allowed to remain wherever they were and not be transported to hospitals. One of the medical officers of the Fifth Division had found Fred in his snug bed in a château, and immediately ordered him to the field hospital in tents along the Meuse River. There he remained on a cold army cot in an unheated space for a few hours, and then was placed in the front seat of an ambulance with little or no covering, and forced to take a six-hour trip over rough roads before he arrived at the little hospital at Fromère-ville. Four lying wounded were taken out of the ambulance and placed in this hospital. Fred remained on the seat with the driver, as he was to go some five miles farther. The receiving officer, seeing that Fred's teeth were chattering and his lips were blue, invited him in to sit by the stove. Taking his temperature, and finding it 104°, he put him to bed. Within twelve hours Fred was dead.

It was so apparent that his death was due absolutely to the outrageous treatment he had received that I investigated and found that he had been moved as a result of orders given by a corps surgeon. I went to see the surgeon of the First Army, Colonel Stark, and preferred charges. Stark admitted that there had been gross disregard of orders, but told me that the officer had been transferred from the First to the Third Army, which was being formed to go into Germany, and that he, Stark, had no jurisdiction.

The course of events in the immediate future prevented my pursuing the matter further, but I have always felt the most intense hatred for this man, who had come into the army as a Philippine contract surgeon and did not treat the army consultants with the courtesy most regulars showed. He was, I felt, directly responsible for my dear brother-in-law's death.

After the Armistice—Accompanying the Third Army: The French Take Over Metz

On November 17, 1918, the Third American Army began its march into Germany to enforce the provisions of the Armistice. In order to discuss problems concerning the Division of Urology, I went along with Captains Bertner and Valentine. We found Major Sanford, urologist to the Second Army, at Toul. He had the problem of bathing and disinfesting not only our own troops, but also a motley crowd of French, Italian, Russian, and American prisoners who had walked many miles from behind the German lines back into France. They were in all sorts of makeshift uniforms and clothing, a tired, pale, footsore lot, but happy to be free. Several thousands of them were temporarily detained in a barbed-wire enclosure that had been built for German prisoners taken in the Saint-Mihiel offensive. With much difficulty Sanford succeeded in providing baths, disinfestation, and clean clothes.   I then went in search of the urologist to the Fourth Corps, Captain Kraft, but found he had moved forward.

We passed through Vigneulles, historic as the town where two American divisions—the Twenty-sixth coming from the west and the First from the east—met on the night of the first day of the offensive and pinched off the Saint-Mihiel salient, capturing some fourteen thousand Germans. It had taken only twenty-seven hours to accomplish this wonderful feat, during which each advanced about twelve miles across formidable fortifications, marshes and hills with every conceivable form of defense.

At Chambley we came across two German "elephant" guns, about seven feet long, and which, operating on a swivel, were able to penetrate our tanks. We next came to Conflans, an important railroad junction for the German army east of Verdun. The French inhabitants were wild with joy and welcomed our troops with boundless enthusiasm. They had improvised flags for all the Allied nations to decorate their homes and streets. Never having seen the American flag, their reproductions of Old Glory were very amusing: stripes running the wrong way, stars with only four points and few in number, and the colors all wrong. We were billeted with a French family—father, mother, and daughter, whose husband had left to fight in the French Army. At her side was a flaxen-haired child of twelve months by a German father who had forced her to submit to him.

The inhabitants reported that on September 13, when, with the rapid advance of the Americans, shells began to approach the city, the Germans had begun to destroy their stores in preparation of flight, but when the Americans had been stopped by the limitation of objective that Marshal Foch had set, the Germans returned and threw up heavy fortifications. Had the American divisions been allowed to pursue their fleeing enemies, they would surely have captured this great railroad center and probably advanced farther, thereby cutting one of the important railroads supplying the German Army, and greatly shortening the war. The inhabitants said that had it not been for the gifts of sugar, flour, cornmeal, and even coffee from Hoover's American Committee, they would have starved. The Germans stole all their farm products and allowed them only a little parched wheat from which to make soup and coffee, and a few potatoes from their own gardens.

My companions begged me, before returning to headquarters, to take a side trip over to Metz. Passing through Gravelotte with its tall shaft surmounted by a French soldier with a bayonet pointing defiantly towards Metz, a reminder of the War of 1870, we entered the city by a road from the northwest, and expected to find Allied troops, but none were to be seen. The French had stationed sentries around the city to prevent any troops from entering, so that General Pétain could come in with a victorious army to take the city. Our machine was immediately surrounded by cheering inhabitants. Small boys scrambled over our fenders and top and remained there as we moved along. I counted nineteen. Among these were two handsome youngsters who seemed very intelligent, so we pulled them into the machine and went, under the direction of our young guides, to visit the cathedral and other points of interest.

Huge statues, generally equestrian and mounted on great pedestals, of Kaiser Wilhelm der Grosse, Kaiser Wilhelm der Zweite, Prince Bismarck, and other German heroes filled the squares and parks. The Germans had just left the day before and the hotel was empty. Near by was a supply depot filled with bayonets, pistols, swords, spiked helmets, and other helmets surmounted by great spread eagles. These last, the inhabitants told us, had been brought there to be used when the Germans triumphantly marched into Paris. We filled the back of our machine with many trophies. The next day we took another tour around the city. During the night the inhabitants, by means of ropes, had pulled the massive equestrian statues off their pedestals and broken them with axes. Kaiser Wilhelm's face, upturned in the mud, had been subjected to every form of degradation. Bismarck and the others had fared no better.

By this time French troops, the elite of the armies, covered with medals and fourragères (decorations of braided cord), had arrived with their bands and artillery. Overhead squadrons of airplanes flew so low that one caught on a telegraph wire and fell into the square, killing several people. General Pétain came last on a fine charger, looking every inch a soldier. General Mangin, who had commanded the army in which the First and Second Divisions A.E.F. had made the great attack against Soissons on July 18, had been thrown from his horse and badly injured. Pétain dismounted, shook hands with the officers of Metz, and then went to the Hôtel de Ville, where formal exercises were held. My friend Prince d'Hénin, a colonel on his staff, greeted me cordially.

Before leaving Metz we visited the hospital, in which the Germans had left behind a good many of their wounded. There were quite a few Americans, who seemed to have been very skillfully treated. We then left the city with our machine filled with souvenirs and hurried back to Neufchâteau.

German Atrocities in Belgium

On November 25 I went with Captain McCague, urologist to the Army of Occupation, through Stenay and Montmédy to Virton in Belgium. We secured an excellent billet at the home of Dr. Antoine Fostie, the most prominent physician in that part of the country, and a member of the Belgian Senate at the outbreak of the war. The doctor spoke quietly, without rancor, and his words carried the conviction of sincerity and truth. I enjoyed talking to him and his family very much, and made notes on the conversation.

According to Dr. Fostie, the Germans regularly took about half the farm products produced in Belgium, principally potatoes, wheat, and tobacco. The milk had to be sent to a central creamery that was run under the direction of the Germans, and the inhabitants were allowed to buy butter and cheese in small quantities. They were taxed on every imaginable occasion. If a light was seen burning through the window at night, the Military Police exacted 20 francs. If anyone was heard to say anything sympathetic with the Allies, large fines were inflicted. Some were sent off to prisons in Germany, and others were shot.

The American Committee furnished the inhabitants with food every week, principally lard, flour, cerealine (crushed corn), sugar, beans, and peas. Coffee was made from malt roasted in their kitchens. Real coffee cost 45 francs a pound. Had it not been for the food given by Hoover's Committee, the people undoubtedly would have starved. The Germans frequently stole quantities of foodstuffs that were sent for distribution to the people by the American Committee. Recently eleven thousand pounds of lard had arrived. Of this, they stole nine thousand pounds at the railroad station before it reached the local committee for distribution. Dr. Fostie thought it probable that some of these stolen goods were sold to profiteers and smugglers from Luxembourg and Germany.

When the Germans came through in their great advance in 1914, they acted like wild animals. The people were rounded up and terrified, the houses ransacked, and wines and liquors stolen from their cellars. Great numbers of soldiers got drunk, particularly those who followed behind the army, and they carried out every conceivable form of barbarism and bestiality. In many places women suffered terribly at their hands, particularly *religieuses* (nuns and lay sisters), whose institutions were broken into, the inmates being raped and then sent away in large numbers to do the bidding of officers and men in the army. The wife of a prominent citizen was shot because she refused their bestial demands. The French were treated worse than the Belgians, were accused of all sorts of unfriendly acts, and often were summarily tried. Almost always the

Germans asserted that they were *franc-tireurs* (snipers) who had fired upon their troops, but Dr. Fostie, and many others with whom I talked, said that this was pure invention.

At Latom, three kilometers from Virton, Dr. Fostie said there were two hundred and ninety-four people living in the town. After a battle near there, the German general ordered all the male citizens to go to the field of battle to bury the German dead. Seventy-six men, including the priest, obeyed this order. After finishing the burial they were lined up, their eyes were bound, and they were killed with machine guns. Only three men, who had not obeyed the order, remained alive in this village. This story seemed incredible, but the distinguished Belgian physician stoutly asserted that it was true.

In Ethe, five kilometers from Virton, two hundred and eighty of the one thousand two hundred and twenty-five of the people were killed for absolutely no reason, but with the usual excuse that some had fired on their troops. Among those taken out to be killed was M. Beaulard, the mayor of Ethe. When he heard the command— Ready, aim, fire!—he fell just before the triggers were pulled, and when the soldiers came along, striking the fallen Belgians with the butts of their rifles, he feigned death, and escaped in the night to his home.

At Gommery, Etalle, and Tantigny, great numbers of citizens were shot, and many of these villages were burned. At Rosignal, a town of nine hundred and fifty-four people, one hundred and thirty were shot, including one woman of excellent position, mother of four children, who had refused to give into their desires. At Tamines one Sunday morning the people were at mass; the Germans ranged troops and machine guns around the church, and when the people came out, slaughtered them, men, women, children, and priest.

The town of Virton escaped with only four people being killed, due to the fact that a large hill overhangs the town, and on it had been placed a large number of French batteries, which forced the Germans to go around the place rather than through it. The Germans frankly admitted that they wanted to inspire terror in the Belgians and the French. No Belgians had been shot since 1914, but on December 4, 1916, every man in Virton and the villages around between the ages of seventeen and forty-five was required to present himself at the gymmasium. It was a sad picture as they passed by in hundreds with little packs on their backs to the "slave market" from which thousands were sent into commercial slavery in Germany. None of the women were sent out permanently, but for three months girls of the town were forced to go into the forest and gather buds from the trees, from which a so-called tobacco was made. Dr. Fostie's daughter barely escaped this inquisition. The Doctor had to draw up papers asserting that she had Bright's disease, and thus got her off.

After the horrors of the first advance, the women were not mal-treated, but they suffered so greatly from hunger and poverty that many accepted the inducements offered by their German tyrants, and a number of children with German fathers were born.

Throughout the war the Germans pillaged and stole right and left. The Crown Prince was in command in this region, and apparently knew of the thievery, as the wagons taking the goods back into Germany were seen in the streets. The Germans forced the people to billet their officers and men in their homes. Dr. Fostie had three officers in his home; his three daughters were required to live in one room. The family always retired early to avoid encountering the Germans.

I have given in detail Dr. Fostie's statement because I think it shows that what the Germans have recently done is only a repetition of what they did in Belgium in 1914. The leopard has not changed his spots!

A Visit to Luxembourg

The next morning I hurried on through Belgium into Luxembourg. On the road we passed American divisions on their way to the Rhine. I saw Captain David M. Davis, who was with the Third

Division. He told a pitiful story of how the men had suffered with their feet on this long march. Their shoes had never been good, and most of the soles had worn out, so that the men were practically barefooted. The temperature was only a few degrees above zero, and the ground was frozen. The Third Division had got completely out of touch with their supply train, and the men were living largely on hardtack. There were a great many cases of pneumonia among the soldiers in our divisions on this fearful march to the Rhine. We eventually lost as many men as we would have lost in a battle to put an end to the war, which was contemplated by General Pershing and would undoubtedly have succeeded quickly, because the Germans were thoroughly disorganized, and ready to quit.

At the hotel in Luxembourg where I put up for the night, I met a number of French officers, and was invited to attend a secret meeting of revolutionaries who were expecting to take over the Government, imprison the Grand Duchess, and make Luxembourg a part of France. They were experiencing opposition among fellow revolutionaries who insisted that it would be better for Luxembourg to be made a part of Belgium. Had it not been for this hitch, the pro-French party probably would have won, so I was told.

The next day General Pershing arrived, and the Grand Duchess invited him to review her army and the First American Division from the balcony of her palace. The General, ever glad to accommodate a charming lady, accepted with alacrity, 'tis said. First came the American division, some twenty-five thousand strong, and then the Luxembourg army of one hundred and ninety-six men, including several generals and colonels. These were followed by civic bodies, many of which contained so many revolutionaries that they refused to pass before the Grand Duchess, took a side street before they reached the palace, went around the block, and joined the procession on the other side.

After conferring with division surgeons and urologists on bathing, disinfesting, and supply of underclothes for our troops, I hurried back to our headquarters at Neufchâteau.

A Trip to the Army of Occupation and Back to Neufchâteau

It was now about three weeks after the Armistice, and troops were being returned to the United States as rapidly as possible, but the Medical Corps still had much to do because the hospitals were filled with sick and wounded. Starting on a tour of inspection, I passed through the great hospital center at Bazoilles where Major J. A. C. Colston was consultant urologist. There were about twenty thousand beds in this hospital center, with the Johns Hopkins Base Hospital as its nucleus. Being fairly close to the front, and receiving wounded from both the Saint-Mihiel and the Meuse-Argonne offensives, the wards had been so crowded that patients had to be rushed to other hospitals in the rear and the staff had been fearfully overworked. Colston had done valiant service with the urological cases, upon many of which he had operated.

At Vittel and Contrexeville was another great group of A.E.F. hospitals in the large hotels of these noted watering-places. In my previous visit after the Germans had swept over the Chemin-des-Dames I had found the hospital filled with wounded British. Their uniforms were tied up in separate bundles, labeled, and placed in the great solarium. Looking at these olive-drab bundles, I was struck with the fact that they had turned gray on top. Thinking it very strange that they had faded so quickly, I walked over with the commanding officer and was shocked to find that the grayness was due to a great mass of "cooties," which had climbed out to the top and were luxuriating in the sunshine.

Passing through Dijon, I soon reached Beaune, near which we had built a great hospital center of twenty-five thousand beds on the plain. Here I made an inspection with Captain Edwin Davis, urologist to the center, and also Captain Gilbert J. Thomas, both of whom had done splendid work there. Near by was the many-century-old hospital of Beaune, celebrated because of its great stone building with high curved ceiling beautifully decorated with murals, and long rows of four-poster oaken beds for the patients, each bed with silken curtains. The Sister Superior informed me that even during the war their celebrated vineyards brought in about $80,000 a year. Hospice de Beaune has always been one of the most celebrated Burgundies.

Taking Davis with me, I hurried on to Lyon to investigate several French hospitals that specialized on wounds of the genitourinary tract. I had with me an artist, a photographer, and a secretary, and with Dr. Davis was engaged in a systematic study of their records and the patients still in the hospital when I received a telegram ordering me to return to headquarters, where I arrived on December 13. I was called on the phone by Colonel Wadhams, G.H.Q., who informed me that I had been ordered by General Pershing to London to attend Ambassador David M. Francis, recently returned from Russia. I spent the day closing up my affairs and initiating Lieutenant Colonel George Walker, who was to follow me as Senior Consultant in Urology A.E.F.

As I had not yet made an inspection trip to the Army of Occupation, I requested Colonel Wadhams to wire London that I would be able to leave in a week. On the following day, as no reply had been received, Colonel Wadhams permitted me to leave for a quick trip to the Rhine. Reaching Luxembourg in the evening, I dined with friends and met a French officer who was one of the conspirators plotting a revolution in Luxembourg.

Leaving early, I followed the banks of the Moselle through the old Roman city of Trèves (Trier) with its ancient Roman colosseum. The precipitous hills on the northern slopes of the river contained wonderfully terraced vineyards, up to which the peasants were laboriously carrying great baskets of manure on their backs. The towns were flattened against these hills, the streets narrow, and the houses tall and slim. On the mountaintops were feudal castles. One could picture the romantic lives of the barons who had lived in those mountain fastnesses, descending suddenly on raids against the people of neighboring feudal chieftans, despoiling them of their property, and carrying off their young women.

Arriving at Coblenz, I reported to headquarters and conferred with Colonel Grissinger, chief surgeon of the Third Army, and Major McCague, urologist. Elsewhere I have described our studies of the venereal situation, our inspection of cafés and of segregated districts occupied by houses of prostitution.

On the following morning an officer from headquarters notified me to go immediately to the office of the chief surgeon. I found Colonel Grissinger greatly perturbed by a message he had received from General Pershing, who demanded to know why I had not stopped at his headquarters at Trèves. "Didn't you know," said Colonel Grissinger, "that everybody is required to stop there before going to the Army of Occupation?" I admitted that I had heard something to that effect, but nothing very definite, and as my trip was a very hurried one, I had not stopped. Whereupon Colonel Grissinger told me that General Pershing had received a telephone message from Secretary Lansing that President Wilson, who was in Paris, was very much vexed that I had delayed going to England to attend Ambassador Francis. General Pershing had ordered that I lose no time getting to London.

I traveled at great speed along the precipitous banks of the Moselle. Darkness fell quickly. The motorcar had not been equipped with lamps, which had been prohibited during the war. The driver complained that it was almost impossible to see, but I explained the great need for haste and urged him on. As he turned a sharp curve he stopped just on the brink of the river and said, "My nerve is all gone; I can't go any farther." Some boys conducted us down the hill to a little fisherman's hotel, but when I knocked at the door, the woman who opened it said that she could not to let us spend the night, because she had no food. I directed my sergeant to bring what we had with us in a sack, and he displayed a magnificent roast, potatoes, and bread. With her eyes popping out, she cried: "Oh, we haven't eaten meat for many weeks! Come on in." About this time her husband arrived with a fine string of trout and the woman, with her two daughters and the sergeant, prepared dinner while the

fisherman and I sampled bottles that he told me had been concealed in panels within the wall during the four years the Germans
had occupied this hotel as their headquarters. After several rounds,
I was in excellent trim for the wonderful dinner set before me.

Hors d'œuvres   Schnapps
Soup   Vin Rouge
Trout   Vin Blanc
Roast Beef   Moselle
Potatoes   Kirsch
Salad
Cheese   Cigars

The next morning we made a quick run through Nancy and Metz
to Neufchâteau, where I had a conference with Colonel Keyes and
Colonel Walker. It was with real sadness that I looked for the last
time at the American Hospital for the Civil Population I had organized more than a year ago. The *sous-préfet* spoke most kindly of
the splendid work that had been done by this organization and the
gratitude that the people of eastern France had for it. I hated to
say good-by to the army consultants, who had been of great service
to the A.E.F. under very trying circumstances. I did not have
time to say good-by to the Princess who had been so kind to me.

I then left for Chaumont. Colonel Wadhams was much exer-
cised because he had been criticized for letting me go to Germany.
I got my orders to proceed immediately to London.

WHEN I got to London on December 22, 1918, I went at once to see Ambassador Francis. He had been taken desperately ill suddenly in Archangel, Russia, whither he had fled with the staff of the American Embassy from Petrograd, having been protected by American troops in Russia from the fury of the Bolshevists in Moscow. He had been transported to England on a battleship. Some English surgeons told his son that the Ambassador was suffering from cancer of the prostate, and that operation was not to be considered. The son was advised to take his father home as soon as possible. His father refused to go, and insisted that I be sent for. After a careful examination I told his son and his wife that I could not agree with the diagnosis the British physicians had made. It seemed to me that the condition was not cancerous, and that an operation would cure him.

Operating on Ambassador Francis

Lieutenant Edwin Davis, who had been resident urologist at the Johns Hopkins Hospital, was ordered from the A.E.F. to London, and instructed to bring with him all the apparatus and instruments necessary. Preparatory treatment was given, and after drainage of the bladder with a rubber tube for ten days the thalein function test showed that the patient's kidneys had improved so much that operation could now be done. He was sent to the Ameri-

can Naval Hospital, which had been organized in a private residence overlooking Hyde Park. Here, on January 16, 1919, I carried
out perineal prostatectomy, removing the obstruction completely,
with the assistance of Lieutenant Davis and members of the hospital staff. The patient stood the operation well and made a splendid
recovery.

Ambassador Francis had had thrilling experiences in Russia,
where for three years he represented the United States Government with wonderful efficiency and was dean of the diplomatic
corps. He was a vigorous and fearless man. As many of the other
diplomats were vacillating and timid, he often had to take matters
in his own hands. He recalled vividly the events of the revolution;
Kerensky's eloquent, plausible, brilliant, but weak personality;
the counterrevolution on the arrival of Lenin from Switzerland,
sent there in a German train; the fall of Kerensky; the Bolshevik
Revolution; the weakness of the Allies in handling the situation,
for which he felt President Wilson was largely responsible by refusing to take steps against the Bolsheviks; the dillydallying and refusal to send troops; the increasing reign of terror, murder, incen-
diarism.

While I was attending Ambassador Francis, I met interesting
Russians who called to thank him for the great work he had done
for the aristocracy and better classes in Russia, and the bravery he
had shown in standing out against the Bolsheviks after all other
diplomatic corps had fled. One of his frequent callers was Miliukov,
Secretary of Foreign Affairs in the first Cabinet of Kerensky.
Miliukov had been professor of history in the university, spoke
twenty-seven languages, English very fluently. He was a charming,
forceful man and undoubtedly sincere. He said the greatest patriot
in Russia was Kerensky, but he was a "trimmer." Miliukov had
urged the arrest and trial of Lenin and Trotsky, but Kerensky,
who was a boyhood friend of Lenin's, refused to arrest him, although
everybody knew that he was busily engaged in plotting destruction
of the government.

Ambassador Francis told us about Kerensky's escape from Russia in one of the automobiles belonging to the United States Embassy, flying the United States flag on the radiator. He said that had Kerensky not insulted and refused to deal with Kornilov, Russia would have been saved from the reign of terror.

On January 8, 1919, President Wilson arrived in London with his staff, and was quartered in Buckingham Palace. A great banquet was given to him by the King, and as Ambassador Francis had improved sufficiently, I urged him to attend. His son, his daughter, and I assisted in getting him ready. An automobile sent by His Majesty was announced to be waiting. The Ambassador was starting to leave the room when he suddenly turned and said, "Daughter, where are my rubber shoes?" "But, Father," said she, "the King's automobile will conduct you to and from Buckingham Palace. Your feet won't touch the ground." However, regardless of her pleading that it would be a disgrace to wear rubber shoes to Buckingham Palace, the Ambassador insisted, and away he went in them. About one o'clock he returned, filled with enthusiasm over his experiences at the party. He had been placed among royalty, and after dinner had been commanded by the Queen to tell her about Russia in a private conference. "But what in the world did you do with the gumshoes?" said his daughter. "Oh," replied the Ambassador, "I had quite a time with them. When I arrived and gave up my coat, hat, and cane, and joined the procession of guests, I didn't think of the rubber shoes until just about to be presented to the Queen, when I looked down and saw them. I couldn't leave the line, so seeing space beneath the rug as it fell over the edge of the platform on which Their Majesties stood, I hastily slipped them off and secreted them beneath it. The Queen entertained me until everyone had gone, when I went to get my coat and hat. Just as I was about to leave I remembered my gumshoes, but where were they? Where was the room in which the King and Queen had received us? I wandered here and there, and finally some high official turned a corner, saw me searching the place, and demanded to know who I was and what I wanted. I told him I was Ambassador Francis and was looking for my gumshoes. 'Gumshoes?' said he. 'What are they?' 'Overshoes,' I replied. 'Do you mean the rubber articles used by common people to cover their feet in wet weather?' 'Yes, I have a pet pair which I took off before I was presented to the King. If you can show me where the reception room is, I can probably find them secreted beneath the carpet covering the dais.' He showed me the room. I walked over and pulled out my gumshoes and put them on. He said, 'Extraordinary—you Americans are extraordinary.'

A Visit to Buckingham Palace

While Wilson was at Buckingham Palace, his physician, Rear Admiral Cary Grayson, Medical Corps U. S. N., took me over there. We sat down to smoke a cigarette in the billiard room, and there I met Jesse Jones of Houston, who was in charge of Red Cross work. Jones soon quit the room, and a little later when we ourselves went back into the great hall I was struck by the horrified expressions on the faces of four flunkies, who were staring at the end of the room to our right. There in front of a blazing fire in a lovely Georgian fireplace sat Jesse Jones with his long legs hanging over the high fender and his feet almost in the flames. Grayson said, "For God's sake, Jesse, what are you doing?" "I'm trying to get warm. I have been so cold in the frigid houses of England that when I saw this fire I made up my mind I was at least going to try to get my feet warm even if I'm drawn and quartered for doing it."

Grayson asked me whether I would like to see his apartment in Buckingham Palace. We mounted the great staircase, and went down a long corridor. He whispered to me that we were passing the apartments of the Duke of York. Suddenly Grayson stopped and asked me to take a sniff. "Do you notice this peculiar odor? All palaces seem to have it. It smells like a urinal to me. The worst odor was in Rome at the Quirinal." I suggested that perhaps "quirinal" was Roman for "urinal."

Grayson showed me the extensive suite of rooms in which he luxuriated. The first afternoon he was there a butler arrived at five o'clock and asked with a cockney accent whether he would have tea. "I said, 'No, but I'll take Haig and Haig.' After a long wait two butlers arrived. One had a large waiter, and the other a table. I wondered what could be beneath the cloth, when I had expected only whisky and soda. I was amazed when the napery was removed, disclosing two eggs."

President Wilson's Speech at the Guild Hall

I was present when Wilson made his oration at the Guild Hall. Before the meeting I had called on Colonel William Robert Smith, M.D., a noted authority on public health. He offered to take me down to the Guild Hall. Excusing himself, after considerable delay he returned in a uniform of many colors with much red and gold lace, the whole surmounted by an immense Napoleonic hat with large plumes. Seeing my evident astonishment, he explained he was also Lord High Sheriff of London. Waiting for him was one of the royal coaches drawn by four horses, an immense and ancient coach, with men on boxes in front and behind, in gorgeous regalia. When I took my seat in the carriage in my service uniform, I felt ridiculously inadequate to the occasion. As we rode through the crowded streets of London we passed a group of American soldiers, and when they spied me they yelled, "Look at our little Colonel traveling with royalty!"

At the Guild Hall I had the privilege of seeing one of the most remarkable functions ever held in London. All the great dignitaries of England and the highest officers of the British Army and Navy were there. As each came up the aisle he halted about forty feet in front of the King, and a herald announced in solemn tones his name. He then proceeded to the rostrum, where he was formally introduced to President Wilson and took his seat.

I was astonished at the lack of sympathy Wilson displayed for the English and the French, and at his boldly championing the freedom of the sea, which during the war had been considered German propaganda and was bitterly detested in England. Prominent English statesmen near me openly expressed disapproval of many of the sentiments that Wilson expressed.

Dinner with Lord Beaverbrook

While I was in London I went to a dinner given by Lord Beaverbrook at the Hotel Savoy at which Lord Montague, Undersecretary for India, and Lady Montague, the beautiful Lady Diana Manners in a gorgeous green silk gown, her fiancé, Colonel Duff-Cooper, and others were present. During the dinner Diana dwelt at considerable length on an article she had written for the press, urging colorful costumes for men, whose attire she thought was much too drab and uninteresting. After dinner we went to the offices of the *Daily Express*, Beaverbrook's newspaper. Lady Diana looked over her dossier in their "morgue," tore up many old photographs they had of her, and also destroyed other documents that she thought uncomplimentary. After that we crowded into one of Beaverbrook's automobiles and took Her Ladyship to the home of her father, the Duke of Rutland. When she got out I was amazed to see that her fiancé remained in the car, and when I saw the beautiful creature struggling to open the heavy gates I could bear it no longer, got out, opened the gate, and accompanied her to the front door. Englishmen are certainly indifferent.

Dinner with Admiral Sims

I also had the pleasure of being present at a dinner given to Admiral Sims by some of his staff. He was like a boy, seemed to be on the jolliest terms with his staff, and poked fun at them all the time. I succeeded in drawing him out about some of his accomplishments during the war, one of which was to persuade the Allies to adopt the convoy system for merchant ships. He had urged this for many months, but met with stern refusal by the British Admiralty. During the early months of 1917 the sinkings increased by leaps and bounds. In the month of May alone three-quarters of a million tons were sunk. Finally the situation got so desperate that the British were willing to listen to Admiral Sims and granted his request to inaugurate a convoy system by which ships could be got together in fairly large groups in mid-Atlantic and convoyed by a considerable number of naval vessels to their ports. After this the sinkings diminished greatly, and the menace to Britain ended.

ADMIRAL GRAYSON told me in London that he was worried about President Wilson's health, and thought he was working himself to death. After the signing of peace, Wilson came home and announced his intention of reporting personally to the people of the United States in regard to his actions in France. He thought that in this way he could obtain their backing for the ratification of the Treaty of Versailles and the League of Nations, against which his enemies in the Senate had raised outcry. Soon after his return, while the intolerable heat still prevailed, he started West in a special train, and after crossing the Mississippi, made rear-platform speeches at almost every station where a goodly number of people had assembled to greet him. So great was his desire to meet and talk to the populace personally that he continued this practice into the night, and even had himself aroused from his slumbers to appear in a dressing-gown before assembled crowds. At the larger cities he gave long addresses, at one city after another in the Middle West.

By the time he reached the Pacific Coast, Grayson informed me that the President had begun again to suffer with asthma, which prevented his sleeping in a horizontal position. He had had a similar attack during the strenuous days of the Peace Conference in Paris, and now on his special car he found it impossible to sleep in bed and got what slumber he could while sitting upright in an easy chair. A very severe neuralgia, or frontal headache, developed, and became progressively worse. At Seattle, where he addressed ten thousand people, Grayson asserted that the President's headache was so severe that it blurred his vision and he was unable to see the faces of those who occupied the front row of the audience. Regardless of this, he insisted on completing his address, which lasted over an hour. From Seattle he turned south and delivered addresses at several cities, but the headache continued night and day, until finally, almost frantic with pain and inability to sleep except in a chair, he turned eastward, and delivered his next address at Denver. From there the train sped east to meet his next engagement at Wichita, Kansas.

At five o'clock in the morning Grayson was called to the President's car. He found him slumped in his chair, ashy-pale and with saliva trickling from the left corner of his mouth, which drooped perceptibly. His pulse was not good, and Grayson saw at once that he had had a slight paralytic stroke. Summoning assistance, he put the President to bed and then notified the President's secretary that all speaking engagements must be canceled, and the train hurried on to Washington. The rest produced a considerable improvement. In Washington the President was able to walk to his motorcar, and arrived at the White House in fairly good condition. For the next few days he seemed to improve, and one night felt so well that he engaged in a game of billiards.

About eight o'clock in the morning on October 2, 1919, Mrs. Wilson, who was in an adjoining room, was awakened by the sound of something falling in the President's room. Rushing in, she found him lying prostrate on the floor in the bathroom. Help was called. Grayson soon saw him, and found that he had had a severe "stroke," with paralysis of the left arm and leg, and also paralysis of the left side of the face. The President weathered this crisis remarkably well, but after a time urination became impossible, and bladder distension to an increasing degree came on. Admiral Grayson decided to introduce a catheter, which he found a little difficult, but he eventually succeeded in emptying the bladder. Still normal urination did not return, and on the following day it was necessary again to pass instruments. Grayson was unable to introduce even the smallest catheter, and decided to summon Dr. H. A. Fowler, who had been my assistant at the Johns Hopkins Hospital. After trying various instruments, Dr. Fowler finally discovered one that would pass and the bladder was satisfactorily emptied. The next day catheterization was again necessary, but when Grayson and Fowler attempted to pass the instruments with which they had succeeded on the previous day, they failed.

I was then summoned by Admiral Grayson, and arrived a few hours later to find that the President had gone thirty hours without voiding urine. This was on October 17. His abdomen was hugely distended. He presented a sad picture as he lay there with his mouth drawn on one side, and with paralytic left arm and leg. The condition was evidently desperate. The patient was greatly weakened by the paralytic stroke. Experts had used almost every conceivable instrument without success. I did not believe I could do any better, and at first sight, it seemed that a surgical operation would have to be carried out through a median line abdominal incision to open the bladder, and relieve the terrific distension. But could he stand the shock of it? I hardly thought so.

We had found in France that wounds in the spine were often followed by retention of urine. The bladder would become greatly distended, reaching above the navel, but eventually the neck of the bladder would relax or give way, and urine would begin to escape through the urethra. This escape of urine would gradually increase. The bladder would become less and less distended, and the patient would recover without operation. The British usually made an opening to drain the bladder in these cases, but hospital statistics showed that most of these patients died of infection. In the *Manual of Military Urology* that we published in France and issued to the Medical Corps A.E.F., we had strongly advised against operation and advocated waiting until urine escaped naturally. As a result of this army experience I believed that the obstruction would eventually be forced open by the great internal pressure present in the hugely distended bladder. I advised waiting. Dr. Fowler and I took an automobile ride, during which we bought a few instruments that had not been tried. When we returned to the White House, I noticed a large wet spot upon the sheet that had not been there before. "Have you spilled any water on the bed?" I asked the nurse, and when she replied in the negative, I said, "Please place a dry sheet beneath him, and let us wait fifteen minutes and see what happens." Again the sheet was wet. It was evident that nature had asserted itself. The bladder neck had relaxed or been forced open. Would this be sufficient to take care of the constantly accumulating fluid? From our army cases I believed that it would, and it was evident that we should wait.

As the hours passed, the escape became greater and greater, and the patient's abdominal pain less severe. By evening he was much more comfortable. The escape of urine was considerable, and the next day the distension was markedly lessened. This continued from day to day. The bladder became progressively smaller. He had been spared a surgical operation. After some weeks of incontinence, natural urination was established. In the meantime the patient gradually recovered from the shock of the paralytic stroke; in a few months the helpless arm and leg began to move voluntarily, and finally muscular control became sufficiently good to allow him to attempt to walk. Eventually he was able to use his arm, forearm, and leg quite well, and to walk with the assistance of a cane. While he never was able to use the fingers of his left hand sufficiently well to hold a fork or other utensil, his general condition was quite good, and he was able to read his books with enjoyment, and to ride out daily in his motorcar with Mrs. Wilson. Procrastination and "masterly inactivity" saved the patient. Had I attempted to pass instruments, failure would have been almost certain, and an operation to relieve the distension would probably have ended fatally.

In her book *As I Saw It*, Mrs. Wilson has given an entirely different account, and credits me with having said that the President's condition could not be relieved without operation, and that the whole body would become poisoned if this condition lasted an hour, or at most two. She admits how distraught she was. This probably is responsible for her failure to remember accurately just what happened. Never once did I advise an operation, because I hoped that nature would assert itself, as I had seen happen so often in France—and it did.

Mr. Wilson was a very patient sufferer, and at times delightful and amusing in his conversation. When on one of my visits I remarked, "Mr. President, you badly need a shave." "Yes," said he, "but I have always shaved myself and I hate to trust myself to a barber." To which I replied: "Why don't you let Admiral Grayson shave you? You know, originally, the surgeons were all barbers." "Yes," said the President, "they are still barbarous."

On another occasion when I was present, a message came to announce that Congress had overridden his veto of the bill to continue wartime Prohibition. Turning to me, the President said: "The war has been over a year. The urgent need for conserving grain, which was present during the war, when this bill was introduced, has passed. There is no occasion for continuing this prohibition on the pretext under which it was passed. I do not believe in national Prohibition. I think that the best thing for this country is to be placed on light wine and beer. Prohibition of all alcoholic drinks cannot be successfully carried out. I was greatly impressed with what Pershing accomplished in the A.E.F. by his orders, which placed the army on a light-wine-and-beer basis. This is what we should have in America." I replied: "Mr. President, your remarks appeal to me immensely, because General Pershing's General Order prohibiting strong drinks, but allowing light wines and beer to our troops, was written by me, and came as a result of an investigation into the horrible conditions at the port of Saint-Nazaire, where the grogshops, with their vile rum and gin, had done incalculable harm to our incoming troops."

While attending the President, I occasionally lunched with Mrs. Wilson. This great-granddaughter of Pocahontas is very charming and has a keen sense of humor. She and Grayson afforded me many an amusing hour at the White House. At times I was able to have a prolonged conversation with President Wilson. One day he had before him a bill to provide additional appropriations for military training of civilians. I was surprised to find him greatly opposed to it, and had an opportunity to express to him, as a medical officer, my strong convictions concerning the immense benefit to be obtained by boys and young men at camps such as that at Plattsburg. I emphasized the valuable information they got on infectious diseases, how to take care of themselves, and how to improve their bodily health and strength. Finally the President acceded to some of these arguments I eagerly put forth. I was delighted some days later to find that he had signed the bill.

About a year later another paralytic stroke occurred, and this one ended fatally. As a medical man, I feel convinced that Wilson's death was due to mental worry brought on by the malignant opposition of his enemies in Congress. The paralytic strokes were undoubtedly caused by the extremely strenuous and exhausting trip that he took in midsummer to make a personal report to the American people of what he had done in France. His enemies did not relax while the President lay prostrate in the White House. An inquiry was proposed, and it was strongly hinted that impeachment proceedings might be introduced to replace him, as incapable of continuing as Executive.

At this time Mr. Frank R. Kent, vice-president of the *Baltimore Sun*, came to see me one Sunday morning. He said that a simple statement from me about the true nature of the President's malady would put an end to the efforts of his enemies to besmirch his character, and that it was my duty to tell just what had happened. After long and serious consideration I decided that he was right, and gave Mr. Kent an extensive interview that was published in the *Sun*. Just as he had predicted, this statement immediately silenced the maligners; the move to impeach the President was dropped. The press of the nation heartily commended my action.

Legislation for Tuberculosis

DURING the winter of 1903 the Maryland Legislature was in session, and the physicians of Baltimore and Maryland were greatly interested in a concerted effort that was being made to pass several tuberculosis bills which were considered of vital importance by health authorities. One bill was for the reporting and registration of tuberculous cases. The second was for the provision of hygienic care and cleanliness in the homes of tuberculous patients, and the third was for a commission to design a state sanatorium for cases of pulmonary tuberculosis. The interest of the Baltimore papers had been obtained, numerous articles and editorials had appeared, committees of prominent physicians, headed by Drs. Osler, Welch, Thayer, Jacobs, and Fulton, had visited the legislature and addressed them. There seemed to be every reason why these bills should be passed, but on the day before the end of the session the evening papers reported that the tuberculosis bills had been unfavorably reported by the Finance Committee of the Senate, and all chance of their passage had been lost.

It was about six o'clock. Phoning Dr. Thayer, chairman of the committee, I told him how sorry I was to hear of the sad fate of the bills and inquired whether there was anything that I could do. I explained that some important officials were patients of mine, and offered my services. Dr. Thayer said he was very sorry to say that everything possible had been done, that Drs. Osler and Welch and other prominent members of the profession had been down there, had urged the passage of these bills without effect, and that although he appreciated my offer, he felt it would be a waste of time to go down. Hanging up the receiver, I put on my coat, telephoned home that I would not be there for dinner, caught the first train for Annapolis, and looked up my old friend and patient General Murray Vandiver, State Treasurer. I found him in the State House attending a banquet given by the president of the Senate. He came out into the lobby and said, "Hello, Doctor, what are you doing here?" I explained that I wanted to see him about the tuberculosis bills. He said, "Those have been killed today, and the session is about to close." "Yes," I said, "but it is a crime not to pass these very important bills." "Well," he replied, "I knew that Welch and Osler had been down here talking to the committee, but they did not come to see me. I am here at this banquet and cannot talk to you now, but I believe the president of the Senate would be very glad to have you come in." I explained that I was in a sack suit and unprepared to join such distinguished company, but he disappeared, soon returned with an invitation for me to join the banquet, and insisted on my going in with him.

I was placed at the head table next to General Vandiver, who said: "Now lap up some of this champagne and eat this terrapin before you attempt to tell me what your mission is. We will be able to talk better after we have had several glasses of wine." A little later he turned to me and asked, "Now what is your trouble?" and I explained the situation. "Those bills," he said, "were reported unfavorably by the Finance Committee of the Senate. Most of the members are here. I will call them over." He then said to a waiter, "Tell Senator Brewington to come here." "Senator Brewington," he said, "this is my friend Dr. Young. He saved my life. He tells me that he is greatly interested in those tuberculosis bills which have been killed by your committee. Why did you do it?" "They seemed to involve a great deal of expense, and we had no idea that you were at all interested, General." "I have not been interested previously, but I am very much now. I shall come around tomorrow at eleven o'clock, and I want you then to get up and propose reconsideration of these bills." "General," said the Senator, "you know that tomorrow is the last day of our session. We have an immense amount of work, and innumerable bills to consider, including the omnibus appropriation bill." "Yes," answered the General, "I understand that, but when I come tomorrow I want you to do as I say." "All right," said the Senator.

Several other members of the Finance Committee were called in turn to the General's seat. Each admitted voting against the bill, was surprised to know that the General was interested, and promised to do what he could. Senator Gill, who asserted that he was a Christian Scientist and was opposed to all medical legislation, said that he could not vote to have the bills reconsidered, but that he would leave the chamber and not vote against them, if the General wished. So the stage was set for the following day. I remained throughout the dinner, drank a great deal of the excellent vintages, and got up the next morning feeling very bad.

I joined the General at the office of the State Treasurer shortly before eleven o'clock. General Vandiver was very busy. A series of political henchmen, Democrats and Republicans, came in turn to report to him the situation of various bills and to get their instructions. At eleven o'clock we went to the Senate. Senator Brewington did as requested, and proposed a reconsideration of the tuberculosis bills. Immediately several Senators were on their feet in violent opposition. "Mr. President," they said, "we have considered and disposed of these bills. We have only a few hours to attend to much important legislation; I object." But as quickly as each got up, General Vandiver went to him, and after a few whispered words from the General the Senator rose and withdrew his objection. In fifteen minutes the Senate had almost unanimously passed Brewington's motion for reconsideration of the bills.

With a request from the president of the Senate in his hands, General Vandiver hurried to the House, where he explained the situation to the Speaker, who, with much misgiving, assented to the question's being brought up. A willing member proposed the reconsideration of these bills. Hubbub arose all over the House, but the protestations were quietly silenced by a word or two from the General, and in a few minutes the bills had been passed by the House and sent to the Senate. There, in a short time, they were passed almost unanimously. Later in the evening they were passed for the third time and sent to the Governor, whose signature was quickly affixed. The papers reported that in some extraordinary fashion, entirely incomprehensible to the political reporters, the three important bills for tuberculosis had been resuscitated and passed by the House and Senate, the most amazing thing, they said, that had ever happened in the Maryland Legislature. Drs. Osler, Welch, and Thayer were not present when these negotiations were going on, but Fulton was there, and soon reported to them what had happened and the part I had played in it. When I met Dr. Osler in the hospital corridor, he cried out: "That was fine work, Young, getting those bills passed! You have demonstrated the truth of that old adage, 'What a powerful thing it is to have a man by the balls.' "

The passage of these three bills had a nation-wide effect in the great campaign against tuberculosis. Many of the provisions that they incorporated for the first time have been copied in other states. The great sanitarium at Sabillasville has come into being, and Maryland has taken a front place in the fight against the great white plague.

Legislation for the Insane

This work for the tuberculosis bills had an unexpected aftermath. In 1908 I received a note from Dr. Welch reading as follows: "Dear Young: The care of the insane in Maryland is in a deplorable condition. The secretary of the Lunacy Commission, Dr. Preston, has just died. There is no state law operating for the care of the insane, who are largely housed in county almshouses, and the provision for hospital care is very inadequate. It is a scandal of the first order. The Lunacy Commission contains several undesirable men, and they are about to appoint a thoroughly unreliable man as secretary of the commission. I have explained the gravity of the situation to Governor Crothers, and he has agreed to appoint you chairman of the Board. It is a matter of great importance to the State. You must accept. Please see the Governor at once."

Nothing could have been more unexpected than this letter. I knew nothing of and had given little thought to the insane. I was interested in my work, and extremely busy, but Dr. Welch's word was law. I saw the Governor, was appointed chairman of the Lunacy Commission, called a meeting, found the majority bent on electing one Dr. Smith, who had been so vigorously condemned by Dr. Welch, as secretary of the board. I managed to postpone the meeting without action being taken, employed legal council to look into the composition of the board, and discovered that several held office illegally, as the law required a fixed number from the city and from the counties, and several of the governors had entirely neglected these provisions in appointing certain of the members who then held office and who, therefore, had been illegally appointed. By this means I was able to force their retirement and get several new members agreeable to Dr. Welch appointed.

Dr. Arthur P. Herring was made secretary and immediately started on a series of investigations, which disclosed a disgraceful condition in the almshouses of many of the counties, and the quite inadequate care that was afforded to many of the insane. These disclosures aroused the people, but they antagonized many politicians and a group of doctors who owned private sanatoria for the treatment of the insane that they feared might be injured if Maryland embarked on a program of state care. When the legislature met in 1910, Herring and I appeared at Annapolis with a bill for state care of the insane and another for an appropriation of $600,000 to build new hospitals. These bills aroused violent opposition. Severe criticisms were hurled at us by certain members of the medical profession and their friends in the Senate. Toward the close of the session it looked as if the bills would be killed.

Herring and I lived in Annapolis and worked incessantly with the members of the legislature, whom we saw personally whenever we could get an audience. We were able to get some members to change their attitude, but when the bill finally came up before the Senate, Senator Campbell of Baltimore, who headed the opposition, came up to me as I stood in the back of the Senate and said: "Doctor, these are nefarious bills. They will do untold harm to private institutions. I have with me a strong group in vigorous opposition, and we will kill these bills or emasculate them." Bowing, I simply said, "Senator, you may be surprised." When the bill for the state care of the insane was read before the Senate, Senator Campbell rose and moved that all words after "A bill" be deleted; in other words, the bill would be wiped out. Then he launched on a vigorous denunciation. He was followed by others of his group, but we had won to our side Senator Gorman, a great power in the Senate. He made a strong speech in our behalf. At my request, other Senators followed his example. Finally, after three hours of violent discussion, Senator Campbell's motion was defeated. After that numerous amendments were proposed by others in the combine against us. Finally the bill, unamended, passed the Senate. We then redoubled our efforts with the members of the House of Delegates, and when the bills came up after another big fight they were finally passed by a good majority. State care of the insane was thus brought to Maryland after a fight of several years, begun by Dr. George J. Preston. The appropriation of $600,000 gave us a chance to add to and improve the two existing hospitals and to start a new institution for the Negro insane at Crownsville.

A Board of Governors was named in the bill to organize the hospital for the Negro insane. Mr. William L. Marbury, a distinguished lawyer, was named as chairman of the board and I as secretary; but also on the board were a lot of politicians, among whom was the secretary of the Senate. When the board met, this secretary proposed that we buy a farm of his for the hospital site. He had a majority of the board with him, and they wished to act at once, but Mr. Marbury finally persuaded them to postpone the vote. We then investigated this proposed hospital site and found that it was on a branch of the Patapsco River, remote from a railroad and good roads. It was a run-down farm and the soil looked poor, but as we knew we had a dangerous clique to deal with, Marbury and I decided to have experts from the United States Department of Agriculture to give us a report on the farm and also to examine other properties that had been offered to us. We had to act speedily, but in a couple of weeks we were able to present to the board expert opinion which showed that the farm offered by the secretary of the Senate was very poor land and utterly unsuited for a hospital farm, and to present the offer of another farm that was much larger, would cost much less, and was much better land. The expert on soils from the Department of Agriculture said it was a Collington loam. When this was announced, two of the members who, though politicians, were practical farmers, at once said that if this other farm was a Collington loam they would vote for it at once. A majority was thus secured, the political cabal was beaten, and we got a six-hundred-acre farm that was close to a railroad for $35 an acre instead of the $200 asked by the secretary of the Senate for his farm.

Here we built the Crownsville State Hospital, which has since grown to be a model institution. The organization of this hospital interested me very greatly, and gave me a chance to study the architecture employed in the construction of the buildings for the insane, and an opportunity to modify current methods greatly.

To superintend this new hospital for the Negro insane, which was to be built on the land we had purchased near Crownsville, Maryland, Dr. Herring secured Dr. Robert P. Winterode. He had made a splendid reputation on the staff of the Spring Grove State Hospital, where Dr. Percy Wade, the superintendent, had achieved great results by providing work for the insane. Winterode was strongly imbued with these ideas. To build a hospital we first had to have a spur from the Baltimore & Annapolis Railroad, near by. Winterode proposed that he organize a work camp on the property and that we send him enough Negro insane laborers to go into the forest and cut trees for crossties and electric-light poles.

The only men available were incarcerated at Montevue, near Frederick, Maryland, which was devoted almost entirely to the violent and dangerous insane. Some of them were murderers. These were considered so dangerous that a number were kept in isolated cells or in strait jackets. Regardless of the bad character of these men, Winterode said he could handle them, and begged us to send them down. We therefore emptied this hospital of its thirty-one inmates and sent them, handcuffed and guarded by a dozen deputy sheriffs, down to Dr. Winterode, who had fixed up a barn to accommodate them. When they arrived on the grounds, Winterode lined them up and addressed them. He told them that they would be treated entirely differently, that they would not be confined to cells or wear handcuffs or strait jackets, and that they would live in the open air and be far happier and healthier. Using the simplest language, he walked up and down the line, looking into the eyes of each man and making him understand the new life that was in store for him. After this "pep talk," to which I listened with the greatest interest, Winterode had the handcuffs removed. He then told the men they were going out with him into the forest to cut down trees, and gave each man an ax.

I feared some tragedy would happen at once, but instead they remained docile, and when Winterode commanded that they follow him into the forest, they went peacefully. With three orderlies to assist him, Winterode worked with these "dangerous insane" Negroes all summer, cutting hundreds of crossties for the railroad and many tall poles for the electric wires, and had not a single accident. Best of all, this active life in the open greatly improved the mental condition of the patients and some of them actually were cured.

In the meantime we had chosen Henry P. Hopkins to design a

new hospital. Herring and Winterode were anxious to incorporate in the plans new ideas for the housing and the treatment of the insane. I became greatly interested in the project and spent much time with them in formulating plans for a building that would provide excellent sleeping-quarters at less cost than heretofore and, in addition, would give what was more important than mere bedrooms, a large space for recreation and rooms adapted to occupational activities of all sorts, work that was expected to be of great therapeutic value. We were able to build a fireproof concrete and brick building with much space for recreation and work as well as with a central heating plant, kitchen, and dining-room, for the amazingly small price of $480 per bed.

Under Winterode's splendid direction, Crownsville became one of the best hospitals for the insane in Maryland. In the workshops willows were fashioned into many beautiful baskets and other products that we were able to sell to the trade. The rugmaking department was also very valuable as a therapeutic agent, and profitable to the institution. One woman who came there apparently hopelessly insane, and so feeble that she had to be fed, as a result of occupational therapy gradually regained the use of her hands and her brain, eventually became one of the most expert lacemakers, and she finally left the hospital, cured.

The work of this hospital interested me so greatly that for a number of years I remained secretary of the board and spent much more of my time on it than I did on the other hospitals for the insane that were under the jurisdiction of the Lunacy Commission, of which I was still chairman. At a meeting of the legislature we secured funds to build a hospital for the insane on the banks of the Choptank, near Cambridge. Here we constructed a lovely group of buildings of the half-timbered type of architecture. We were able to put into practice the principles of farm labor and other forms of occupational therapy with which so much had already been accomplished at Spring Grove, Springfield, and Crownsville.

As secretary of the Lunacy Commission, Arthur P. Herring was

an inspiring man to work with. Modern in his viewpoint, and indefatigable, he developed his program for the state care of the insane
beautifully. He carried the press with him, and at the legislature
we were able, year after year, to pass laws and appropriation bills
that created for Maryland one of the best groups of hospitals for the
care of the insane in the country. The state administration has been
remodeled by the organization in 1923 of a Department of Welfare,
with Colonel Stuart Janney as its first chairman. Under this was
placed the State Board of Mental Hygiene, and Dr. Herring became the first Commissioner of Mental Hygiene. And then,
suddenly, while still in his prime, Herring came down with intestinal
cancer, too far advanced when we first saw him to be cured by
operation. When he discovered the inevitable end he stretched out
his hands to me and said: "Dr. Young, you have conquered many
apparently insuperable difficulties successfully. I know you will
not fail me now." But nothing could be done—and I left in tears.

After the death of Dr. Herring, Dr. George H. Preston was elected
to fill his place. Dr. Preston's father was one of the first important
figures in the treatment of the insane in Maryland. Under his son
the care of the insane has made steady progress. Wonderful new
methods of treatment have been developed in the hospitals. The
Mental Hygiene Society, organized by Dr. William H. Welch in
1915 with a fine group of interested citizens as well as doctors, has
co-operated actively. The Lunacy Commission, of which I had been
chairman for years, now became the State Board of Mental Hygiene.
Our function remains the same as before, but with wider co-operation with other state boards and local societies the scope of its work
has been broadened and become increasingly valuable.

The care of the feeble-minded has not yet been mentioned. At
Rosewood, we have gradually developed a great institution for the
care of these unfortunates. Here the principles of occupational therapy are also stressed, sometimes with amazing benefit. The necessity
of placing in an institution the feeble-minded, who, on account of
their absolute lack of morals and strong sexual proclivities, are a

great menace to the population, has been stressed before the legislature, which has been generous in providing adequate funds for that purpose. As a result of the splendid law for state care and the development of five great institutions, the care of the insane and the feeble-minded in Maryland now is ranked very high.

Killing a Prohibition Bill

During one of the sessions of the legislature (1915–16) Mr. Robert F. Crain, a prominent lawyer and a considerable power in Democratic circles, who had frequently been of much assistance to me in my efforts to get the legislature to pass certain bills, requested our help in fighting a Prohibition bill that was before the legislature. I found on looking over the bill that it prohibited the use of alcoholic spirits by the medical profession. It even prohibited the use of sacramental wines by the clergy. This gave me a ready excuse for getting into the fight. It occurred to me that it ought to be easy to form a combination of doctors and clergymen against this bill, which vitally affected both professions. I had no difficulty in securing strong support, and drew up an advertisement to be published in the *Baltimore Sun*, which was signed by four clergymen and four physicians. It simply stated that the bill was radically destructive of the age-long privileges of the medical profession and the sacred rites of the clergy, and should be defeated. It was signed by Cardinal Gibbons, Dr. Kinsolving, Pastor Hofmann, and Rabbi Rubenstein, and Drs. William H. Welch, William S. Halsted, Lewellys F. Barker, and Hugh H. Young. The advertisement occupied one entire page of the *Sun* and created a sensation. When the bill came up before the legislature on the following day, it was defeated by a large majority. Why such an absurdly radical Prohibition bill was ever attempted I cannot understand, but as a matter of fact laws that prevent the medical profession from using liquors and even light wines and beer have been placed on the statute books of many of our states. The fact that the use of spirituous liquors should not be prohibited to the medical profession is shown by the following case:

Dr. Osler had sent me the Governor of North Carolina, Mr. Daniel Russell. He was a huge man, six feet two inches tall, and weighing three hundred and twenty-five pounds. His right kidney was filled with stones. His heart was bad, and we dared not give him a general anesthetic. The operation was carried out under spinal anesthesia. A large incision was necessary and I had to go in up to my elbow to reach stones as big as golf balls, which filled the kidney. With great difficulty a huge one was dragged from its adhesions, and when it emerged the Governor, cursing loudly, asked to see. When he looked at it, he burst out, "God Almighty, I'm a regular stone quarry!"

The operation passed off successfully, but about a week later the patient's heart went suddenly to the bad and Dr. Osler was hastily summoned. The pulse was imperceptible and the heart dilated. His wife was present as Dr. Osler examined him and said: "Young, the case is hopeless; nothing can be done. His heart is so bad he will surely die. Good-by." As soon as Dr. Osler left the room the patient opened his eyes and said slowly to his wife: "Mary, I've heard every word Dr. Osler said. Send this telegram to my people in North Carolina. Say 'I'm dying—as a result of a surgical operation— performed—by Dr. Young,'" and with that he lapsed into unconsciousness. I felt his pulse. It was imperceptible and the patient was apparently rapidly passing out. I turned to my assistant and said: "Caulk, we can't afford to let that message go out to the people of North Carolina. We'll have to save the life of this old scoundrel. Get some brandy." A bottle of excellent French cognac was produced and I quickly gave the patient a hypodermic syringeful into the muscles of the arm. The pulse was still imperceptible, but after a time I felt one beat come through. "Give me some more cognac." A second injection was made, and then two beats were felt. Another injection, and six or eight beats came through. Finally, after eight injections the pulse was fairly regular, and he got well. Some of my friends insist that if the patient hadn't dictated that telegram he would have died.

Legislation for a School of Engineering at the Johns Hopkins University

Another experience at Annapolis was with the "Tech School Bill." During the session of 1912 I was completely occupied in efforts to obtain adequate appropriations for the insane. I frequently saw Mr. B. Howell Griswold, who had charge of a bill that proposed that the State of Maryland build and help to maintain a school of technology at the Johns Hopkins University. About four days before the end of the session, the bills for the insane having been passed, I was able to respond to an invitation from Mr. Griswold to join him in his campaign. There had been opposition from other institutions, and members of the Senate from rural districts could not see why Maryland needed a school of engineering. After numerous conferences it was possible to change the votes of only a few of those in opposition. We still had a majority against us.

Finally it occurred to me that we might attract members of the Senate by offering to let each one of them name two applicants for free scholarships in the proposed school. This bait proved effective, and we soon were able to get the bill passed by the Senate with a comfortable majority. We had no such bait to offer the members of the House of Delegates, but our Senatorial friends helped us there and the bill was finally passed and signed by the Governor. It provided $600,000 for building and equipping the School of Engineering and a yearly appropriation of $50,000 for maintenance. In return free scholarships for students from Maryland were offered. At this time the Johns Hopkins University was near the center of the city in old, very inadequate buildings. A beautiful site, Homewood, had been given for the future location of the university, but no money was at hand to make the move. The funds provided by the state for the School of Engineering gave the first opportunity to build at Homewood. The lovely Colonial structures that were placed there under the direction of Dean John B. Whitehead formed the nucleus around which the present university buildings were built. The Dean's aspirations of organizing not only a practical School of Engineering of great value to the state, but also a place where research and investigations of high order could be carried out have been realized.

Legislation for a Municipal Hospital in Baltimore

In 1914 the papers had been full of the need of a municipal hospital, and a bill for this purpose had been sent to the legislature. Dr. C. Hampson Jones, the Commissioner of Health of Baltimore City, worked night and day to obtain favor for the bill among the legislators. He was met by the opposition of Mayor James H. Preston, who for some unaccountable reason violently opposed the bill, even though Baltimore was sadly in need of such a hospital, as buildings at the old city hospital (Bay View) had been declared unsafe by the building inspectors several years before. Regardless of this, the Mayor and the city organization vigorously opposed the passage of a bill which simply provided that the citizens should be allowed to vote at the next election on the question as to whether they wished to have a city hospital.

Here, again, Dr. Welch appeared on the scene and said that I must join in and work for this bill. I protested that I had to ensure the passage of bills carrying large appropriations for the insane before attempting anything else. When these bills were passed, I was able to join Dr. Jones in active work on the bill for the creation of a municipal hospital. Practically the entire city delegation had been voting with the Mayor, who worked openly on the floor of the House and Senate. After a week of strenuous lobbying we were able to bring to the support of the bill members who had become interested in our bills for the state care of the insane, until finally we had a majority of the city delegation with us. Although the Mayor and the heads of the city organization stormed and threatened, the bill was finally passed. The building of the hospital was afterwards

approved at an election There now stands on the hill overlooking
Lake Montebello a beautiful series of buildings that have resulted
from the passage of this bill, a great hospital group that does credit
to Baltimore and has done away with the scandalous conditions
which previously existed.

The State Medical Society

In 1912 I was elected president of the Medical and Chirurgical
Faculty of Maryland. It is one of the oldest state medical societies
in the country, founded in 1799. It has had on its rolls the names of
some of the most distinguished men in American medicine. Three
years before, I had been chairman of the committee for furnishing
and decorating the new building that we had constructed on
Cathedral Street, Baltimore. In the auditorium, which we named
for Dr. Osler, I placed copies of slat-back Colonial New England
oaken chairs with rush seats, which are so durable that now after
twenty-eight years they are still in good condition.

The state medical society has an annual meeting in Baltimore,
and a semiannual session in the fall in some distant portion of the
state. In 1912 this was to be held in Cambridge on the Eastern Shore
in the latter part of October. An interesting program had been
arranged, and Governor Goldsborough, who hailed from Cambridge,
agreed to be present. The only practical transportation from Baltimore to Cambridge was by boat. A short time before our meeting
we discovered to our dismay that the ship on which we expected to
go had been taken off. The ships available would get us there either
too early or too late for the meeting. The other officers of the society
said that I had to do something to meet the emergency. The president of the line was an old patient of mine, and to him I went with
my troubles. He listened sympathetically. Finally he said that as
a special favor he would put in commission the *S. S. Dorchester*,
which had just been delivered from the shipyard, and would charter
her to me personally for only a few hundred dollars. As the situation
formed a crisis in my presidency of the society, I gladly accepted

his offer, and invited the members of the society from all over the state to go as my guests.

We took along a glee club that had been formed in the Baltimore City Medical Society, and also a symphony orchestra that Dr. Herring and I had organized among the members of the Medical and Chirurgical Faculty. They had been playing for several months and were quite good. With these two musical organizations aboard, and countless kegs of beer and other liquid refreshments, the overnight trip down to Cambridge was a "howling success." Parades, preceded by the orchestra and the glee club, were made from stem to stern of the ship, the last one in the small hours of the morning with the members in nightshirts. For years there had been much dissension—medical-school rivalries and professional jealousies—among the members, but before the night was over these had disappeared like snow under a tropic sun. As I made final rounds of the ship I found many of the former enemies sleeping in the same bunks.

The citizens of Cambridge gave us a delightful reception and a luncheon. Everybody had a wonderful time, but my joy was greatly lessened by the fact that the liquid refreshments had been completely consumed on the trip down, and Cambridge was in a prohibition county where local option was so strict that nothing spirituous could be obtained. In desperation I turned to my friend General Vandiver, the State Treasurer at Annapolis. Over the phone I explained my predicament to him. "Don't worry, Doctor. I'll send over a large supply by the state police boat." When I reminded him that Cambridge had local option, he said, "The captain will get the beer and whisky aboard while the Governor and the city officials are busy at your reception." The trip back to Baltimore was highly successful. I am told that the meeting of the Medical and Chirurgical Faculty in Cambridge is still considered one of the most memorable in the annals of the society, and is recognized as having done much to bring complete harmony to the medical profession in Maryland.

The State Aviation Commission of Maryland

In 1929 a law providing for the creation of an aviation commission was passed by the legislature. I had often talked a lot about aviation to Governor Ritchie, and it probably was on this account that he asked me to assist him in the selection of the commission and to become its chairman. The other members were Clarence W. Whealton, Benjamin H. Brewster, 3rd, Lieutenant Commander De Witt C. Ramsey, U.S.N., and Captain Charles A. Masson, secretary-treasurer.

Soon after the organization of our commission I went to Europe. During my stay in London I met Lord Brancker, president of the Imperial Airways, and his chief engineer, Major Mayo. The Imperial Airways had in consideration the establishment of a transatlantic line. Major Mayo had been to America and reported on the relative merits of various locations along the Atlantic coast for seaplane bases. I found that his report was very favorable to Baltimore, and invited him to visit me. I attended a lecture by Blériot in celebration of the twentieth anniversary of his first flight across the Channel, which he repeated on the day of the celebration. With Major Mayo I visited some of the important airplane factories and went to see the R-100 and R-101, great dirigibles in the course of construction, which afterwards came to disastrous endings. Luckily I could not stay to participate in one of these flights, which ended in a crash that killed nearly all aboard, including Lord Brancker.

In Paris, after visiting the airplane factories, I was present at a round-Europe flight of some fifty planes representing most of the European nations. There I saw for the first time revolutionary designs of the low-wing monoplane type, which have now been universally adopted. Flying with my son and his wife from Paris to Amsterdam, I visited the works of Fokker and then went on to Berlin, where conferences with airplane officials and manufacturers were had. Remarkable stories of the work of the gliders in Germany led me to the Röhn mountains. Here I saw the beautiful sail-planes made on the mountain top by students of a technical school.

Members of the glider club had already traveled fifty miles across country and had begun cloud flying, in which they had reached the height of a mile by utilizing the currents within storm clouds.

I next went to Lake Constance, where I saw Captain Eckener come in from America in his first Zeppelin on the trip that was to carry him around the world. Inspection of this wonderful ship with his first officer proved very interesting. A few miles away on Lake Constance was the great Dornier works. Here I saw the world's greatest flying boat, the DO-X, that subsequently flew to America.

After visiting airplane factories in Italy I joined Ambassador Garrett on his cruise, and at Athens saw the great ships of the Imperial Airways come in from Alexandria.

Soon after my return to Baltimore Major Mayo came to visit me and in a series of conferences with the Maryland Aviation Commission and city authorities, Mayo told of his investigations, in which he had come to the conclusion that Baltimore would be the best terminus for a transatlantic airline. It occurred to me that following the co-ordination that had been arranged between the Pennsylvania Railroad and a transcontinental airline a similar arrangement might be made between the Baltimore & Ohio and the Imperial Airways. President Willard of the B. & O. and his staff conferred with Major Mayo and myself and took the proposal under advisement. Mayo's visit had a far-reaching effect in the arrangements by which the Imperial Airways and the Pan-American Airways co-operated in starting the scheduled flights to Bermuda and subsequently to Europe. In the meantime national and state aviation had been making rapid progress. I joined the Association of State Aviation Officials and went to national air meets in various parts of the country.

After consultations with the Bureau of Aeronautics, United States Department of Commerce, model laws governing all aspects of aviation were passed by Maryland legislatures.

Since its inception the Maryland commission has always had as one of its members the chief of aeronautics at the United States

Naval Academy. These successive naval commanders have given much time to the meetings on state aviation questions and in the study of sites proposed for airports.

Work with this commission has brought me into close contact with many of the great figures in aviation and has added another interesting chapter to my life.

The Purse Net Bill

Devotees of fishing in the Chesapeake Bay were often outraged by "purse-netters." When, on cruising about in our small boats, we discovered a large school of rock or striped bass, not infrequently a schooner would come sailing down upon us, put off a rowboat piled high with a great net, and surround the school with it. These nets had lead sinkers which carried them to the bottom, and corks at the top by which the upper end floated on the surface. When the school had been surrounded, a drawstring closed the bottom of the net, transforming it into a huge purse in which the fish were entrapped. It was only necessary then to draw the purse systematically across one of the rowboats until the fish massed in the lower end were reached. Tons of fish were often scooped up in a single haul; I have been told that a single catch of ten tons was not rare.

For a number of years bills had been introduced in the legislature to prohibit the use of purse nets. Finally, in 1931, after conducting a vigorous campaign in the newspapers, a concerted effort was made to get a bill through. It was a hard fight, which I was called in to lead, and a good deal of trading on other bills had to be done to get it passed. The market fishermen were there in force, but we finally beat them.

Before the passage of this bill, when rock were "running," they were caught in such quantity that the market was glutted and the fishermen received very little for their immense catches. Rock were getting scarcer every year. Since the passage of this bill the number of rock in the bay have increased, but the amount of fish, and crab also, in the bay would greatly increase if Virginia would enact conservation measures similar to Maryland's. The prices received by market fishermen, who now use pound nets and other legal methods, have been so much better than before that they have lost nothing. I prize highly the gold pen and holder with which the bill was signed, a present from the Sportsman's Club.

The Potomac River Bridge

In 1932 a committee of southern Marylanders came to my home and proposed that I accept the presidency of a company to build a bridge across the Potomac River at a point halfway between Washington and the Chesapeake Bay. They pointed out that in this one hundred and forty miles there was only one small ferry, and that the great section of southern Maryland and the even larger northern neck of Virginia were separated by the broad waters of the Potomac, which prevented intercourse and greatly hindred trade and the development of the country. I had often visited and fished in the Potomac, and realized the sad situation in which these great Colonial sections of sister states had gone backward from lack of communications. In recent years Mr. John D. Rockefeller, Jr., by his reconstruction of Williamsburg, had aroused great interest in Colonial Virginia. The thousands of visitors had to take the circuitous route through Washington. The Colonial homes and plantations of southern Maryland still languished. Acquisition of the Calvert Papers and the portraits of the Lords Baltimore had aroused a keen interest in Colonial Maryland, and I was glad to join these men in this worthy effort to build a bridge just above Morgantown. It was first proposed that we form a company to sell bonds to build the bridge, after having passed the necessary legislation and secured a charter. It was then discovered that money might be secured from the Reconstruction Finance Corporation, and we laid plans accordingly.

The Maryland State Roads Commission co-operated by preparing careful studies of the Potomac River at the proposed site for the bridge. This was the narrowest point of the river, and in Colonial times was the site of Ludlow's Ferry, which Washington often used and across which his army passed on its way to Yorktown.

The necessary borings of the river bottom were complicated by the depth of the mud that filled the great gorge through which ice had passed in the glacial era. It was discovered that some of the piles would have to go down two hundred and fifty feet to get a firm foundation. The John Greiner Company, which undertook the preparation of plans, found that this would not prevent the construction of a bridge on firm foundations, having had similar experience in building a bridge across the Severn River at Annapolis.

We presented our plans and estimates to the RFC, and my old friend Mr. Jesse Jones, the chairman, gave us sympathetic hearings, and then turned our proposal over to their engineers. Unfortunately they did not prove sympathetic, and in fact made an adverse report claiming that there was not sufficient traffic in sight to make the bridge self-liquidating. About this time the PWA was flourishing, and assisting with its millions many similar projects. Mr. Jones advised that our application be transferred to it, and promised that our papers would be sent over with no adverse report attached to them. We transferred our efforts to the Department of the Interior, and one day in Georgia, while hunting with Ambassador Bingham, I received a wire saying that our plans had been approved and would probably be passed at a meeting on Saturday morning. But the Secretary of the Interior disallowed our request for assistance in building the bridge, along with many other propositions, I am told.

So the matter rested for many months. It looked as if the bridge would not be built. Then came the primary election of 1938, in which Senator Millard Tydings was opposed for re-election by Mr. David Lewis, a close friend of the President. During this campaign the President decided to make a trip through Maryland to speak in the interest of Mr. Lewis. When I learned that the President had planned to go in his yacht from Washington to the Eastern Shore, where he was to make his speech, I felt that this was an opportunity to have him visit in person the site of the bridge. Months before this

I had talked to the President about the project, and found him sympathetic, as he had often sailed on the Potomac River and Chesapeake Bay, and was familiar with the country generally. For two or three days the wires were kept busy between Baltimore and Hyde Park. At last the President promised me that he would motor through Charles County, look at the site of the bridge, and take his boat at Morgantown. He invited me to accompany him, Governor Nice, and Mr. Lewis on the trip, but previous engagements prevented this. On his visit to Charles County he appeared greatly impressed, and in a brief speech said that he would give the matter earnest consideration, and he hoped sincerely that the bridge could be built.

In the meantime the State Roads Commission had drawn up an ambitious program, which comprised new bridges across the Susquehanna River, across Baltimore Harbor, across Chesapeake Bay at Sandy Point, and our Potomac River Bridge.

For some time we were very much afraid that our bridge would suffer the same fate as the proposed bridges across Baltimore Harbor and the Chesapeake Bay. Mr. Jesse Jones, Mr. Sumner Welles, who lived on the Potomac, and Mr. R. Walton Moore, who lived on the Virginia side, and whom I had importuned, became very active in their support of the project. However, the President's interest in the matter, and his firsthand knowledge of what was to be accomplished, were finally responsible for a happy culmination of our efforts of many long years. Thus, in 1939, the bridge that Marylanders and Virginians had looked forward to for generations was begun. It is now (June, 1940) nearing completion, and will, according to the drawings, be one of the most beautiful spans in America, rising to a height of two hundred feet above the waters of the Potomac in a single span over eight hundred feet long.

The Visit of Anthony Eden to Maryland

In November, 1938, the newspapers announced that Anthony Eden was coming to deliver an address before the National Association of Manufacturers in New York. Officials, national and state, civic organizations, and leaders of society were excited at the prospect of having this distinguished Britisher come to our shores. His visit was of particular interest to Maryland because he was a descendant of Sir Robert Eden, the first Baronet of Maryland, and the last proprietary governor. Sir Robert had married Caroline Calvert, the daughter of the fifth Lord Baltimore, and through her the Edens had fallen heir to the portraits of the Lords Baltimore that I had the good fortune to acquire in London in 1933.

Mr. Eden had made it known that he would visit Annapolis, where his ancestor had lived, and was buried. The Association of Commerce had invited Mr. Eden to be their guest at a banquet in Baltimore, but received word that he could not possibly accept invitations that had been extended to him by the Mayor and the Governor. It occurred to me that he would surely be interested in seeing the portraits that had come from his home. I proposed to the Mayor that we suggest to Mr. Eden that he allow us to give him a banquet in the great hall of the Enoch Pratt Free Library, where, surrounded by the portraits of his ancestors, the Calvert Papers, and other documents of much interest to his family, he could be given an intimate dinner, entirely different from the huge banquets he was slated to attend elsewhere. The Mayor received the proposition enthusiastically, and asked me to present the invitation to Mr. Eden. I realized that it would be extremely difficult to reach him. It occurred to me that the widow of my dear friend Robert W. Bingham, recently Ambassador to the Court of St. James and an intimate friend of Mr. Eden, was at her cottage in Virginia near Stratford, General Lee's ancestral home. It was on Thursday afternoon, twenty-four hours before the scheduled arrival of Mr. Eden, that I reached her by phone and begged her to go to New York with me the next day to secure an audience with Mr. Eden. She had planned to go on Saturday, and said she couldn't leave before. It was arranged that I was to meet her on the 1:40 P.M. train in Baltimore. During the night I awoke from a troubled sleep with the presentment that Saturday would be too late, and at 3 A.M. indited a note to Mrs. Bingham begging her to go to New York a day earlier and saying I was sending the note by my chauffeur, who would assist her in packing and take her to Washington in time to catch the five o'clock train and that I would join her in Baltimore. This arrangement would get us to New York about the same time that Mr. Eden arrived on the *Aquitania*. Then I sent the chauffeur off at 8:30 A.M. with instructions that if the lady didn't phone me, he was to do so himself. In the middle of the afternoon he called me from Fredericksburg. "Doctor, I have the lady and we will be in Washington on time, but she is awful mad." When I boarded the train she was still rather peeved. When I unfolded the plan for bringing Anthony Eden and his wife to Baltimore, and giving him the banquet in the great hall near the portraits of his noted forebears, she forgave me.

It was impossible to intercept Mr. Eden, who was rushing to the banquet where he was to speak. A note was written that would reach him when he returned, in which Mrs. Bingham mentioned my mission and also her desire to greet him. The next morning we waited in suspense until eleven o'clock, but received no reply. I found that he had gone to the City Hall to meet Mayor LaGuardia and from there would go to a luncheon with the staff of the *New York Times*, from there to the World's Fair, from there to a tea, then to dinner, then to the theater, and then to a night club. All hope of reaching him seemed gone. Discouraged, I pondered what to do next. Remembering that the editor of the *New York Times*, Dr. John H. Finley, had been a professor at the Johns Hopkins University and that I had met him, I took advantage of our slight acquaintance and telephoned to ask for the privilege of speaking to Mr. Eden either before or after the luncheon. There were objections that it was a private affair, and that so distinguished a guest could not be disturbed, but finally Dr. Finley agreed that if I would come to his office before Mr. Eden left for the World's Fair, he might be persuaded to see me. I went. Dr. Finley appeared with him, and I presented the invitation to come to Baltimore. He said, "I must certainly go to Annapolis but I can't come to Baltimore, because I am scheduled to dine with the Foreign Policy Association in New York that night." I proposed the following program: "Leave Washington early in the morning, see Annapolis, come to Baltimore, visit the Enoch Pratt Library to see the portraits of your forebears, come to a luncheon at the Maryland Club, then take the 2:43 P.M. train, which will get you and Mrs. Eden to New York at six o'clock, in ample time for your dinner engagement." He said he was amazed that all this was possible, and eagerly accepted. I returned to Baltimore, and the Mayor announced in the papers that this great Englishman, in whom the whole of Maryland was so interested, would honor us with a visit. Only two days remained to prepare for him. I was besieged by patriotic and historical societies, personages of distinction, and descendants of the Calverts and Edens for the privilege of honoring Mr. Eden in one way or another.

At 9:45 A.M. we left the British Embassy in Washington, accompanied by a fleet of motorcycles, and got to Annapolis an hour later. We went to the Hammond-Harwood House, a Colonial mansion, where he was greeted by an enthusiastic group who represented the Federated Garden Clubs of Maryland, the Society of the Descendants of the Ark and the Dove, the Southern Maryland Society, the Colonial Wars, and the Society of the Descendants of Colonial Governors. Mr. and Mrs. Eden showed the keenest interest in this mansion, its charming exterior, lovely rooms, and stairways. They even inspected the vast kitchen, where the implements of the Colonial cuisine hung around the great fireplace. Standing beneath the portrait of his ancestor Sir Robert, he was snapped by a score of photographers from the press. He was then led to a microphone, where after preliminary speeches by Mrs. Harry Slack, representing the Garden Clubs, and Senator George L. Radcliffe, Mr. Eden talked of the Baltimores and the Edens and his pleasure in being in the territory that his distinguished ancestor had governed so admirably. After toasts to the King and the President had been drunk in old sherry, hurried visits were paid to other lovely Colonial homes, including one in which Sir Robert had lived and another in which he had died, and to St. Anne's churchyard, where his remains were buried beneath a marble slab extolling his virtues in ancient script. Although more than the allotted time had been used up, Mr. Eden begged to make another rapid tour past the old houses and the ancient State House. As we rushed to Baltimore with the sirens blaring before us, Mr. Eden's enthusiasm over Colonial Annapolis and his keen interest in all he had seen and heard of his distinguished ancestors were delightful.

The crowds that surrounded the entrance to the Pratt Library were enthusiastic. In the interior the columns of the great entrance hall were roped off so that the surging crowd would not interfere with his reception by the Mayor and the officers of the library. Keenly he surveyed again the majestic figures of the six Lords Baltimore, commented on the splendid setting that this magnificent hall affords and his pleasure in seeing the portraits in the city that bears their name and among people who revere their historic past. He then made a hurried inspection of the Calvert Papers that his progenitors had assembled for their solicitors to fight the heirs of William Penn in the courts of England in their effort to regain the territorial strip of twenty miles that had been stolen from them by the Penns. At the Maryland Club were fifty distinguished men of Baltimore I had invited to meet Mr. Eden. As he was presented to each his charm captured everyone. The menu had to be short. No attempt was made to have the traditional terrapin and canvas-back ducks. After a few words by the Governor and the Mayor, I explained to Mr. Eden that this luncheon was given in an effort to make amends for the rude way in which my great-grandfather had treated his great-grandfather. "When the Maryland colonists arrived at Old Point Comfort they were met by one of my progenitors, Captain William Claiborne, who announced that he already had received a patent to the large Island of Kent in the Chesapeake Bay, had established a trading-post with the Indians and cultivated the lands, so he seriously objected to the occupation by the colonists sent over by Lord Baltimore of land that embraced his territory. "As the brother of your great-grandfather refused to listen to his objections, my great-grandfather fitted out and armed two pinnaces and attacked three pinnaces of your great-grandfather in the waters of the Chesapeake, the first naval battle in American waters—and was badly defeated. A little later, my great-grandfather suddenly attacked the forces of your great-grandfather again upon the water and won. I hope, sir, that you will accept this simple luncheon as a peace offering to make amends for the treatment of your great-grandfather by my great-grandfather." Mr. Eden's reply was charming and amusing.

Hastily bidding adieu, Mr. Eden, accompanied by Lord Hinchingbrooke, Sir Martyn Beckett, and Mr. Roland Tree, made his way to the station, where Mrs. Eden and Lady Hinchingbrooke, who had lunched with Mrs. John Garrett, joined him. Mr. Eden said he felt rather dazed by all he had seen in Maryland but that he had enjoyed his visit greatly and would carry back to England a vivid picture of the home of his ancestors.

Preparing an Exhibit for Maryland at the New York World's Fair

When I left early in January, 1939, for a vacation in Florida, the Maryland Legislature was in session. The indications were that no money would be appropriated for a Maryland exhibit at the New York World's Fair. I returned home the middle of March and found awaiting me a letter from the Governor of Maryland asking me to take the chairmanship of a commission of twenty-one that he had appointed "to insure the participation of the State of Maryland in the 1939 New York World's Fair."

The Baltimore newspapers had been hostile to the proposal for weeks and had taken a violent stand against an exhibit, both in the news and in editorial columns. They were even suggesting that the best thing Maryland could do would be to exhibit "Wally's" bathtub, referring to the Duchess of Windsor.

General Dennis Nolan, an old friend, who also crossed on the *Baltic* to enter the A.E.F., was "Director of States Participation." I telephoned him and explained my predicament. Only six weeks remained before the fair was to open, and I had given no thought to the problem. General Nolan was encouraging, said his office was prepared to assist, and proposed to send one of his staff, Mr. Scarborough, to tell us what other states had done. With Senator Emanuel Gorfine, vice-chairman, and Mr. Charles W. Galloway, who had been chairman of a previous World's Fair Committee, we met Mr. Scarborough at luncheon and then went to Annapolis to confer with Governor O'Conor.

Most of the states who were participating had appropriated sums ranging from $100,000 to $1,000,000. Our neighbor Delaware had appropriated $50,000, and Mr. Scarborough thought this sum would be required to prepare even a modest exhibit for Maryland.

Governor O'Conor called in the president of the Senate and the Speaker of the House. It was their opinion that no more than $35,000 would be appropriated, but we decided to ask for $50,000. I then came down with influenza and my physicians put me to bed. Realizing that every moment was precious and that if we were to prepare an exhibit for Maryland no time was to be lost, and having no idea how long I would be confined to my home, I considered it my duty to the state and to myself to resign. I notified Governor O'Conor accordingly. Ten days later, when I returned to work, I was surprised to find that the Governor had not accepted my resignation— and nothing further had been done. There were only four weeks left. I went to see the Governor and begged to be allowed to give up the job, but he insisted on my keeping the chairmanship.

Several of us appeared before committees of the Senate and of the House. Many of the legislators were hostile to the idea of Maryland's participating at all. Finally, on March 31, a bill appropriating $35,000 to prepare an exhibit for Maryland at the World's Fair was passed, and for the first time the commission was officially authorized to go ahead.

I called the commission together and asked for suggestions, but during several hours' conference no one offered any concrete ideas. An Executive Committee was chosen, and for several weeks met daily, often several times a day, and sometimes working far into the night. A visit was made to the World's Fair and exhibits that had been installed by other states were carefully inspected. Specialists on exhibits presented their views. Some brought illustrative plans and extensive programs, but most of them became discouraged when they found out how little money had been appropriated. On May 28 I was able to report to the Governor as follows:

Two spaces were available in the Court of States for one of which the Fair demanded $15,000 and the other $11,000. We decided that we could afford only the $11,000 space.

The location is very attractive—immediately on Rainbow Avenue, the main artery of travel through the Fair, on which busses pass every few minutes. Near by, on the same avenue, are the important exhibits of Missouri, Arkansas, Tennessee and Utah. Adjacent are the exhibits of Texas, Illinois, West Virginia and Ohio.

The building which houses the Maryland exhibit has a charming colonnade which surrounds a lovely pool. Maryland is fortunate in obtaining a space so well located.

A study was made of what other states had done and consultations with persons and organizations from all over Maryland were held. The views presented were various and often entirely impracticable.

Our space measures approximately 56 x 45 feet. On account of its irregularity it was easily divisible by a broad arch into two rooms, one about 16 x 33 feet and another about 40 x 43 feet. We decided to devote the smaller room to historic Maryland and the larger one to present-day Maryland.

In the smaller room we have placed large portraits of the first and second Lords Baltimore painted by Miss Florence Mackubin thirty years ago at the ancestral home of the Baronet of Maryland, a descendant of the fifth Lord Baltimore. Between these portraits are excerpts from the Maryland charter surmounted by the coat of arms, beautifully sculptured and painted. The glorious history of tolerance and liberty, which has led to Maryland being called the Free State by the Sun papers, is stressed.

To the left of George Calvert's portrait is a large photomural of Kiplin Hall, his castle in England. To the right of the other painting, which contains not only the portrait of Cecil Calvert but also his infant son Charles, is a photomural of Mattapany, the home which Charles built on the Patuxent River.

At the ends of this room are twelve exteriors and interiors of famous Colonial Maryland homes. To furnish adequately this Calvert room we were fortunate in securing the loan of old seventeenth century furniture and on a large Jacobean chest we are placing exquisite models of the Ark and the Dove.

An attractive space has been devoted to Francis Scott Key. On each side of his portrait are facsimiles of his poem and the first musical score of "The Star-Spangled Banner." Above are two old prints—one of the bombardment of Fort McHenry and another of the Battle of North Point. Surmounting all is a replica of the original Star-Spangled Banner. Beneath the portrait of Key is a model of a ship on which he [may have] composed our national anthem.

On the wall is a large map mural of Maryland painted by Mr. Edwin Tunis depicting historic events, monuments and homes. To the left of this map are nine photomurals showing the various sporting activities of the Chesapeake and our Atlantic seaboard. To the right of the map are photomurals of commercial activities on the Bay, in which the interesting workboats and their cargoes of produce are shown. Beneath the map are ship models of the early clipper and its successors and the "Constellation," which had such a gallant record in the War of 1812.

Another wall is devoted to Maryland breeding farms, racing and hunting. Above these photomurals is a large painting by Mrs. Marion Butler Ewald of the Maryland Hunt Cup. A thrilling scene at the twelfth jump is vividly depicted.

A large space is devoted to educational and cultural Maryland with photomurals of important institutions.

Another large area is devoted to rural and industrial Maryland. Beneath these photomurals is an interesting diorama depicting the organization of the Baltimore and Ohio Railroad.

Your Commission has endeavored not only to portray the glorious colonial history of Maryland with its splendid monuments and historic institutions but many phases of modern Maryland. Literally hundreds of photographs have been scrutinized to do justice to our great state.

The Maryland Commission has been the recipient of great assistance: our consulting architect, Mr. Henry P. Hopkins; the muralists, Mrs. Marion Butler Ewald and Mr. Edwin Tunis; the ship modelers, Mr. John Dernoga and Mr. William Hurst, Jr.; the artistic photography of Mr. and Mrs. Aubrey Bodine and Mr. M. Edward Grogg; Mr. George H. Pouder and Mr. William G. Ewald, of the Baltimore Association of Commerce; and the Consolidated Gas, Electric Light and Power Company for splendid slides showing the great industrial development of Baltimore and adjacent Maryland; and our director, Mr. Warren T. King.

Varied as is our exhibit, it is only slight evidence of the steady growth

of Maryland and its principal city in industry and commerce. Modern
Maryland is ready to take a worthy place in the world of tomorrow.

On May 31, eight weeks after the money was appropriated, the
exhibit left Baltimore, and a few days later was installed at the
World's Fair by Mr. King. Mr. Paul Berge and Miss Margaret
Andrews were appointed to assist him.

July 28 was designated Maryland Day at the World's Fair. Governor O'Conor was to be the principal speaker and be tendered various
functions by the officials of the World's Fair. Many states had made
a big feature of the musical section of the program. It occurred to me
that we could not do better than to take the Naval Academy Band
and the Baltimore & Ohio Glee Club. We set about to secure them.
Through Vice-President Galloway no difficulty was encountered in
getting the services of the Glee Club, but with the Naval Academy
Band serious obstacles were met. The Commandant of Cadets referred us to the Admiral and the Admiral referred us to the United
States Navy Department. The Navy Department referred us to the
President of the United States and the President notified us that the
permission would have to come by act of Congress. By that time
only four days remained. Senator Radcliffe hastily prepared a bill,
which was presented to the Senate and then referred to the Naval
Affairs Committee. By our bringing great pressure the committee
promptly gave it a favorable report and the Senate passed it. Senator
Radcliffe immediately took the bill to the House, where the Maryland Representatives were waiting to receive it, and secured immediate consideration. It was again referred to the Naval Affairs Committee, but its chairman, Mr. Vinson, I had prevailed upon
beforehand to give it immediate attention and our bill was soon
before the House of Representatives, where it received special consideration and was passed. When at last it reached the President, he
was so engrossed with other important legislation that for a time
it looked as if our bill would not get to his attention in time. Finally
the Maryland delegations prevailed upon him to act at once, and

permission was granted just two days before Maryland Day was to be celebrated.

A special train had been arranged for. It started from Annapolis with the Naval Academy Band at six in the morning, and at Baltimore picked up the Glee Club and several hundred patriotic Marylanders who had been personally invited by our commission and urged by the Baltimore Association of Commerce to attend. Governor O'Conor and his staff went up the day before, and participated in a full program arranged for him. These included a call on Mayor LaGuardia at the summer City Hall near the fair, a call on United States Commissioner General Flynn, a luncheon by Grover Whalen, a serenade by the Naval Academy Band. At two o'clock the Maryland Day exercises began. As chairman of the commission I acted as master of ceremonies. The Naval Academy Band and the B. & O. Glee Club furnished the music. General Dennis Nolan spoke for President Grover Whalen. Governor O'Conor delivered the address, and the chairman briefly described the exhibit and invited the audience to be present when the Governor officially opened it.

During the summer Mr. King and his assistants were taxed to the utmost to take care of the visitors, estimated at some seven hundred and sixty thousand, who came to the Maryland exhibit.

Although the Governor realized that the exhibit had been very successful, he was forced to notify the World's Fair officials that Maryland could not participate in 1940 because the legislature had failed to make an appropriation for this purpose. During the winter the exhibit was brought back to Baltimore.

I prepared a report to the Governor in the form of a profusely illustrated brochure that presented in attractive form the scope of the exhibit, and what it had accomplished for Maryland. Nearly a hundred thousand booklets of various types descriptive of Maryland had been distributed. Although Maryland spent less than any other state, we are confident in the belief that it received lasting benefit from its exhibit at the New York World's Fair.

Building the Baltimore Club

Early in my career there was an accident at the Baltimore Club that did much to introduce me in Baltimore. I was sitting at my desk late one night, wondering when I would have another patient and how I would ever make my expenses, when the door opened and in came my friend Markham Marshall, who said: "Come over to the Baltimore Club at once. A man is bleeding to death." "Where is his wound?" I said. "In his forearm." Hastily picking up some clamps, scissors, needles, and ligatures, I followed him across the street to the club, and was led through the lobby past the bar into a large washroom, where I found an excited crowd of club members in evening clothes, all very tight, surrounding someone on the floor. Pushing my way through, I found Rowland Harvey, from whose right forearm there spurted intermittently a jet of blood, evidently from the radial artery. The blood-bespattered shirt fronts of the friends around him showed that they had not hesitated to get into the line of fire while attempting to put some dozen tourniquets around his arm and forearm, none of which did any good. It was only a question of a second to clamp the bleeding artery and stop the hemorrhage. Immediately there arose from the startled gang a cry of joy, and some member declared that it was the most marvelous thing that had ever been done in surgery.

On my request to get the patient into a bedroom where I could complete the operation, willing hands caught hold of various parts of his anatomy and started for the second story, but as they went out the door and climbed the circular steps, one by one fell by the wayside and rolled down the steps, upsetting others, so that finally I was forced to carry him up almost alone. Getting him into bed, I said, "We had better remove his clothes." With that one friend caught hold of each tail of his coat, split it up the back, and removed it in two halves. The vest was similarly removed, and the shirt came away in pieces. There was still a little bleeding and I thought it wise to apply a tourniquet, and asked for a stick with which to twist a handkerchief around his arm. A beautiful gold-headed cane was promptly handed me. "No," I said, "this is much too long." With a crash it was broken in two, and the short piece was handed to me with which to twist the tourniquet. The operation of ligating the vessels was then carried out, and a few stitches closed the skin. Bacchus was the anesthetist. No anesthetic was required. It was an ushers' dinner, and Rowland was doing a beautiful toe dance upon the table when he slipped and fell, and the fragments of a champagne glass cut the artery. I was immediately urged to join the club, and soon picked up a great deal of practice among its members.

A few years later I was made a member of the Board of Governors. We then decided to buy an old Colonial mansion and make it into an attractive clubhouse. As a member of the Building Committee, of which Sherlock Swan was chairman, I took great interest in planning the club, and was soon made chairman of the committee on decorations and furniture. In a little while I was head over heels with work in the study of club furniture and decorations, and made visits to clubs in Boston, Philadelphia, New York City, Montreal, and elsewhere.

While in New York I visited the exclusive Brook Club, organized by the younger Vanderbilts and Astors. Mr. Thomas Benedict Clark, chairman of the House Committee, was very kind, and invited us to see his collection of antique English furniture, which was on exhibition at the Tiffany Studios. He even offered to let Tiffany's copy for us any pieces that seemed suitable for our club. I took advantage of his kind offer and had many chairs, sofas, and tables made by the Tiffany Studios from pieces that appealed to me. For many of the pieces lovely copies of old tapestry were used as coverings. The whole formed a collection of which any club might well be proud. The other furniture was largely made in Baltimore, the designs being worked out from books showing the interiors of old English homes. The dining-room chairs were copied from an old Hepplewhite chair belonging to Dr. Joseph S. Ames, afterward president of the Johns Hopkins University. The billiard-room chairs were made in Paris. They were copies of an old priory chair known as *la chaise caqueteuse*, models of which I found in the Louvre.

For the hangings and wall coverings we organized a contest between Baltimore and New York artists. The Tiffany Studios and
the Hayden Company sent representatives with beautiful water-
color sketches and large pieces of material. This display of decorating
schemes proved of great interest to our committee, and showed
wonderful possibilities for doing the work in a very attractive way.
Unfortunately, the program submitted by the New York firms was
far beyond our means, but with the intelligent co-operation of a Baltimore firm we were able to approximate fairly closely the designs
submitted, at very much less cost.

When the furnishing and decorating of the club was completed, we
had one of the most attractive buildings of its kind in the country.
On the second floor was a long drawing-room with two splendid
Colonial mantles with broad chimney breasts above, just the place
for two fine portraits. It occurred to me that the Baltimore Club
should have two portraits of the Lords Baltimore. Without much
difficulty I secured permission from Sir William Eden to have copies
made of the portraits of the first and second Lords Baltimore that
were among the six family portraits at Windleston, the ancestral
home of the baronets of Maryland, near Durham, England. Miss
Florence Mackubin agreed to make the replicas for us, and spent a
summer in the work. She brought back beautiful reproductions of
the fine portrait of George, first Lord Baltimore, by Daniel Mytens,
and of Cecil, second Lord Baltimore, by Gerard Soest. A group of
club members chipped in and paid for one, the other I presented.
With these in place we had one of the finest clubrooms in America.

Another job of our committee was to purchase silver, china, and
the multitude of other articles required. During this period my private office was largely filled with samples. The quest became so
interesting that I rather neglected the hospital and my family, so
much so that Mrs. Young finally remonstrated, asserting that the
Baltimore Club would be my ruin. For a time I continued as chairman of the House Committee of the club, and during the formative
period all this constructive work was very interesting. The new club-

house was opened in 1908. After things had become systematized, I was glad to turn over the responsibilities to others, much to the satisfaction of my wife and my associates at the hospital. But the three years' service in these capacities in the club had been very interesting and instructive. It is a pity that, with the depression which began in 1929 and the great difficulties that most social clubs had at that time, the members decided to close the Baltimore Club and join the Maryland Club. It grieved me much to see the beautiful furniture and decorations on which we had spent so much time and effort eventually go to the mortgagor.

The Baltimore Museum of Art

In 1916 I joined a group of men interested in building an art museum in Baltimore. We had a fairly large society of contributing members, and with annual subscriptions, donations, and legacies eventually had accumulated about $40,000. It seemed wise to the Executive Committee to make a start toward an art museum by purchasing two lots on the southwest corner of Biddle Street, with a frontage of forty feet on Charles Street, on which to construct a small building for exhibitions and meetings. I was on a vacation during these discussions, and on my return to Baltimore I saw in the morning paper that the Executive Committee had voted to buy this property and intended to present the matter to the meeting of the members that afternoon at two o'clock. It seemed to me that they were making a great mistake, that to build a small museum would stop the great impetus to have a real museum of art for Baltimore. If a fine site for the future museum could be offered to the Executive Committee, I believed that this proposal to build on Charles Street could be thwarted. It occurred to me that the trustees of the Johns Hopkins University might be persuaded to donate the lower end of their property, which projected into Wyman Park, for the construction of a museum, if they could be shown that it would be of great benefit to the university.

Instead of going to the hospital, I went at once to the office of

Mr. R. Brent Keyser, president of the Board of Trustees of the Johns Hopkins University, and put my proposition up to him. After a long discussion Mr. Keyser agreed to it, and took the time to telephone other members of the Board of Trustees. He obtained, in a short time, an agreement from the majority of the board. He then gave me a letter to the Executive Committee of the Baltimore Museum of Art, offering the property. With this in hand I attended the meeting and listened to the report of the Executive Committee, which presented plans for a building at an estimated cost of $70,000. As we did not have half enough money to buy the property and build the proposed tiny museum, I opposed this expenditure, and then presented Mr. Keyser's letter. This came as a bombshell. There was much discussion, but it was finally decided not to buy and build on Charles Street, but to accept the splendid offer of the Johns Hopkins University, which amounted to a donation to the museum society of property worth about $100,000.

Then came the war, and for some years the movement for a museum was in abeyance. Finally it was decided to rent the Mary Garrett house on Monument Street, at the west end of Mount Vernon Place. Here some very attractive exhibitions were held. The active board, under the presidency of Mr. Blanchard Randall, continued to excite interest in art and to keep before the people the importance of a Baltimore art museum. In this propaganda the newspapers took an active part. Finally the Mayor and the City Council became so interested that they agreed to give the citizens of Baltimore an opportunity to vote for an appropriation of $1,000,000 for the construction of a municipal art museum. This was carried by a large majority.

Our board realized the great importance of divorcing the museum from politics. It was decided to follow as closely as possible the plan of organization of the Metropolitan Museum of Art. Mr. Henry Walters appeared with our committee before the Board of Aldermen and backed our proposals. Mr. Edwin Baetjer, in a masterly analysis of the situation, showed how the plan of organization of the

Metropolitan could be adopted for a municipally owned museum in Baltimore, and his suggestions were carried out.

The Committee on Site then considered many proposed locations. After much discussion it narrowed down to two sites, one in the middle of Druid Hill Park, on a hill just above the lake, and the other the Johns Hopkins site. The latter was finally accepted.

The next question that arose was the choice of an architect. The city statutes require that for all public buildings a Baltimore architect must be chosen, but not infrequently an associate architect from another city had been called in. It seemed to me very desirable to secure the services of Mr. John Russell Pope of New York, considered by many to be the outstanding architect in this country. His plans for the Lincoln Memorial had been accepted by the commission, but his appointment was thwarted by politicians. Mr. Pope's great buildings at Yale, Columbia, and Dartmouth stamped him as one of the greatest architects. Other advantages, it seemed to me, were that he was closely associated with Mr. Henry Walters, having married Mrs. Walters's daughter, and had designed the private art gallery in the home of Mrs. Henry Barton Jacobs on Mount Vernon Place. To have an architect thus closely connected with the two greatest art patrons in Baltimore was urged by me as of prime importance. I hoped that if we brought him to Baltimore to design our building, he could get Mr. Walters and Mrs. Jacobs interested in the municipal museum. Finally, Mr. Howard Sill was chosen as the Baltimore architect and Mr. Pope appointed associate. Shortly after the work had been begun on the plans, Mr. Sill died suddenly. Mr. Pope after that had sole charge of the designs and ultimately presented plans that the board heartily approved.

The City of Baltimore co-operated by building a boulevard to pass in front of the museum on the Wyman Park property. When completed, the Baltimore Museum of Art stood in classic beauty on an eminence looking down across Wyman Park to Charles Street.

Before long, just as I had hoped, Mrs. Jacobs showed her interest in our museum by offering to donate her wonderful collection of pictures, on the condition that the museum be considerably enlarged to take care of them and that a lecture hall be provided. Mr. Pope prepared beautiful plans, which were presented to the Mayor and the City Council. The proposal to build this addition was presented to the voters of Baltimore at the height of the depression and was defeated by a small margin. Fortunately, it was possible to arrange with the PWA to obtain funds, and Mayor Jackson and the City Council found ways and means to provide additional money to build this splendid addition, in which the great Jacobs collection has been installed and which has made the Baltimore Museum of Art one of the most attractive in the country.

The first director, Mr. Roland McKinney, was able to stimulate great interest by a fine series of exhibitions that brought the Baltimore public into intimate contact with the museum. Mr. Henry Treide had been elected president of the Museum Board. When Mr. McKinney left to head the art commission for the San Francisco Fair, Mr. Treide was very effective in arousing public interest in the museum. With the appointment of Mr. Leslie Cheek the museum has been brought still closer to the hearts of Baltimoreans. In a great series of exhibitions, loan collections, lectures, and motion-picture demonstrations for both adults and children the museum has become one of the most important factors in the civic life of Baltimore.

Just as I had predicted, the museum has been brought into close association with Johns Hopkins University, which has provided workers and lecturers of much value to the museum. At the same time the museum has been of great importance in the cultural and art work of the university and has justified the splendid donation of land by the Johns Hopkins trustees.

The War Memorial

In the spring of 1919 at the organization of the American Legion in Baltimore I offered a resolution requesting the legislature to appropriate a sum of money to build a suitable memorial to Maryland soldiers who had died in the World War. In this resolution, which was unanimously passed, it was proposed that the memorial be in the form of a building that in addition to a large auditorium would provide numerous rooms in which patriotic organizations could have their offices and meetings.

I took the resolution to Governor Albert C. Ritchie and was asked by him to be the chairman of a committee on which he appointed Colonel Redmond Stewart and Captain William C. Coleman, to prepare a bill to be presented to the legislature. The bill carried an appropriation of $400,000 on condition that Baltimore appropriate an equal amount and furnish a site for the memorial.

The bill passed unanimously and was taken to the Mayor, who appointed a committee of which Colonel Harry C. Jones was the chairman. After consultations between our two committees and an architect, it was decided that we would need at least $1,000,000. The city finally agreed to appropriate $600,000 and to authorize the construction of the building on a site facing the City Hall, with an intervening plaza.

To put through the program, Governor Ritchie appointed a State Commission on which he placed E. Brooke Lee, William I. Norris, Richard C. O'Connell, Emory L. Coblentz, and Hugh H. Young. The commission to represent Baltimore consisted of Charles F. Goob, Mrs. Henry F. Baker, S. Johnson Poe, Walter B. Brooks, and Harry C. Jones. Mr. Laurence Hall Fowler was selected to prepare designs for the building. Eventually a satisfactory plan was accepted and bids were asked.

The building is of classic design. It has an auditorium seating approximately two thousand, and around it are medallions of the divisions that served in the A.E.F. and the engagements in which they took part. With an excellent organ on the stage, the War Memorial has furnished a beautiful meeting-place for large patriotic gatherings. On the floor below are several meeting-rooms with capacities varying from fifty to three hundred, and in addition numerous smaller rooms that are used as offices and meeting-places for some sixty patriotic organizations. The members of our board participated with the City Planning Commission in designing a special forum of the sunken-garden type between the War Memorial and the City Hall. The plaza that we designed is known as the War Memorial Plaza, and is a part of the civic center that includes the City Hall, the Plaza, the War Memorial, and the City Police head-quarters building. We were able to get the adjacent streets widened, and this civic center is one of the most attractive architectural features of downtown Baltimore.

Documents Relating to Early Days of the Maryland Colony

In the summer of 1929, while in London, I was called upon by Mr. W. A. S. Douglas, correspondent of the *Baltimore Sun*. He said that an important collection of papers relating to Maryland was being offered for sale by Quaritch, who had bought them at a sale at Sotheby's auction rooms. When I read these old documents, I was so fascinated that I decided they must go back to Maryland, and bought them.

These documents had been sent by Charles, third Lord Baltimore, to his solicitors in England for use in a lawsuit against the Penns. The charter issued by Charles I to Lord Baltimore defined the limits of the Maryland Palatinate as the fortieth parallel of latitude. William Penn had come across and located Philadelphia below the fortieth parallel. Then began the celebrated dispute that culminated in a lawsuit before the courts of England that lasted for years.

The papers comprise forty items, and were originally the private papers of Lord Cecilius and Lord Charles Baltimore, proprietors of the Colony of Maryland. Among the documents is a letter signed by George, first Lord Baltimore, and addressed to Charles I. Baltimore wrote from his plantation in Avalon, Newfoundland, which colony he had founded. He described the rigors of the winters and prayed for a grant of land in a warmer climate. This document is of great historic interest, as it led to the foundation of Maryland. Then follow warrants of the King directing the preparation of a patent to Lord

Baltimore for a new colony to be called Maryland. These papers described Lord Baltimore's difficulties owing to opposition in Virginia, which caused the Maryland charter to be recalled and reissued several times.

An interesting document was a treaty with the Sachems of the Indians declared owners of the country on the west side of the Delaware Bay. The Indians signed their names with the outlines of animals, their totems. In return for the territory, which now comprises the large part of the State of Delaware, they received jack-knives, mirrors, boots, socks, and various trinkets.

Among the papers is an original letter from Charles II to the third Lord Baltimore announcing that he had granted a charter to William Penn to locate a colony north of Maryland and asking Baltimore to have a conference with Penn. Ten letters from Baltimore to Penn are among the most important documents in the collection. In the earlier of these letters Baltimore writes in dignified and friendly terms protesting politely against some of Penn's actions within the confines of northern Maryland. In his last and terribly angry letter Lord Baltimore throws off the dignified restraint exhibited in his former correspondence and speaks his mind fully to Penn, ending up with "your pen is as dirty and rude as many of your late actions."

These letters have never been published. In the library of the Historical Society in Philadelphia, I found only a copy of one by an amanuensis, which Lord Baltimore signed and sent to Penn. The collection includes other original letters, documents, and maps. It is on exhibition at the Enoch Pratt Free Library in Baltimore.

The Lords Baltimore Portraits

On July 26, 1933, a sale of portraits of great importance to Maryland was held at Sotheby's in London. These consisted of the family portraits that had come down to Sir Timothy Eden, sixth baronet of Maryland, from Carolyn Calvert, sister of the last Lord Baltimore. She had married Sir Robert Eden, Governor of Maryland.

He governed the colony until the Revolutionary War. He afterward returned and died here.

I was spending a few weeks with my friend Robert Bingham, at the American Embassy. I was notified of the sale by Thomas Agnew and Sons, Ltd., and went to see the portraits, which were hung in Sotheby's auction rooms six days before the sale. Agnew suggested that I let him bid on them for me. The next day I was called up by Mr. Robert Garrett, who said that he had come to London at the request of the directors of the Walters Art Gallery with instructions to buy these portraits. I told Mr. Garrett that I was delighted at the prospect of these portraits going to the Walters Gallery and assured him I would not be at the sale, but would go to Paris to see the Davis Cup matches.

On the day after the sale the Paris newspapers carried the information that the portraits had been sold to various bidders, one of whom, Lord Duveen, had paid £4,600 for the one of Cecilius Calvert, second Lord Baltimore, by Gerard Soest. The names of the other purchasers were not given.

When I returned to London on August 1, I went at once to Agnew's. I was told that the pictures had been bought by various commissioners, the names of the actual purchasers not being disclosed. I asked Agnew to discover the buyers of the various portraits. I was soon informed that Sir Timothy Eden had bought in, to withdraw them from the sale, the portraits of the first, third, fourth, and sixth Lords Baltimore, but that the one of the fifth Lord Baltimore had been bought by a person whose identity was unknown. Through Agnew I got in touch with Sir Timothy and asked him at what figure he would be willing to part with the four Baltimore portraits. In a few days negotiations were completed, and I secured them. As the sum asked was not at hand, the American Ambassador kindly guaranteed the sale.

In a short time it was discovered that the owner of the portrait of the fifth Lord Baltimore was Alfred, Lord Fairfax, who was born in Maryland and went to England when he became of age, to assume the title of his forefathers and his seat in the House of Lords. Lord Fairfax offered to sell the portrait to me. He informed me that the portrait of Benedict Leonard Calvert, Governor of Maryland and a son of the fourth Lord Baltimore, had been bought by a former Baltimorean, Mr. Hallam Tuck, who was living in Belgium. Lord Fairfax offered to begin negotiations to secure this portrait also for me. A month later he cabled me that Mr. Tuck had agreed to sell it.

Before I left London I arranged that the portraits should be carefully cleaned under the scientific direction of Agnew. Although they were in excellent condition, there were many coats of varnish, which marred their beauty and had to be removed. Ambassador Bingham proposed exhibiting these portraits at a reception in the Embassy before they were shipped to America. Lord Fairfax participated.

The portraits were shipped to Baltimore, where they were exhibited by the Tercentennial Commission in conjunction with the celebration on November 22, 1933, of the sailing of the *Ark* and the *Dove* from Cowes, England. These small ships brought the first colonists to Maryland.

The portraits were subsequently exhibited at the Baltimore Museum of Art, and are now, for the time being, loaned to the Enoch Pratt Free Library in Baltimore, where they have attracted great interest. Just what final disposition I shall make of them is still uncertain.

Interest in Musical Affairs

When I joined the Colstons, I had my first experience with a family steeped in music. Mr. Colston came to Baltimore as a poor Confederate captain after the Civil War. He spent almost every penny that he saved on musical events. One Sunday, on an afternoon stroll, as he passed a home on Eutaw Place the lovely notes of a soprano floated through the windows. Fascinated, he waited until the singing was over. He then made inquiries and found that the singer was the daughter of Justice John Archibald Campbell, who had left the United States Supreme Court to serve in Jefferson Davis's Cabinet and after the war had come to practice in Baltimore. Arranging an early meeting with the singer, the gallant Captain fell desperately in love and finally won the fair lady's hand. When his four daughters married, we outsiders were brought into the most closely knit family organization in the city. Every Wednesday evening we went to the Captain's home to dinner, where music occupied a large part of the conversation. Wednesday night had been chosen because the Boston Symphony Orchestra came to Baltimore then. We had to hurry through dinner in order to get to the Lyric early, as the Captain insisted. In common with other music-lovers, we sat in the gallery, where the acoustics were best.

In this highly musical family the in-laws, particularly myself, felt our dense ignorance. One day when Mr. Huber told me of his desire to organize a string quartet with four fine musicians at the Peabody, I readily assented to his proposition to finance the venture, just to prove to the family that I did have some interest in music. Mr. Huber arranged six concerts in the lovely statuary hall of the Peabody Institute and there among palms and flowers gave one of the most charming series of musicales ever held in Baltimore.

Captain Colston was secretary of the company that built the Lyric. He and Mr. Frank Frick had been the chief propagandists for a music hall for Baltimore, and finally raised enough money to build it. Mr. Henry Randall had prepared ambitious plans based on the great music hall in Leipzig. Funds subscribed by the Lyric Company, which they organized, were not nearly enough to complete the building. A grandiose curved façade with carriage drives and so on had to be left out, and a mortgage was necessary. As it was difficult to make money on musical affairs at that time, the company sank deeper and deeper in debt and the mortgagors took it over. After passing through several reorganizations it was finally sold to a group representing the Metropolitan Opera Company in New York, who bought it to keep Oscar Hammerstein from having a house in Baltimore. Mr. Otto Kahn, who was said to own a majority of the Metro-

politan stock, also controlled the Lyric. After preventing Hammerstein from getting it, he took little interest in his Baltimore purchase
and allowed a vulgar manager to apply atrocious arches beneath
the classic columns that supported the gallery and let the furniture
and decorations deteriorate greatly. Mr. Colston bewailed the sad
state to which his pet venture had fallen.

His daughter, Esther Colston Coale, had formed a committee of
six for the promotion of music, of which Mrs. Harold Randolph,
Miss Ellen Starr, James Swan Frick, Ral Parr, and I were the other
members. One day in 1920 Mrs. Coale called the committee together at her home and announced that the Lyric was about to be
sold, either for a garage or for a movie house, that such a happening
would break the hearts of music-lovers in Baltimore, and that
something must be done. A meeting was arranged at which some
forty were present, and I was asked to preside. All agreed that immediate action must be taken to save the Lyric. I talked too much,
and as a result was nominated to take charge of the campaign.
We assembled a large group of Baltimore music-lovers, stirred them
to activity, and organized a vigorous campaign.

In the meantime, Mr. Otto Kahn gave us an option for $225,000
and also offered three stores adjoining the entrance, which we felt
we should have, for $80,000. In one of the most intensive drives ever
seen in Baltimore we secured in twelve days subscriptions for stock
to the extent of $250,000. This campaign was conducted without a
professional manager or clerks, and without overhead. We bought
the Lyric, giving Mr. Kahn a mortgage for $100,000. During this
drive Mr. Frederick R. Huber, secretary of the Peabody Institute
and himself a musician and connoisseur of great ability, was of much
assistance. He was asked to be managing director. Mr. R. E. Lee
Taylor prepared plans for the improvement and modernization of
the theater, on which we spent over $80,000. In the company that
had been formed to run the theater I was forced to take the presidency.

We were fortunate in securing Mr. Albert Young, a man of great theatrical experience, as active manager. He assembled a fine group of workers, and under Mr. Huber's expert directorship made the duties of the president comparatively light. Mr. Huber had been made Municipal Director of Music, and organized the Baltimore Symphony Orchestra. This he brought to the Lyric, and soon made it a musical organization of high class considering that the musicians got little pay and had only Sunday evenings for their performances.

The Lyric had been designed primarily as a music hall; the stage was not large, there was no orchestra pit, there was very little provision for scenic effects. There were only four dressing-rooms on the level of the stage. It was therefore a difficult place in which to give grand opera, but we would not be satisfied until we brought these great musical events to Baltimore. Regardless of our inadequate arrangements, the Chicago Opera Company was induced to come. Mary Garden was the manager and sang beautifully in *Thais*. At Mr. Huber's suggestion I arranged an after-theater supper for the artists and my musical friends after the last opera, in which Chaliapin sang in *Mephistophele*. This great singer and actor was never so wonderful as on that occasion. The audience, which filled every seat and included eight hundred standees, was thunderous in its applause and called him back many, many times. After the performance the stars came out to my home. Mary Garden, however, for whom the party was given, was not on hand to greet the guests. As I was wondering what had happened, I was called to the telephone. "This is Miss Garden's secretary. Miss Garden has a bad headache and presents her excuses." The first person to whom I announced the sad news was Chaliapin. His face beamed with delight. "Yes," he said, "she must have a very bad headache. I gave it to her. I had three times as many standees and four times as many encores as she got."

After a few seasons we approached the Metropolitan Opera Company with the request to come to Baltimore. They answered that our arrangements were too inadequate. Securing an architect, we found it possible to prepare a pit for the musicians and to hang on the side of the building eight dressing-rooms. The money for these important additions I secured from Captain Isaac E. Emerson. With the stage enlarged and lighting arrangements greatly improved, the Metropolitan presented beautiful performances. An Opera Club had been formed to guarantee us against loss, as it was necessary for us to pay them about $16,000 for each performance as well as to furnish the Lyric and make all necessary arrangements. Since then the Metropolitan has come every year for three or four performances, and the Opera Club guarantors have never had to contribute one cent. Some seasons we broke even and in others we made money. We were able to make donations to the orchestras of the public schools and on several occasions to assist the Lyric in redecorating and furnishing. While the Opera Club succeeded in having the Metropolitan here year after year without a deficit, other cities, Washington, Pittsburgh, Cleveland, Atlanta, required their guarantors to contribute thousands of dollars to make up deficits.

Our success in Baltimore is largely attributable to the fact that about twenty-five hundred families participate in the ownership of the Lyric, and although they have received nothing in dividends, continue to take great interest in their property. During the twenty years in which the present Lyric Company has been in existence, we have made many improvements to our building. With the increase in costs, the symphonies and the opera company notified us that unless we could enlarge the building they would have to stop coming to Baltimore. Behind the main auditorium was a small, second-story theater for which we had little use. I finally discovered a way in which, by taking down the rear wall of the main hall, the gallery could be continued upward and thus increase the seating capacity from twenty-two hundred to approximately three thousand. This change had been proposed before, but the architect's staircase took up so much room that few additional seats were provided by the plan. With a builder of steel fire escapes, I developed a plan by which stairs and fire escapes could be combined in one outside construction, thus giving the entire interior for additional seats. The money for this addition was mostly raised at a small meeting of friends at my home one afternoon. In a short time the fund was complete. In addition to adding vastly to the seating capacity of the Lyric, we were able to carry out much needed refurbishing.

In 1934 the affairs of the Lyric reached a critical stage with the failure of the Baltimore Trust Company, which held a mortgage for $140,000 against our property, then valued at about $600,000. In the midst of the financial crisis no other company would take the mortgage. It was necessary to have another campaign to raise funds. A group of prominent businessmen that I assembled at a luncheon gravely warned that the money could not be raised at that time. Regardless of that, we went out and raised all we needed to pay off the mortgage and to put the Lyric in a position so that it would have no more crises. Since then we have prospered; we have been able to improve our building greatly, to extend our interests, and to reduce the prices of grand-opera seats. We have no mortgage on our property. Under the able directorship of Mr. Huber the operations of the Lyric Company have been very smooth. The Lyric holds, indeed, an important place in the hearts of Baltimoreans, and is hardly exceeded by the Museum of Art as a civic enterprise.

Recently the Baltimore Opera Club made a donation of $1,000 to the fund of the campaign to save the Metropolitan Opera Company. In order to stir up public interest I presented the check on the stage of the Lyric Theatre to Mr. Edward Johnson, the director of the Metropolitan, between acts of *The Barber of Seville*.

A Trip with Frank Munsey to Germany

IN JUNE, 1921, Bessy and I took the children to France. On the *Ile de France* we met Frank A. Munsey, a patient of mine, and four of his friends—Wilde Hammill, Charles H. Sabin, Jr., Leonard Replogle, and Philip Lydig. They were on their way to visit the properties of the Archduke Frederick of Austria, which had been taken over by Munsey and his associates. When they arrived in Paris, they were met by Thomas Felder, formerly of Atlanta. Tom Felder had been living in Switzerland, where he had encountered the Archduke Frederick of Austria and his wife, along with other aristocrats who had escaped to neutral Switzerland during the World War. Tom loved mingling with the great, and it was not long before he and the Archduchess were fast friends. Sympathetically he listened to her story of how their great properties, which comprised hundreds of thousands of acres of mineral, timber, and farm lands and before the war had been valued at about $400,000,000, were in danger of confiscation. He was flush, and before long she had borrowed some $20,000 from him, but as she needed much more, she finally proposed that Tom form a company to take over their properties, and pay her $80,000 and a third of the yearly income from them. He was fascinated with the idea, and before long had persuaded Munsey and his friends to go in with him.

The group put up at the Hôtel Ritz. Almost immediately Wilde Hammill came down with a heart attack, and although I called in distinguished Parisian specialists and Dr. Thomas R. Brown of the Johns Hopkins Hospital, who was in Paris then, Hammill died. Greatly upset over his death, Munsey asked me to go with them in their private car, which was to leave immediately for central Europe. The first property we visited was a great steel mill in Silesia. Leaving the private car on a siding in Czechoslovakia, we proceeded in two open touring cars to a bridge over the Vistula River, intending to cross over into Silesia, but we were stopped by a barrier similar to an American tollgate. A group of officers whose gold braid and decorations suggested high rank appeared. The interpreter showed our passports and papers, but made little headway. The conversation became fast and furious. Finally Frank Munsey rose from his seat and said: "You tell those fellows that I am Frank A. Munsey, owner of the *New York Herald*, and if they don't let us through I'll show them up in the press and shut off any more American contributions to their damned country." The gates were then opened, but we had proceeded only a hundred feet before we encountered another barrier on the Silesian side of the river, and more high officials and more palaver. Whereupon Frank Munsey arose and repeated his philippic, with the same result.

After inspecting steel mills and also a brewery that belonged to the estate, we hurried on to Vienna to see the Albertina Art Gallery, which was valued at $100,000,000 and formed the most important part of the Archduke's properties. This gallery was particularly rich in Rembrandts and other great paintings. We had time only to pass hurriedly through its beautiful galleries, as it was necessary to return to the hotel to meet Samuel Untermyer, who, as legal council for the company, had come to Vienna to hold a conference with the Archduke and Archduchess.

These aristocrats had been keen to have the Americans take over their properties when the Social Democrats had got control of Austria and Czechoslovakia and threatened confiscation. Now that this danger had passed, they were trying by artful devices to put the Americans out and get their properties back. Untermyer was very positive that the plan he had evolved would put a stop to their schemes. When they left the Hôtel Bristol about ten o'clock in the morning, all dressed up in frock coats, striped trousers, high hats, and gold canes, Untermyer called back to us, "You wait and see what I will do to that troublesome Archduchess." Philip Lydig and I, not being members of the company, waited at the hotel. Three hours later they came back, the most bedraggled, disappointed-looking bunch I have ever beheld. When they assembled in our suite, no one said anything for a while, and then Untermyer said, "Well, did you ever see such a terrible woman?" Gradually it developed that they had been no match for the Archduchess, who had made monkeys of them.

Hoping to have more success in Czechoslovakia, we went to Prague, where conferences were held with President Masaryk and Minister Beneš, the results of which were more satisfactory, and the party adjourned to Carlsbad for a rest cure, which they badly needed.

Meeting Marguerite Harrison, Just Out of a Russian Prison

I went on to Berlin because the papers had stated that an old friend of mine, Marguerite Harrison, had just been liberated from a Russian prison because of tuberculosis, and would soon be in Berlin. While waiting for her, finding that at that time Berlin was the greatest center for Oriental pearls in the world, I devoted myself to procuring a nice string for Bessy. The aristocrats and wealthy people, their fortunes depleted by four years of war, were selling their jewels. One district of Berlin was filled with pearl merchants.

At the Hotel Adlon were Mr. and Mrs. Fred Allen, whom we had met on shipboard. She had shown me a necklace her father had bought from Cartier some years before, one of the most beautiful and perfectly matched strings, she said, in existence. At one of the great wholesalers I found hundreds of thousands of pearls carefully classified. Spurred on to accept nothing but the best, I finally got together a string, each pearl of which was perfectly round, with no imperfection, with fine skin and a lovely rosée. When I told her what I had assembled, Mrs. Allen offered to inspect them, saying, "Of course, you won't be able to duplicate my Cartier necklace," but when we placed her necklace beside the other she was amazed to find that they were of the same perfection, though her pearls were larger. It was because of the great fall in the value of the mark that I was able to procure this necklace. I had kept the project a secret and Bessy was overwhelmed when I slipped the necklace around her neck on my return to Paris.

When Marguerite Harrison reached Berlin, she was pale and thin, dressed in the shabby khaki dress she had worn in prison. She was immediately surrounded by correspondents, because her liberation made front-page material. I had seen her when she came to Paris as a correspondent of the *Baltimore Sun* during the latter part of the World War. With the Armistice, she disappeared into Germany, and the next I heard of her she was in a Russian prison. She had been in Berlin during the Revolution, narrowly escaping machine-gun bullets, and was about the only correspondent at the secret Weimar convention. In German dress and speaking the language perfectly, she had no difficulty in being accepted as a delegate.

Before long she was a correspondent with the Polish Army. Desirous of getting into Russia, one night when things were quiet on the front, with the permission of some Polish officers, she had boldly climbed out of the Polish trenches and walked across no-man's land into the Russian lines. The Russians were so surprised to see a woman approach that they held their fire. A Lieutenant took her in hand, and passed her on to the captain. She had learned to speak Russian, and told such a plausible story that he took her to the general, who was so greatly intrigued by her exploit that he put her up at his mess, and eventually took her by motor to Moscow.

Before long she was denounced as a spy, tried, and imprisoned in the Cheka. In this notorious prison she occupied with sixteen other women a room so small that as they slept on the floor they completely filled the space. During the six months she spent in this room, there came prisoners with all types of loathsome disease, even acute fevers, from which a number died. The food was terrible, but they were given great quantities of tea, and with this she was able to wash herself, so that she was distinctly tea-colored when she arrived in Berlin. Our Government had frequently demanded her release, but it was granted only when the prison physicians declared that she had pulmonary tuberculosis.

I insisted that she consult a specialist in Berlin whom I knew. At first he said that he could not see her because he had thirty people waiting in his office, but when she reached him, he became so interested in her story of Russia and her experiences that he kept the other patients waiting two hours. Finally he reported to me that she did not have tuberculosis. I took her to a fashionable modiste to get clothes, but when she was asked to remove her dress, she said that she could not, because she had nothing on beneath it. We got back to the hotel in time for her to get into her new garments and go to the American Embassy for dinner. The French and British Ambassadors were there and kept her well beyond midnight discussing the Russian situation and reciting her own remarkable story.

I left the next morning for Paris, carrying a diplomatic pouch that had been placed in my care for delivery to the Embassy in Paris.

With the American College of Surgeons to South America

In the spring of 1923 members of the American College of Surgeons chartered the S.S. Van Dyke for an extensive cruise to Central America and South America. The object was to visit members of the College of Surgeons in Latin American countries, hold scientific meetings there, and strengthen the bonds of friendship between the Americas. The program was similar for each country. An official call was made on the President, who usually gave us a reception attended by high officials and local members. A scientific session was held, at which medical papers were presented by the resident members of the American College of Surgeons and prominent physicians as well as some of the visiting surgeons. The points of interest in the principal cities usually were visited, a banquet was held, and there were many private receptions.

The visits occupied from one to several days and were remarkably successful, particularly in stirring up interest in the American College of Surgeons and fostering goodwill between the Latin American nations and the United States and Canada. There were some three hundred members and their wives and friends aboard our ship. While at sea a portion of each day was given up to medical meetings, that were organized according to specialties, at which interested groups got together. General medical meetings, which were attended by all on board, were also held. There was in addition much time for sport and recreation, and almost every night the orchestra furnished music for a dance. It was an interesting and enthusiastic group of men and the trip was a very profitable one. We had a lot of fun on board ship and also on land, and made many new and lasting friendships in the fourteen countries we visited.

One of the attractive women aboard was Portia ——— of Pittsburgh, who was traveling with her mother. She was a charming young woman who had just returned from Paris, where she had sung in the Opéra Comique. Her lovely Paris gowns attracted attention at once. She was amusing and gay, and we became fast friends. At Trinidad while traveling in the country she spied some natives with gold nose and ear pieces. Fascinated, she stopped to bargain with a woman. While we were talking the woman's husband came out of a banana patch and joined us. Saying that she had other prettier pieces, the woman went to her cabin about a hundred yards away.

As soon as she left, her husband asked if we would like to see a young boa constrictor. I was not at all interested, but my companion said she would be delighted. The native appeared with a ten-foot boa in his hands. The snake apparently was tame, and moved its head and neck gracefully around in front of the young woman, who was fascinated and exclaimed at the beauty of the green eyes and the lovely forked tongue that darted out frequently. Seeing her admiration, the native asked if she would like to hold the snake. She said she would and took it in her hands. At that moment the native was called by his wife to join her in the cabin, leaving us with the snake. Portia continued to admire the reptile and then suddenly cried out: "Oh, the snake has wrapped himself around my arm and is beginning to constrict! I'm afraid he is going to break my arm!" I turned, and sure enough, the snake had wound itself four or five times around her arm and forearm, and I could see it tightening its coils. Now terrified and crying louder, Portia demanded that I pull off the snake. I holloed to the native, but he was still in the cabin. Fearing that the arm would be crushed, I realized that something must be done at once. Grasping the snake by its neck to prevent its biting me, I struggled, and finally pulled it off the lady's arm and dashed it to the ground. The native was much upset when he found that his pet had wriggled off into the bushes.

I reprimanded Portia, but without much effect. A few weeks later we were at the great Brazilian snake farm where sera are made from hundreds of poisonous reptiles that are kept in pens there. Portia allowed the director to present her with a snake, which she put in a large gold mesh bag that she carried on her arm. When I demanded to know what she was going to do with it, she calmly said she intended to take it back to the ship. The director had given her a box of special food, which she asked me to carry. When she got back to the ship, Portia said she intended to keep the snake in a shoe box in her stateroom.

The next morning one of the stewards asked me to come immediately to Room 75. The lady wanted to see me right away. I found Portia greatly excited. She had been awakened to discover that her snake had made its escape from the box and entered the bunk of a lady near by. Portia had arrived just in time to prevent the killing of her pet snake. She demanded that I go to the Captain and plead with him not to have the snake thrown overboard. At another port Portia acquired a pet turtle that she led around the deck on a pink ribbon. This little beast inspired the following:

TO A PET TURTLE

The fancy of a lady fair
  Has changed your sordid lot,
And saved your gizzard from the knife,
  Your liver from the pot!

And now henceforth a luscious life
  Your joyful lot will be,
To linger in the scented rooms
  Of her, Your Majesty.

To eat from out her dainty hand
  The rarest kinds of sweets,
And munch in your reptilian mouth
  Most fascinating eats.

But best of all will be the charm
  Of *grande intimité*,
In which you'll live with such a queen,
  All petted day by day.

How *ravissant* it is to be
  Permitted thus to roam,
Amidst her silken lingerie
  And call yourself at home!

Oh, little beastie, turtle small,
  I envy you your lot,
To serve so near a Princess fair
  And thus escape the pot.

When Portia arrived back in New York she had with her the snake, the turtle, several parrots, and a monkey.

After a delightful visit to many ports, including Rio, we arrived at Buenos Aires, where we were greatly impressed by the beautiful university and hospital. We were surprised to find surgery expertly done. At Buenos Aires the party divided. Most returned on the *Van Dyke*. Some of us crossed the mountains to Chile and came up the West Coast. Before leaving the *Van Dyke* I gave a dinner to my friends, and indulged in a friendly gibe at the high-priced surgeons on board.

OUR IMPROVED TECHNIQUE

And now we've sailed the Southern Seas
　　Once claimed by buccaneers,
We surgeons, who at cutting throats
　　Are easily their peers!

We've traveled where Pizarro burnt
　　And killed with bloody hands,
But we have spilled more blood than he
　　E'er dreamt of, with his bands!

When Morgan pillaged Panama
　　And robbed them of their gold,
He was an amateur, compared
　　With some aboard, I'm told!

And Captain Kidd, the cruel beast,
　　Was nothing but a piker,
At sending to the great beyond,
　　Compared with a Van Dyker.

At Santiago we found another excellent medical school and hospital. At Lima we were struck by the high character of the medical profession.

Passing through the Panama Canal, we eventually reached New York after an absence of two and a half months. The trip had been delightful and very profitable.

The International Society of Urology at Rome

In 1924 I went to the International Society of Urology, which was meeting in Rome. They did me the honor of electing me president of the next congress, which was to meet in New York. After the meeting, with my wife, her mother, and three children, we toured through Italy, visiting the hill-towns and spending a lot of time in the art galleries in Florence. From there we motored to the Adriatic, and on to Venice, where all of us enjoyed hugely the bathing at the Lido, then through Switzerland and France to Paris, where we had portraits of the children painted.

A Mediterranean Cruise and a Trip to Egypt

In 1926, with our friends the William Keysers, we took another Mediterranean cruise. In Cairo I called upon another member of the International Society of Urology, and told him I wanted to see a harem. He said it would be impossible, because there were only three left and he had no entree to any of these. He explained that with the mounting of living-costs the maintenance of harems had become increasingly difficult, and finally a law had been passed that made them unnecessary. It was now only necessary for a husband to write a polite note to his father-in-law, explain that as he had no longer any need of his daughter, he was returning her, and accompany this announcement with the equivalent of a $20 bill. After this the husband was free to marry again. "You have a new favorite when you want a change, and no troubles with the deposed one, and no need of eunuch guards" he said.

In London I had met Lady Carnarvon, who had given me a letter to her husband. At Luxor we found Lord Carnarvon, who was busy with Mr. Howard Carter opening the tomb of Tutankhamen. They kindly gave us a private view of the tomb and its gorgeous furnishing. Returning to Cairo, we sent a messenger to Lord Allenby with a letter of introduction that had been given me by Lord Balfour, whom I had met at the home of Ambassador John W. Garrett in Baltimore. Having left early the next morning on a sightseeing trip, I failed to see a note from the Governor General inviting our party to lunch. On returning to the hotel too late to accept, I was soundly upbraided by the ladies. A note of apology brought an invitation to tea, where we were delightfully entertained by Lord and Lady Allenby.

A Trip to India

The next year, after Christmas we were off again on another cruise, which was to take us across to Paris, to Marseille, through the Suez Canal to Colombo. At Ceylon Mrs. Young acquired some sapphires. Crossing over to India, we "did" the celebrated temples and arrived at Calcutta. On the ship I had met a big-game hunter who thrilled me with his descriptions of how he had gone into the jungle on foot attended only by natives with their spears. He had supreme contempt for those who shot tigers from platforms in trees to which the animal was attracted by a carcass fastened down near by. The thing to do was to go in, shoot your tiger—follow him in the jungle, kill him, and have the natives bring him out triumphantly. I decided not to use the letters I had to the Viceroy, with which I had hoped to participate in a hunt on elephant back, but to stalk my tiger with a bunch of natives, as my hunter friend had done.

At Calcutta I went to a gun shop to secure a rifle and to make arrangements for a tiger hunt. The proprietor said he knew an excellent place. It was one of the islands near the mouth of the Ganges. There was a tiger there that had terrified the native population, and a trip there would be interesting. Recently two Englishmen on the staff of the Bengal Railroad had had the same idea. They got rifles from the proprietor, went to the island by boat, and were enthusiastically received by the natives. They knew where the tiger could be found in a jungle, and a hundred men volunteered to accompany the Englishmen. In they went, preceded by a few natives. They had not gone far when out of the thicket bounded the tiger. The natives faded away. On rushed the tiger, and felled the first Englishman. Menaced by the animal, the second Englishman shot, missed, then followed the natives. He could hear the brute crushing the bones of his friend. Frantic with remorse, he decided to kill the beast and rescue the body, although the natives had fled. He had not gone far when the tiger unexpectedly burst out from a thicket and attacked him. But being more interested in his first kill, the tiger left him. Having finished his meal, the tiger went back into the jungle, At nightfall the natives stealthily returned and rescued the second Englishman. I saw him in the hospital, where he was recovering after amputation of his arm. In a feeble voice he gave full particulars of his horrible experience. I decided not to go after a tiger.

I was invited to address the British Public Health Institute at Calcutta, and showed slides of our work on antiseptics and intravenous therapy. At Darjeeling we had a wonderful trip up the mountain, each of us carried by four coolies, and had a gorgeous sunrise view of Mount Everest. At Benares we wondered why those who came to worship, bathe, and drink the waters of the sacred Ganges, filled with the filth of the city and the remains of the bodies cremated on its banks, did not acquire fatal infections.

At the Viceroy's ball we met some maharajahs. At dinner there was a pretty English girl who had purchased at a curio shop a silver heart, which she was wearing on a silken cord around her neck. It happens that this silver piece is worn by the native girls up to the age of six, but it is suspended by a cord around the waist, and hang below as their only modest apparel. The young lady was pleased with her purchase and asked a British officer what he thought of it. He nonchalantly replied that he thought it was very attractive, but wasn't she wearing it a bit high?

At Jaipur a ride to the palace on elephants almost shook out our insides. How such rides could have ever become popular with the aristocracy I cannot understand. At this palace we were beset by jewelers, many from prominent firms with magnificent collections, some of which had come from rajahs. Mrs. Young was fascinated with an old emerald necklace, and I had to mortgage the farm to get it.

The Maharajah of Baroda had invited us to visit him. He was an

Oxford man, and spoke English without an accent. His Maharanee was no longer in purdah and entertained us at tea. The Maharajah gave us a delightful dinner, which was attended by some forty of his principal men and their wives. The plates were of gold and the food typically Parisian. He and his wife were not present, as such food was forbidden them. The Chief Justice and other members of his court were not so punctilious. After dinner Baroda and his wife met us in a great drawing-room. We were entertained by poets, singers, players, and dancers. Much of the music was mystic and entirely beyond me. I later complained to Mr. Stokowski that I been unable to see any beauty in the singing or the music. He explained that it was because my ear was not educated, that the Hindus had twenty-one notes instead of our octave, and many notes that my uneducated ear could not get. He insisted that their music was beautiful and said that he had made trips there to study it.

At Bombay I found an excellent Parsee medical school. These Zoroastrians who leave their parents' bodies in the towers of silence for the buzzards to devour are otherwise very charming people. I dined with the professor of ophthalmology. I saw him perform twenty-one eye operations in sixty minutes, seventeen being on cataracts. I know of no ophthalmic surgeon in Europe or America who has such dexterity. At his invitation I addressed the students. The tall amphitheater was filled with eager brown faces. I have never had such an enthusiastic audience. They applauded every successful case I described, and discreetly remained silent when I reported failures.

We called at the office of the greatest pearl merchant in the world to get a few studs, and saw nine natives squatting on the floor engaged solely in the work of boring holes into pearls. The whirling needle was operated by a fiddle bow while the pearl was held in position with the other hand, assisted by the left great toe.

The homeward trip through Egypt and the Bosporus, and stopping at Constantinople (now Istanbul), Constanza, Bucharest, Budapest, and Vienna, was completed by a motor trip through the flowering fields of Holland. The gorgeous acres of tulips were at their loveliest.

A Cruise to the Aegean

In 1929 Ambassador and Mrs. John W. Garrett invited me to join them in a cruise through the Aegean Sea. Leaving the Embassy at Rome, they joined us at Genoa, where we went aboard the Drexel yacht *Sayonara*. The ship's company included Mr. and Mrs. Garrett, Mrs. Mary Benjamin Rogers, Mrs. Arthur Woods, Sir Rennell and Lady Rodd, Marc Connelly, and myself. A brief stop was made at Naples, then on to Capri and the Blue Grotto. Next we hurried on to Taormina and Malta and reached the area of the Grecian islands, where we climbed the criscross path that led to the top of Thera.

Anxious to put to test my knowledge of modern Greek, on which I had spent several months at the Berlitz School, I fired some of it at a tall native who offered to guide us. I was distressed when he apparently understood nothing that I said. At Crete I had better luck, as I have elsewhere related.

At Rhodes I was fascinated by the great hospital of the Knights of St. John. The huge ward with its vaulted ceiling is one of the most magnificent in the world, and would still make a splendid hospital after many centuries of nonuse. Around it were the great granite balls that were fired by the powderless cannon at the Turks who besieged them for years before the place fell—by treachery, I believe.

The island of Cos interested me most, because Hippocrates had lived there. Here were written those immortal works which for centuries were the foundation stones of medicine and still contain many golden truths by which we moderns may well profit. One of the first things encountered was the great tree, some fifteen feet in diameter, under the branches of which Hippocrates is said to have taught about four hundred years before Christ. The remains of the great health resort are many and interesting. One of the first we

saw was the baths, which must have been elaborate. The foundations and ruins of hospitals and beautiful temples were also clearly
seen. We next visited Patmos, Samos, and Athens, then went on to
Epidaurus, the ancient shrine of Aesculapius, still perfect in many
respects. We first came to the great amphitheater, which I believe
seated twenty thousand and which is still almost perfect, with only
the stage gone. Mounting a pedestal, Marc Connelly delivered an
oration, which we, on the topmost seats, heard with great distinct-
ness. Sir Rennell Rodd also declaimed beautifully to us. The acoustics were wonderful. We then visited in succession the ruins of the
great hospital, the home for doctors, and that for nurses, and then
saw the splendid stadium. Undoubtedly this was one of the greatest
health resorts the world has ever seen, with a large hotel for guests
and ambulatory patients, the hospital beautifully equipped, the
great theater and stadium. In attractiveness it unquestionably
surpasses anything we have today, and even in its fallen state dis-
plays a beauty of architecture and design excelling any of our
modern institutions. In the small museum were gathered tablets
recording the maladies of some of the patients, and they were most
interesting to study. One left with a great admiration for the medicine of ancient Greece that flourished here some seven centuries
before Christ, although it was based on the worship of the god
Asklepios.

The trip led through the Corinth Canal, to visit Delphi and the
island of Ithaca, which Sir Rennell had studied so brilliantly, and
then on to the Adriatic Sea, where we visited the charming cities
ranging along the coast, and finally to Venice, where we spent several delightful days before leaving for our various destinations.

This wonderful cruise was made even more delightful by the
evenings we spent on deck in the moonlight while Sir Rennell read
from a book of his poetic translations of Sappho's verses, or Mr.
Marc Connelly recited scenes from his *Green Pastures* and hummed
the spirituals he intended to include in this forthcoming play.

Some wonderful colored motion pictures of Mrs. Garrett and her dozens of gorgeous pajamas, and Mrs. Woods and Mrs. Rogers in colorful Parisian costumes, gave Marc and me opportunity for some interesting movie parties after our return.

A Trip to Mexico

During the meeting of the Pan-American Medical Congress in Dallas in March, 1933, I accepted an invitation to go to Mexico City as the guest of one of the family of General Calles, the Dictator, and to present a paper before the Medical School at the university. Other members of the congress were also invited. Those in our party included Dr. and Mrs. Joseph J. Eller, Dr. Foster Kennedy, Dr. J. J. Valentine, and Dr. A. I. Folsom.

We went by plane to San Antonio, where we took the night train for Brownsville, Texas. Here we boarded a three-motored Ford monoplane of the Pan-American Airways. We traveled for quite a distance over the Gulf and came into Tampico, with its forest of oil derricks. From there we rose rapidly over the great Cordilleras, which we crossed at a height of about sixteen thousand feet. In a short time we were over the ancient Aztec pyramids, which the pilot circled in order to give us a good view of them.

We were met at the airport by a group of high officials and physicians and taken to the Ritz Hotel, where we were introduced to the highly potent tequila, for which you have to prepare your mouth by sucking a lime and dashing in a lot of salt, which is necessary to prevent excoriation of the mucous membrane by the liquor when it is drunk straight. One was enough for me.

The old Aztec canals where Cortés met and destroyed Montezuma and his wonderful people are still lovely. The native boatmen handled their delicate dugouts with great skill, and a pretty girl in one only fourteen inches wide hooked on to our launch and offered bunches of flowers, which our party promptly bought.

The next day we took a trip in the country to the hacienda of the Dictator. On the side of the road we came across six small crosses, mute evidence of the way General Calles treated officers who rose against him. During the evening the General's three daughters and their husbands (one of whom was Dr. Eller) took us to a game of frontón, the Mexican name for jai alai, the marvelous Spanish game.

The next day we visited the beautiful new Institute of Hygiene, where we saw bacteriological and immunological work of high order. This institute is more extensive and beautiful than anything in the United States.

At the Hospital Central I stopped long enough to do a prostatectomy for the professor of urology. That evening we were the guests of the Medical School and addressed a large audience. Dr. Eller presented a dermatological paper, Dr. Foster Kennedy a neurological one, and Dr. Folsom talked on prostatic resection. These three spoke in English. Then came a paper by Dr. Valentine, who was born in Cuba and spoke perfect Spanish. The audience followed him closely; I had noticed that they understood very little of the three previous papers. I had lantern slides on the surgery of the prostate to show, and essayed to do it in Spanish. The audience apparently appreciated my using their language, although my effort was very crude. After complimentary remarks by the president of the university, we were taken to the home of General Calles, which we found surrounded by soldiers who were nonchalantly boiling their coffee on the sidewalk. Before being admitted we had to pass the scrutiny of several officers.

After a trip of several miles into the country we reached the home of the secretary to the Dictator, said to be the richest woman in Mexico. She had recently married a young surgeon, but still continued her secretarial work with the General. She was credited with being the smartest woman in the country. Her house was on a pretty lake and had been presented to her by the Dictator because of her excellent stenography. In the ballroom was a regimental band, whose music was so violent that the Dictator's daughters decided to send to the Ritz for a jazz orchestra. When it arrived, a serious situation was created. The military band refused to leave, and both played at once. On one side you danced to a foxtrot and on the other side ran into a tango. Food and drink were abundant. I had been told of the hostess's wonderful bedroom and got her to show it to me. In the center was a bed fourteen feet square with deep box springs that rested on the floor. There were no posts. There were four quilts seven feet square, which joined each other in the center and reached the outer limits of the fourteen-foot bed. I was so amazed at this remarkable piece of furniture that I said to the husband, "You must have a harem." Whereupon the hostess said, "Not at all. I'm the only woman in this establishment."

Cruises to the Caribbean with the Pan-American Medical Association

The Pan-American Medical Congress in 1934 had a delightful cruise through the Caribbean. At Havana Dr. Soiland of California appeared on deck in a gorgeous white uniform with the three stars of a yacht-club commodore. He said, "Young, you are a commodore of a yacht club on the Chesapeake. Why don't you come with me to the Havana Yacht Club, where I am to be made an honorary commodore?" We started off. We had not gone far when Dr. Soiland suddenly remembered that he had forgotten to bring the parchment making the commodore of the Havana Yacht Club an honorary officer of the yacht clubs of the Pacific Coast, and he had also forgotten the official button and pennon that he expected to present. I persuaded him not to turn back, but to bring the officials of the Havana Yacht Club back to the ship with us, and have another party.

Arriving at the Havana Yacht Club, we were conducted to the veranda overlooking a beautiful bay. We sat down to a table with the commodore, the vice-commodore, the rear commodore, the fleet captain, and other officers of the club. "*Primero*," said the Commodore, "it is necessary to go through the ritual of twelve Bacardi cocktails. After that we'll have the ceremonies." A fleet of waiters appeared with the drinks in champagne glasses. The first toast to the commodore of the yacht club of the Pacific. No heel-taps. Down. A second series to the commodore of the Gibson Island Yacht Club. Down. To the commodore of the Havana Yacht Club. Down. I remember six more rounds, and the next thing I knew I was on board ship. My memory is not clear about the latter part of the ritual or the ceremony. Soiland said we must have brought these Cubans back with us, as the paraphernalia was gone.

With the advent of balmy weather the mornings were spent in medical meetings. These were completed in time for a swim and a cocktail before luncheon. With afternoons given to sports on deck and sun baths, and a dance every evening after a formal lecture or two in the ballroom, the days passed profitably and delightfully.

We touched various ports and returned home in sixteen days, during which we had met the medical faculties and principal members of the profession in various Latin American countries, had participated in interesting medical conferences, and had had a very good time.

Four years later the Pan-American Medical Society had another cruise. I was on a fishing trip in Florida and joined them in Havana. We had a fine round of parties as well as serious scientific sessions. From there we went to Port-au-Prince, Haiti, where we were surprised to find that many of the inhabitants of the black republic were white and spoke beautiful French. In many cases the color of the others was so slight as to be imperceptible, and they danced so well that the women were real belles at a tea-dance that was given us at the country club on the mountaintop.

At the Dominican Republic we stopped at Ciudad Trujillo, which the dictator had named after himself when he had ousted my old patient, Vasquez, from the Presidency. Here we found a pure Spanish population speaking the Castilian language and almost no French.

We got to San Juan early in the morning. I was awakened by the ringing of my telephone. "Is this you, Dr. Young? Please come up and see what you can do about a crowd of Puerto Ricans who are assembled on the dock, waving banners containing in large letters the words, 'Welcome, Dr. Young.' " I hastily dressed, and arriving on deck saw my patient Rafael Martinez Nadal, surrounded by some fifty citizens on the dock, across which stretched a thirty-foot poster printed in red—"Welcome, Dr. Young, who has restored to health that great leader of the Constitutional Party, Senator Rafael Martinez Nadal." By this time fellow members of the medical cruise, disturbed by the racket, had hastily come on deck to see what it was all about. It was very hard to make them believe that I was just as surprised as they were. The Senator insisted that he be allowed to conduct me to the Governor's palace. He led the way to a line of automobiles, across the backs of which stretched bunting with "Welcome, Dr. Young." The procession was preceded by the band playing "Maryland, My Maryland." The cavalcade slowly wended its way up the crooked, narrow streets of old San Juan to the massive gates of the Governor's palace, Fortaleza, inside which a small military guard received us. I was conducted to Governor Winship, who quickly saw my embarrassment at the overenthusiastic reception I had received and invited me to retire to a room that he had kindly reserved for me at the Government House.

Not satisfied with his extraordinary reception, the Senator informed me that on the morrow I was invited to meet some friends at his hacienda in the country. This party started with a cockfight at three o'clock in the afternoon. The Senator was an ardent sportsman and had in his pens and runways hundreds of cocks of the finest breeds from Spain and South America. From these he selected his greatest fighters for the arena, around which, in circular rows, were seated an enthusiastic group of the island's most distinguished men in political and professional life. The brave little warriors staged mortal combat before them. I haven't the space to describe adequately this typical Latin sporting event, at which the prize gamecocks showed their marvelous skill and fought to the death. About five o'clock the ladies began arriving at the garden party, and a band soon started playing charming Spanish and Latin American melodies. On a great dance floor on the lawn, señoritas and señoras and their graceful hidalgos were soon giving wonderful exhibitions of the tango, the rumba, and the conga.

Having had scant acquaintance with these Spanish dances, I remained in the audience, but I wasn't allowed to stand inactive for long and soon found myself attempting to do the rumba with Señora Martinez Nadal. The crowd suddenly formed a ring around us and by cries and gestures incited us on. One could not help entering into the spirit of the occasion and I wriggled and hootchy-kootchied until I almost dropped dead. Other dancers were singled out, and these in turn were surrounded by a ring of tormentors. The couples thus isolated showed amazing versatility in the movements they were able to perform, to the intense amusement and delight of those who were surrounding them. Soon drinks of all sorts and food appeared. After feasting the dancing became more and more fantastic and the onlookers more and more enthusiastic. Thus the party went on far into the night, until finally the six hundred guests left for their homes.

At a medical meeting that I addressed the following evening the Senator insisted on making the opening remarks. Rarely have I heard such an orator. The next morning I left by flying boat for the States. The Senator and his friends were at the airport to wish me bon voyage. Recently the Board of Commissioners has named a street in San Juan after me!

Honolulu, Hawaii, and Molokai

In 1935 the American Urological Association met in San Francisco. I had been nominated to give the Guiteras Lecture, a formal event for which previously some European lecturer had been chosen. My subject was "Genital Abnormalities and Related Adrenal Diseases," and I presented my investigations and new operations. The collection of material for this lecture led to my writing a book on the subject.

After the meeting I crossed over to Honolulu with my daughter Elizabeth and Miss Virginia Watts, and gave lectures in three cities in the Hawaiian Islands. I was much interested in the scientific work done by the pineapple-growers. They are greatly bothered by a pest known as the meanie bug, which has a proboscis somewhat like a mosquito's but infinitely stronger. This it drives into the pineapple leaves, sucking the sap and leaving a poison that causes the leaf to wilt. By glands at the side of its mouth a form of sugar is secreted, and this causes the insect to be pursued by a parasite ant, which gets its living robbing the sugar secreted by the bug. When the meanie bug has completed its destructive work on one pineapple plant, it is ready to move to another, but its feeble legs are apparently unable to transport it across the intervening rough ground. Here the parasite ant comes to the rescue, picks up the succulent bug, and carries it over to a new pineapple plant, where it begins anew its borings and excretion of delectable sugar, on which the ant lives.

As soon as the wilt disease, as it is called, is recognized, the growers surround the infested plants with boards sunk into the ground and extending about six inches aboveground. These are planed smooth, and the parasite ant is unable to carry its meanie-bug burden over this little fence. The spread of the disease is thus prevented. Laboratories manned by very scientific staffs are maintained by both the pineapple and the sugar-cane corporations for the study and prevention of pests that, if unchecked, quickly lead to widespread destruction and great financial losses. The strictest quarantine is maintained to prevent new infestations from getting into the country. Likewise, the Pacific Coast quarantines against pests from Hawaii.

After a lecture at Honolulu I traveled on to Hilo on the largest island, not far from the great volcano. There were dinner parties, at which native orchestras and hula dancers furnished the entertainments at Hilo. Then on the islands of Maui and Kauai.

When one thinks of the Hawaiian Islands, there generally comes to mind the leper settlement of Molokai, in which world-wide interest was aroused years ago by the wonderful description by

Robert Louis Stevenson of the heroic life of Father Damien among the lepers there. Most people think that leprosy is rampant in the Hawaiian Islands, and do not realize that the disease is to be found in many parts of the United States, and that in various places in Europe it is not uncommon. When I arrived in Honolulu, one of my first thoughts was to see the leper colonies and obtain firsthand information about these unfortunates.

I reached Molokai by airplane. The leper colony is on a flat plateau about four miles in diameter, which projects into the ocean below a precipitous row of cliffs about three thousand feet high. This low plateau was selected because it is practically impossible to escape up over the beetling cliffs. As we circled this plateau before landing, we could see the colony skirting the shore of the lovely coral beach. Then came groves of tropical trees, among which appeared the hospital buildings, numerous cottages, churches, amusement halls, the theater, and so on that make up the Molokai settlement. Landing on the small airport, I was met by the medical director and driven about two miles to the colony. The main hospital was of wood, attractively constructed, with large porches and abundant windows. The director, Dr. Tuttle, had been there for years. He was a tall, athletic-looking man of perhaps sixty, with graying hair, sympathetic blue eyes, and a charming personality. With great pride he conducted me through his hospital, where I saw for the first time the awful deformities produced by this singular disease—faces distorted by great swellings, enlargements, tumorous elevations, so that it was almost impossible to recognize the patients as human beings. The hands were very prone to invasion, with consequent loss of fingers and thumbs and terrific ulcerated areas. Similar conditions were seen on the legs and feet. Most of the lesions were covered by extensive bandaging, but they were apparently causing no pain. In the wards and on the verandas the patients were chatting as nonchalantly as if nothing was the matter. I was attracted particularly to a handsome young girl in a gay kimono, evidently of Japanese and Hawaiian blood. Only a

week before, a baby girl had been born to her. In accordance with
the rules of the hospital, the child was immediately removed to a
special maternity hospital in Honolulu, where babies of leprous
patients are cared for until it is demonstrated that they are free
from the disease. In the great majority of cases they grow up to be
healthy children. The girl was philosophical about the removal of
her child, and was chatting gaily with a young man leper. Out of
pity for these poor outcasts, no attempt is made to prevent *affaires
du cœur* among the men and women. "They deserve any happiness
they can get," I was told.

I was amazed at the absence of any appearance of suffering or
sorrow on the faces of these patients; they seemed to be uniformly
content and apparently happy. At the end of one ward was a large
Hawaiian sitting by a radio of the latest type, his face wreathed in
smiles. "Oh, what a joy," he said, "this machine is to me! Our
President Roosevelt gives me great delight. I never miss his broad-
casts. He has the best radio voice of them all, but what I enjoy most
is to listen to the thrilling prize fights. The Max Baer-Louis fight,
which I heard recently, had me spellbound. I am glad the much-
pampered Max was badly beaten." I looked at him and saw the
ravages of the disease all over his body. He had lost many fingers,
his mouth was puckered by the scars of many ulcers, and in his
throat he wore a silver tube through which he breathed, his larynx
being greatly involved. In order to talk he placed a finger across the
tracheotomy tube and whispered raucously through his leprous
vocal cords, and yet despite this tragic disease he was content, leading an interesting existence, suffering no pain, and was apparently
happy.

In one part of the colony, surrounded by lovely flowers and trees
in brilliant bloom, was a small hospital for women, maintained by a
group of Roman Catholic sisters. These religious women were serene
and happy in their self-sacrificing work. Protestant and Catholic
chapels provide for the spiritual needs of the lepers. The theater
and motion-picture establishment gives them frequent entertain-

ment. A pretty dance hall is the scene, every few weeks, of a gay evening in which, to the strains of an orchestra with leprous musicians, the ladies of the colony, in low neck and short sleeves, dance with swains often in evening dress, so I was told by Dr. Tuttle. His description of the lepers' dances was so intriguing that I promised myself another visit to the colony, but was unable to go when I was notified that a dance was to take place.

A few years ago they organized two football teams among the men, who went after each other hammer and tongs. The leprous lesions being anesthetic, they did not realize the damage they were doing. One man is said to have kicked off a part of his foot. The teams were then disbanded.

There are four hundred and thirty-five lepers living in the settlement. They are free to come and go as they wish; their residence there is voluntary. They receive excellent board and lodging from the Government, and a certain amount for spending money. Many of them are occupied in various functions about the hospital, the gardens, farms, and so forth. Those who work receive pay. The Government paid them $45,000 in wages in 1936. The lepers are comparatively rich. Many of them own their homes, which they have built on garden plots allotted to them. I found them working among the flowers and vegetable gardens or reading on the porches. Ninety of the patients had automobiles, one in five. The longest distance they could go was five miles. The great precipitous cliffs prevent their visiting other parts of the island. One road runs to the grave of Father Damien.

Some die early, generally of pulmonary involvement. Many live for years. I saw one who had been in the colony for thirty years, and many others were aged men and women. Leprosy, being an only mildly contagious disease, is not much feared by their families. Many patients are accompanied by wife or husband, who generally do not contract the disease. Nonleprous workers in the colony sometimes marry lepers. The gardener, who had been there for twenty years, is now living with his third leprous wife, but he himself is free from the disease. The doctors and nurses apparently have no fear of infection. Some of them have grown so careless that I was horrified as I saw the flagrant breaks in technique, as we surgeons say. These doctors went freely from ward to ward, touching the patients, handling doorknobs, while I cringingly walked behind, refusing to touch anything and sterilizing my hands frequently. These nurses and doctors assume no role of martyrs, and are so interested in their work that they are content to spend their lives with the lepers. As a result, leprosy is gradually decreasing and is no longer a menace.

The social ramifications of the lepers of Molokai are extensive. Some come from exclusive families. What the leper wants the legislators never deny him. His political influence is so great that before elections the island is visited by political aspirants. Before a recent election one candidate came with three large airplanes, one filled with dancers, another with speakers, and a third with an orchestra. Although the lepers are not numerous, if they are combined against a candidate, his chances of being elected are slim.

A few years ago, on the island of Kauai, a systematic effort was made to persuade the lepers to go to Molokai. My charming friends the Philip Rices gave me the following story: The work of segregating the lepers was in the hands of the sheriff, and he assigned to the job one of his deputies, a native Hawaiian, who brought many suspected of leprosy together to the medical examiners. When the work was completed, one of the doctors turned to him and said: "My dear fellow, I am sorry to tell you that you yourself are a leper. Since these others have agreed to be transported to Molokai, you should also go." The deputy accepted the diagnosis calmly. "I believe you are right, and I shall go if my wife is allowed to go with me." This was assented to, as other wives of lepers were there ready to embark with their husbands.

Now it happened that the deputy had a beautiful Hawaiian wife who had excited the fancy of the sheriff. He had already attempted to steal away her affections, but unsuccessfully. He saw now a chance to achieve his aims. The ship arrived to transport the lepers to Molokai. There was no dock, and it was necessary to use boats. As the deputy appeared on the beach with his wife, he was told that he must go first with the other lepers, and that the nonleprous wives would come last. Unsuspecting, he went aboard. Finally all the lepers were embarked. The boat returned to shore and came back with a boatload of wives, but the anxiously waiting deputy discovered that his wife was not among them. He realized that a trick had been played on him by the sheriff, who he knew was after his wife. When the ship was a mile from shore, overboard he jumped with his clothes on, managed to reach the land, and made off to the mountains. There he went to a cave high up on a cliff in a beautiful gorge, which I visited with the Rices.

Soon he sent for his wife, who brought with her their infant child. There, friendly natives furnished them food and bedding. It was not long before the sheriff missed the woman and in searching for her discovered their whereabouts. Whereupon he organized a posse. As these men approached the foot of the cliff, the deputy called down to the sheriff that if he dared come any closer he would shoot. Relying on their numbers, the sheriff's posse made a rush for the path that led to the cave. The refugees aim was unerring, and three of the posse fell. The others fled. The National Guard was then invoked to capture the refugees, but again several were killed and the remainder fled from the leper. In another attempt an artillery piece was actually carried up the mountain to bombard the leper's cave, but without result, and all attempts to capture him were finally discontinued. Four and a half years the leper lived there with his wife and child. The beautiful waterfall that dashes to the valley across the mouth of the cave irrigated a taro patch, from which he made the poi on which the Hawaiians live. In a near-by stream he was able to net fish at night, and thus the three lived until the child died of pneumonia. The father too was soon to pass away. The sorrowing widow then returned to her people on the seashore. In the meantime the sheriff also died.

Operations at Sea

Returning from the International Congress at London in 1913 were some hundred surgeons. One evening we heard that Dr. John B. Murphy of Chicago was going to operate on a case of appendicitis. Owing to lack of space below, it was to be done in the dining-room. Many of us found we might see the operation by slipping into the gallery. The patient was wheeled in draped in sterile sheets. Dr. Murphy made a long incision, put in his hand—and pulled out a chain of frankfurters and a bottle of beer. We went down and enjoyed the viscera that he had removed from the abdomen.

There were, however, real operations at sea in my experience. During a trip through the Caribbean a woman came down with a large pelvic abscess, and although a storm was raging and the ship was tossing, we were able to operate and evacuate it. I saw her only in rough hospital clothing and did not recognize the lovely lady in furs and silks a year later when she dropped into my office to thank me.

On a trip from Bermuda we ran into a hurricane. The ship carried very little ballast and rolled violently from one beam end to the other. Attempting to cross the main hall, I was pitched through a glass door. When I recovered my senses, I was standing in the middle of the hall. Around me were several stewards who were tying towels around my arm. I demanded to know what they were doing, and they pointed to the floor, on which was a big pool of blood. A large spicule of glass had gone up my sleeve and made a triangular wound several inches in length. The radial artery was spurting vigorously. Making pressure upon my brachial artery just above the elbow, I stopped the bleeding, which the stewards' tourniquets had failed to do, and walked to the surgeon's office.

The ship's doctor had no assistant and proposed that he give me ether while his hospital steward sewed up the wound. Being a little dubious of the steward's surgical technique, I suggested that there might be some doctors aboard who would like to assist. He brought in a list of four. On investigation we found that one was a dentist, one an obstetrician, and the third a horse doctor. We sent for the fourth. He was very young, and very seasick. I asked if he were a surgeon and he said no, but he had recently ridden an ambulance in New York. As it was evidently necessary to do quite a plastic operation, I decided to take no anesthetic and to direct the affair. I showed him where to cut off the badly frayed skin, how to clamp and ligate the bleeding artery in the depths of the wound, where to place some stitches to draw the torn bodies of muscles together, and how to do a T plastic so as to get the skin to close the wound. When the pain seemed unbearable, I thought of my father's experience with the Yankee surgeon who poured pure nitric acid into his foul wound, and gritted my teeth.

CHAPTER 27. TRAVEL BY AIR

Santos-Dumont and His Dirigible

IN THE Summer of 1903 the International Tennis Match was held
in Paris at the Ile de Puteau, about five miles below Paris. The
Doherty brothers represented England. In the midst of the final
doubles match with France the onlookers heard the put-put of a
gasoline motor in the distance. Almost immediately a shout arose
from the assembled crowd—"*Santos-Dumont!—Le dirigible!*" All
eyes were directed up the Seine. In a short time a small, ovoid
balloon appeared above the river. As he approached, the crowd became so excited that it was necessary to stop the International Tennis Match. In a little while the tiny dirigible, one of the first to be
constructed, approached the island. Beneath the oval bag was a
runway suspended by ropes, and at the rear end of this a small
two-cylinder gasoline motor that operated a propeller. In the runway was a man who worked a vertical rudder with ropes and moved
backward or forward in his runway to make the balloon ascend or
descend.

He was soon over the tennis courts. The enthusiastic crowd demanded that he come down. He threw ropes overboard; many of us
grabbed for them and were dragged for a short distance, but we soon
brought the slowly moving balloon to a halt. Other strong arms
grabbed the dangling ropes from all sides, and the balloon was

hauled down to within fifty feet of the earth. The intrepid Santos-Dumont slid down a rope and was surrounded by enthusiastic admirers. In the meantime the Dohertys, greatly bored, were leaning on their rackets and demanding that the tennis match be resumed, but nothing could be accomplished until Santos-Dumont again climbed the ropes up into his runway. The crowd let out the ropes, the balloon slowly ascended to about two hundred feet, and Santos-Dumont started his tiny motor, circled the island, and made off back to Paris amid the cheers of the crowd.

My First and Almost Last Flight

At Vincennes, just outside Paris, in 1909, where an aviation meeting was being held in France, I saw for the first time flights with heavier-than-air machines. It was just six years after the Wrights had demonstrated the possibility of flight at Kitty Hawk. Some ten crude planes of various makes were assembled; most were of the Wright type, but two were constructed after Blériot's model. Among the planes was a crude affair made by a French mechanic who offered to take people for a ride for 20 francs. It was made of gas pipes, which formed not only the central structure but also the framework for the wings, around which were stretched strips of canvas held tight by leather straps. Some sort of crude ailerons had been provided. The engine was a heavy Panhard automobile motor, which operated two propellers by means of slender chains. Immediately in front of the engine sat the aviator in an oak dining-room armchair that was fastened to the gas pipes with wire. In front of him were the usual stick and foot brakes. Farther in front and protruding about three feet beyond the forward edge of the plane was a seat for a passenger. This was also an armchair, and in front of it was a footrest.

He had just returned with one passenger, and I was the next. I took my seat and held onto the arms of the chair. There was no fuselage or body of any sort, not even a strap to hold me in the chair. The motor was cranked up and we went with increasing speed along the field and finally got into the air. With difficulty the machine cleared the forest of Vincennes, over which we traveled for perhaps three miles, across the river Seine, and then we turned to go back. As we did so the ship banked greatly, we were caught in a cross-wind, tossed crazily back and forth, and came near plunging into the treetops, but we finally rose, crossed the Seine, and arrived at our starting-point.

Much relieved, I climbed down from my perch and vowed never again to get into such a freak airplane. Shortly after I landed a small plane flew overhead at a height of about two hundred feet. Suddenly it lost speed and nose-dived into the earth, carrying the poor pilot deep into the ground about fifty feet away from me. With difficulty, those of us who rushed to the scene were able to pull away the motor and wreckage and extricate his mangled body.

The Second Aviation Meet in America

The following year I went to the Belmont Park race track and saw the second aviation meet in America. There were some twenty planes there to take part in the races, which were around a one-mile track. A pylon was erected at each end of the oval. Wright was there with his biplane, which was provided with two skids. The plane was placed on a runway, the rear end of which was about five feet from the ground. At the signal a trap was sprung, a weight descended, the machine shot forward down the inclined runway and slowly rose in flight at a speed of perhaps twenty-five miles an hour. Wright made his way down the race track, around the pylon, and came back toward us.

Machines of the Blériot type were there, and Santos-Dumont flew his *Butterfly*, which he called the *"demoiselle"*—a beautiful and delicate fabrication.

The Boston Air Meet

In 1912 I attended another aviation meet near the water front at Boston. Beachey took a prominent part. His plane was similar to that of the Wrights, but he had cut off the anterior horizontal elevators, and had a simple transverse rudder behind. His oil tank had been leaking, so he got a five-gallon kerosene can, to which he fastened a simple rubber tube through which the gasoline flowed to the carburetor. A few small wires attached the can to the gas pipes above his head. In this contraption, off he flew to win the prize for speed and altitude. Before many months he was looping the loop and amazing the world by his daring aerial maneuvers, in one of which he was finally killed.

The Halethorpe Meet

The next aviation meet I attended was at Halethorpe. A few planes were assembled, and thrilled the crowd with flights that would be considered trivial now. A Frenchman named Hubert Latham won $5,000 for flying from Halethorpe over Baltimore and out through the northern suburban district, in a graceful monoplane, the *Antoinette*. The housetops of Baltimore were loaded with humanity. Ross Winans, an interesting recluse, had added $500 to the prize on condition that the aviator fly over his house.

The American Air Corps in France

I first saw the celebrated Lafayette Escadrille at their hangars a short distance north of Toul in Lorraine. They were provided with French machines, and had made a fine record, but many a valiant pilot had been killed.

After we entered the war both French and British planes were sent to Washington, and able engineers assisted in the building of American airplanes, but for some reason the War Department decided that it could design better motors than the Allies, just as they thought they could build a better gun than the French seventy-fives. A group of automobile engineers were called to Washington, locked in a hotel room, and told to design an aviation motor. After some weeks they emerged with plans for the Liberty motor. The papers hailed it as a marked improvement over foreign motors.

News of the ballyhoo reached us in France, and for months we eagerly awaited its arrival. Finally, an American plane with a Liberty motor arrived at our field near Colombey-les-Belles. The next day, it is said, a plane with British markings landed on the field. The aviator, in the smart uniform of a British Air Corps captain, with a broad English accent explained that he had been forced to descend because he had run out of petrol. He asked for enough to reach their field some twenty miles away. It was about time for the evening meal, and the American officers invited him to dine with them while the mechanics filled his tank. Reference was made to the Liberty-motored, American-built airplane that had just arrived. The visitor evinced great interest and begged to see it. In order that the plane could be inspected properly it was taken onto the field. The visitor inspected it eagerly and said, "I believe I would have no trouble in flying it myself." The Americans invited him to get in and try it out. As the machine mounted higher and higher, it turned to the east, and rapidly became smaller in the distance. Finally it disappeared completely. The Americans wondered at the length of the Britisher's flight, but kept expecting him to return. That was the last they ever saw of him or the plane, because the pilot was a German in a British uniform in a captured British plane.

Once I saw a German plane that had crossed our line attacked by two Americans. Apparently badly hit, the German plane tumbled like a falling leaf. The Americans followed him a short distance, but feeling that he was "done for," soared up as the German fell toward the earth. About eight hundred feet from the ground the German plane suddenly ceased its crazy fall, straightened out, and made directly for an American observation balloon and set it on fire with a burst of machine-gun bullets, then rose gracefully in an inside loop and returned to the German lines.

The American Air Corps fought throughout the war with cast-off machines against a greatly superior enemy. Along the Lorraine front was a squadron of six planes commanded by a Major Brown who, although holding rank, was not highly regarded by his associates and was frequently taunted for his failure to fly with his men. Stung by criticism, so I am told, he announced one morning that he was going to take his men up across the German lines to bomb a railhead. The more experienced youngsters in his squadron pointed out that the weather was unfavorable, with the wind strong from the southwest, and that it would be difficult to return in their slow planes. The Major retorted that he was going to show them what he could do with that squadron, and off they went, loaded with bombs. As they rose high into the air the gale caught them, and on they rushed across the German lines. When they came down through the clouds, they found they had been carried beyond Luxembourg and were over the German city of Trier (Trèves). They tried to get back home, but soon ran out of gas and had to land in German territory. It is said that that evening a laconic message came from the Germans: "Thanks for the airplanes and the six officers." Someone in the American command replied: "Please be kind to the lieutenants. Don't give a damn what you do to the major!" On November 16 I met one of these lieutenants making his way back to the A.E.F. He was still violent in his language about the Major.

Across the Irish Sea by Air

In 1928 Mr. Van Lear Black flew me from London across to Dublin, where I had some medical business. His plane, which he had named the *Maryland Free State*, was celebrated because of the wonderful long-distance flights that he had made in it, the last being around the world. On his return from this I had gone up with the squadron of the Maryland National Guard to meet him over Washington and conduct him back to Baltimore.

I saw Van Lear in London, with his plane in a hangar at Croydon. Knowing that I had to go to Dublin, he offered to fly me across. His two Dutch pilots had a remarkable record for millions of miles flown without an accident. We crossed in splendid style, and the rest of the party, consisting of his daughter, her husband, Mr. T. B. Blakiston, and his valet, interested themselves in the Dublin horse show while I repaired to the old building of the Royal College of Surgeons of Ireland, where I was made an honorary fellow at a small private session. This was followed by a delightful little dinner in the spacious rooms of the college. There were only a few members present, but they were a delightful and amusing lot and members of the St. Patrick's choir were there to sing for us. These youngsters were anything but religious, as their anecdotes disclosed. I was delighted with the informality and their charming hospitality.

The next day we returned to London. The day was not propitious for flying. It was hazy, and there was a gale out of the southwest. Mr. Black, who rarely stopped because of bad weather, insisted on going. We crossed over Dublin at considerable height, but as the clouds lowered it was found desirable to keep beneath them. As we sped along at perhaps one hundred and seventy miles an hour (a good speed for that day) we dropped to one thousand, then five hundred, two hundred and fifty, and finally one hundred feet above the water. The sea below us was rough with tremendous whitecaps. The visibility ahead was poor, only a narrow strip about a hundred feet above the water. Suddenly dead ahead rose the great Holyhead cliff, several hundred feet high. I braced myself for a head-on collision. With a great pull at the levers, the pilot, Geysendorffer, brought the ship on her beam end and barely missed the cliff. As soon as we had passed it we were caught in a great downdraft as the southwest gale dropped over the precipitous ridge. Down went the plane with such speed that before the pilot could stop our descent the left wing actually dug into a wave, and water came aboard through the windows. With superhuman effort Geysendorffer met the situation, and up we zoomed out of what seemed to be a watery grave. The pilots said that this was their closest shave in a million miles of flying.

Across the Mediterranean Sea to Marrakech

In 1930 at the Congress of the International Society of Urology at Madrid, Dr. Heitz-Boyer of Paris urged me to go with him to

Marrakech in Morocco. He had operated upon the Grand Pasha of Marrakech, uncle of the Sultan, and was going to visit him. He painted a picture of the palace where we would be entertained and the harem with two hundred beauties into which he would take me. I explained that I had first to go to Rome to deliver a lecture. He urged that it would be possible by fast trains and planes to get to Marrakech almost as soon as he did by motor. Intrigued with the idea of having this entree into a great harem, I promised Heitz-Boyer to go if I could arrange it.

Immediately after my lecture in Rome I bade farewell to Ambassador and Mrs. Garrett, who had kindly invited me to stay at the Palazzo Rospigliosi, and took the night train for Marseille. I reached the airport about thirty miles west of the city early of a morning. It was blustery with intermittent showers, and not at all propitious weather for flying, but the Aéro Postale Française prided itself on leaving with the mails on time every day. The plane was brought out of the hangar. It was an old army pursuit plane with two cockpits.

Just before we took off a woman arrived with a baby of about fifteen months. She begged the pilot to wait until she could give the child a bottle of milk. I have never seen a baby consume so much milk. Finally, when over a pint had disappeared, we three were stowed away in the rear cockpit with our heads sticking out. As we made off in the gray dawn across the northwest corner of the Mediterranean we mounted higher and higher, and before long were over the Pyrenees. The peaks were covered with snow, and as the sun came up out of the Mediterranean they were tinted a beautiful pink. Suddenly the baby became seasick. Seeing a package of paper bags at my side, I succeeded in opening one of them and getting it beneath the baby's mouth just in time. Throwing it overboard, I hoped that that was the last of the baby's seasickness, but during the next half-hour I was busily engaged in filling and throwing overboard one after another of the paper bags.

Before long we were over Barcelona, and made a nice landing.

We took on the mail, and reached Valencia, where we landed for gas and mail. The country was rough and covered almost entirely with olive trees. As there were no places where the plane could land, the pilot decided to travel over the sea, although we had no floats and no parachutes. We stopped at Alicante, and then ran into fearful winds and rainstorms. The progress of our ship was so greatly delayed that it was evident we could not make it across the straits, so the pilot decided to come down and land at Malaga, where we secured another army pursuit plane with a little more power. In a short time we were up again and diving through black rain clouds filled with lightning. When we passed over Gibraltar, it was raining so hard that we could not see the old rock. The trip over the straits was very rough, and we arrived very late at the airfield of Tangier. The wind had increased greatly, and the pilot said we could not go farther.

Securing a conveyance, I reached the railroad station in time to get the night train, and the next morning I was at Casablanca, which I should have reached the day before. Marrakech was about two hundred miles away. The road across the level plain was fairly good, and we arrived before sundown at the great gates of the thirty-foot wall that surrounds El Glaoui's palace. I was expected, and a messenger conducted me to a small residential building where Heitz-Boyer and his wife were awaiting me.

My room was large, with cornices of typical Moorish architecture reminiscent of Granada. Adjacent was a bathroom almost as large, with no toilet but with two large marble tubs. I hastened to dress, as El Glaoui was waiting for us. With the Heitz-Boyers I walked across to his palace through fantastic gates and down narrow Moorish corridors. At one side was an alcove which led to a barred door, in front of which sat the largest, most unpleasant-looking woman I have ever beheld, with a large cutlass at her side. I softly asked Madam Heitz-Boyer who she was, and she replied that she was the guardian of the harem. I had no desire to crash that gate. We were soon in the reception room, which was shaped like a Red Cross

symbol, with a continuous line of day beds, or rather low benches
covered with mattresses, on which were hundreds of silken cushions.
There was not a chair or a table in the room.

The Sultan's uncle arrived with his attendants, deftly shed his
shoes in the court, and entered in his white silk stocking feet. After
greeting us cordially he sprang up on the day bed, curling his feet
beneath him. We sat close by him, but with our dirty shoes it
was impossible to assume any such comfortable position, and we
hung our feet over the edge. He spoke perfect French, and was quite
demonstrative with Heitz-Boyer, for whom he showed sincere
affection because of the great relief he had received from an operation at the Doctor's hands. Shortly other guests arrived, among
whom were Count Robert Rothschild and his nephew. After a time
we were taken through a court around a crystal pool to the dining-
room, which was almost identical with the Red Cross room with its
continuous day bed. El Glaoui picked a corner and we arranged
ourselves around, some of us on large ottoman cushions that were
set around in a circle. A low table was placed among us.

Next came two slaves, one bearing a large copper vessel filled
with water and the other towels. Our host stuck his right hand into
the water and had it duly wiped by the second attendant. As the
bowl was passed around each of us did the same. Why no one put
in the left hand I did not know, but I dared not break the technique. Other slaves arrived with a great board on which was almost
a whole sheep, lying on his stomach. We waited for our host. With
lightning speed he dived in with his nimble fingers and pulled out
a large hunk of dorsal muscle. The rest followed suit through the
hole our host had made with his strong fingers. There were no knives,
forks, or other utensils. Our left hands were reserved to handle the
glass of drinking-water. When we had demolished the loin of the
mutton, it was spirited away. In its place came six ducks, with
their brown breasts up. Without a knife I could not imagine how
it would be possible to break through the thick skin of these roasted
ducks, but El Glaoui's fingers broke through as if the breasts were

paper, and came out with a large piece of pectoral muscle. The rest of us followed suit as best we could. Between courses we each took sips of the tepid water with our unwashed left hands. There was no bread. There were ten courses in all, most of them meats of various kinds.

Finally a great platter arrived with a mound upon it. It looked like Vesuvius. It was at least two feet in diameter and had a crater at the top of which were small pieces of boiled celery. The volcano was composed of couscous, which I was told was of granular farina, somewhat like the grains of rice but different. I waited to see what my host would do. He dashed in with that deft right hand, scooped up a handful, manipulated it with his fingers and thumb until he had formed a ball about half the size of a golf ball, and with great dexterity shot it into his mouth. It was wonderful to watch him, but the procedure looked perilous. I waited to see Rothschild negotiate the problem. He grasped a handful of the granular mass and tried to fashion it into a ball, but the more he worked on it, the less easy the ball became to handle. Finally in desperation he tried to throw the mass into his mouth, but most of it landed on his shirt bosom and rolled into his lap. The couscous course was not a success. After that we had a simple ice cream, with which the first implement we had seen was offered us, a wooden spoon several times normal size. This and the other courses were washed down with the tepid water. As our host was a strict Mohammedan, there was no wine, no champagne, no liqueurs, all of which we vulgarians longed for during this interminable meal.

After dinner was over I firmly expected to be invited to take a stroll with our host through his harem, but he did not mention it. To my left was a portly Arab, an intimate friend of the host whose job I heard was to find new girls for the harem when the older ones left, but he also showed no tendency to discuss the subject. Finally when the Heitz-Boyers and I went back to our small Granada palace, the Doctor admitted that his promise of a visit to the harem was simply put out to lure me, and finally admitted that he had not seen any of the ladies himself, although he had spent several weeks here while attending our host.

The next morning I clapped for a boy and ordered breakfast. He spoke a little French, and with great difficulty I explained to him that I wanted some eggs and bacon, honey, coffee, and a pot of hot milk. I then shaved and bathed, dressed, went out on the porch, and waited. After half an hour had passed I clapped violently and another attendant arrived. When I demanded my breakfast, he said that my wishes were unusual and it would take some time to prepare it. After waiting fully an hour, I saw a retinue of servants crossing the lawn carrying great trays covered with large conical domes of metal. These were placed on the floor of the porch, and I took a cushion to sit upon. The metal covers were then removed. On one tray was perhaps half a pint of honey, on another a dozen scrambled eggs, on another some substitute for bread. Slices of hog supposed to be bacon covered another platter, and the coffee and milk filled large receptacles. There was almost food enough for a battalion, and the six servants who had transported it stood around and eyed me while I struggled with it. Heitz-Boyer and his wife, who had simply had coffee in their room, almost exploded when they found me surrounded by my English breakfast.

A little later we were off in automobiles to visit the mountain fastnesses from which these fierce Arabs had come to conquer the plains of Morocco. There are still tribes that have not been defeated by the French and continue to elude them. The road through the mountain passes was wet with recent rains, and slippery. I expected to be dashed into some of the turbulent streams below, but our driver was skillful.

Leaving the rest of the party, I dashed back to Casablanca, which I reached late at night. After a few hours' sleep I was taken to the airport. It was four o'clock and not yet light. It was raining hard, and there was a violent wind from the southeast. The mails were put aboard. The pilot said that we could not wait. The plane was a monoplane still smaller than the one I had come in, and I was the only passenger. Into that tempest we went, and it looked for a time as if we were not going to make it. Finally the pilot said that he could prevent a crash only by turning into the wind and going out into the desert. For a half-hour it was rough going; after that it became calmer, we turned west, and before long we were over the broad Atlantic. We continued westerly until out of the region of the storm, then north, still flying over the ocean and many miles from land. Finally the pilot turned in toward shore near Rabat, where we came down for gas. In a few minutes we were off, passing over the interesting villages along the shore and coming down at Tangier, where after a short wait we traveled along the Straits of Gibraltar until we were over Algeciras. I had told the pilot that friends of mine would be in Algeciras because they expected to sail back to America that day. I had wired them that I would be passing over them by plane, and I thought I saw someone waving at me as I hung out of the cockpit and frantically shook my hand, but the pilot would not go low because of the rough country ahead. The view of Gibraltar and the cliff in the brilliant sunshine, with the warships nestled behind the breakwater, was attractive. We made the usual stops at Alicante, Valencia, and Barcelona, and late in the afternoon, after sixteen hours in the air, arrived at Marseille, where I caught the night train for Paris.

I rushed on to London, where I arrived just in time for an address I was scheduled to make before the Royal Society of Physicians.

CHAPTER 28. A SMATTERING OF LANGUAGES

AS I thought I might settle on the Mexican border, I took, as I have noted, a one-year course in Spanish at the University of Virginia under Professor Maximilian Schele de Vere, an ancient member of the faculty who taught various languages. It had been discovered that the way to "pass" old Schele's classes was to make frequent presents to him. We followed the rule and made gifts at Thanksgiving, Christmas, and Easter, with such success that every member of the class graduated. It is not surprising that I learned very little Spanish and that when I made my operating trip into Mexico several years later my knowledge of Spanish did little else than to come near getting me married. With the passage of time, more and more Latin Americans came to our clinic, and I took conversational courses with native teachers and by phonographic methods. Some years later I had the hardihood to deliver a lecture in Spanish at the University of Havana and again at the Medical School at the University of Mexico. At the International Medical Congress of Madrid my smattering of Spanish helped a good deal, but my frequent mistakes were often found amusing. At the palace of King Alfonso, in my feeble Spanish I asked one of the guests who a particularly beautiful woman was. He replied, "*Señora X, una cortesana.*" I showed my surprise at King Alfonso's having a courtesan at the reception, but soon found that a *cortesana* was a member of the court (*cortes*), and not what I suspected.

495

A knowledge of German and French was required of all students applying for admission to the Johns Hopkins Medical School, in addition to a college degree. It is said that Dr. Osler remarked to Dr. Welch, "It is a good thing we got in on the faculty, because we would never have been admitted as students." Osler had been taught by his mother and had no university degree. When I came to the Johns Hopkins, the German medical literature was so superior to all others that it was widely quoted at all medical meetings. It was essential to learn the language. I have recounted how Douglas Duval and I went to live with a German family, and I subsequently supplemented this with a course at the Berlitz School. In furtherance of my desire to become more proficient in German I spent the summer of 1900 in Berlin. I have already spoken of my work at Casper's clinic. The pension of Frau Rinkel, on Schadowstrasse, gave an excellent opportunity for conversation, and by mingling with the corps students I got more practice in the language as well as in quantity consumption of beer. Every Sunday morning the corps with which I was affiliated had dueling matches, at which I was brought in to determine whether the wounds were sufficiently serious to halt the match. I never became really proficient in German, but could follow the lectures and take part in medical discussions at future congresses. I subsequently published a number of papers in German journals and had many friends among those artistic and scientific people.

After Bessy Mason Colston and I were married in 1901, we spent a delightful summer at her father's home, then took a small space in the St. Paul Apartments. Bessy spoke French very well, with a delightful accent. Her mother was also a fine French scholar and her three sisters were proficient in the language. Every day after lunch Bessy and I would have a half-hour of French, using Rosenthal's system. From this I learned enough to whet my appetite for more, and during the following winter a teacher came to the house twice a week. My study was mostly while traveling on streetcars in my practice at the various hospitals. In the spring of 1903 I decided to go to France to learn to speak French and to study at the Hôpital Necker, the urological center of the world. In order to facilitate my methods and improve my technique, I arranged for a student of medicine to assist me in my studies. He met me every day at two o'clock at my pension and we walked to the hospital, where we went systematically through a series of specimens of which there was a beautiful descriptive catalogue. The student would read me the history of the case and the pathologist's description. Then we would discuss the findings and try to recognize everything that had been pointed out in the pathological report. I then dictated notes in French of important details that I wished to record. In this way I was getting a practical knowledge of medical French, and had it been possible for me to stay several months, I might have become quite proficient. I also attended lectures and took private courses in pathology with Dr. Boleslas Motz.

When my young French friend and myself had finished our work at six o'clock, we went to a café, where he was joined by student friends and their girls. His girl was a charming little creature. His alliance with her had gone on for the four years that he had been a student of medicine. She was a midinette, worked at a shop, and joined him at six o'clock. After coffee and a stroll they had dinner and repaired to their little home, where he worked at his medical books while she mended his socks and did other useful chores. Breakfast of coffee and rolls was prepared by her before they parted for the day until the rendezvous at six o'clock. I wondered how such a scheme would work in an American college.

Soon after I arrived in Paris, I was walking down one of the boulevards when I was stopped by a nice-looking young American who said: "You are evidently an American. I am going home; I have been a student here three years. I have had a charming girl, and we have had a delightful little home together for these years. She is a fine girl, and when I leave I want to see her get a nice fellow. I have made bold to introduce myself to see if you would not like to take charge of her." I explained that I was married, and he then said, "Well, if you see someone you can recommend, please let me know, because I am greatly worried about her future."

I lived at 61 rue de Vaugirard, at the pension of Mlle Marie Leclerc. She was sixty, weighed almost three hundred pounds, and had lost all her hair, so that she wore a white wig kept thoroughly dusted with powder. Her blind brother Jules was a very literary and charming man. He carried on an extensive correspondence in Braille. Mlle Leclerc and I lived in the attic. To reach it there was a rickety circular cast-iron staircase about three feet in diameter, which rocked and creaked when she pulled her three hundred pounds up it. My room was about six feet wide and ten feet long and had only a small dormer window, but Mlle Leclerc's room was only half the size of mine and ventilated only by an opening in the roof over which lay inclined a pane of glass. Between us was a thin paper partition through which we carried on conversation until one or the other fell asleep.

I had breakfast with her in the salon. She would not wear a wig then, but covered her head with a cap of netting through which I could plainly see her shiny pate without a sprig of hair. She was a charming woman, and I can never forget the amusing breakfasts we had together, at which we read the morning newspaper, discussed the happenings of the day and the most risqué illustrations in *La vie parisienne*. From her I got the "lowdown" on Paris society and many a scandalous story. At night she was always dressed de rigueur; a large ruffled, low-necked dress exposed her enormous bosom, upon which, during mealtime, she would drop crumbs, so I dubbed it the "balcony." Across her back was another plateau produced by her stays, and this we called the "promenade."

At the right of Mademoiselle sat Paul Breton, a young lawyer and one of the most amusing and charming fellows that I have ever met. Mademoiselle had a pet name for almost everybody. Mine was *le grand chirurgien Américain*. After dinner, in the salon over our benedictine, Paul Breton often recited. One of his stories, I remember, was called *"Le culbute,"* and described how a young girl was madly in love but was constantly accompanied by a chaperon, even when she rode a bicycle into the country. One day she was joined by her admirer, and as they rode along they concocted a scheme to get rid of the chaperon, who was somewhat old and short-winded. Arriving at a long, steep hill, the two young rascals peddled furiously ahead, and when the chaperon finally reached the top of the hill they were nowhere to be seen. At the bottom of the hill at a *culbute* (culvert) that was being constructed across the road, she came across their wrecked bicycles. Terrified, she made inquiries and discovered that they had been injured and carried into a peasant's home. The peasant said he had seen the two bicycle-riders fall into the ditch, rushed over, and found them both unconscious, so he and his brother had carried them to the house and put them in bed together. When the English governess saw them, she could not bear the humiliation and immediately sent out for a priest and had them married.

One day I saw a fakir on the street who had a pasteboard box on the sidewalk, in which little artificial animals were running about in a very lifelike manner. He was offering envelopes that he said contained similar papier-maché animals which would be just as lively as those in his box. Thinking to amuse my friends in the pension, I bought an envelope and the fakir then showed me the secret. Beneath each paper back he had pasted a fly. After dinner I went into the kitchen and, with the assistance of the cook, captured some flies and pasted their outstretched wings upon the previously gummed animal backs. I then joined the company in the salon with my box under my arm. Mademoiselle asked what I had and I told her that it was a recent invention of Mr. Edison's and a secret.

On her pleading, I finally put the box on the floor and removed the top, after exacting a promise that they would not touch nor demand to see the mechanism. The little animals were scurrying around the box, backing and filling in a lifelike way. Mademoiselle cried out in amazement and demanded to see this marvelous invention of M. Edison. I reminded them of their promise, but they grew more and more insistent. Making them promise they would say nothing and make no outburst if I gave them an intimate view, I allowed the Mademoiselle to pick up the turtle. When she saw the fly fastened beneath the back, she gave a cry of horror, and the entire group accused me of great cruelty. The outbursts were so unpleasant that I finally picked up my box and went to bed.

After spending two months in Paris I ran over to Berlin for two weeks and was amazed to find that my head was so gorged with French that I could not speak German at all. Starting in the most simple way to answer my old friends with whom I had previously lived, I would almost immediately lapse into French, and it was several days before I could get back into my German conversation again.

My stay in Paris had been a great success from the standpoint of urological pathology, and I had learned a good deal of conversational and medical French. Many a time since, however, I have been sorry that I was away for so many months, and I can frankly advise young married couples not to be separated so long. It is much better to take their trips, even when on science bent, together.

In 1930 one of my Italian friends sent me an invitation to address the surgical society of Rome. The meeting was to occur immediately after the International Congress in Madrid. I accepted, but explained that as I did not know Italian I would present my paper in English or, if that was not acceptable, could do it in a rough way in French, or possibly in Spanish. The reply came that if I presented it in English no one would understand it; that French was so unpopular that no one would listen; and that if I could do it in Spanish I could surely do it in Italian. It seemed a presumptuous thing to do, but nevertheless I secured as a teacher, through the Berlitz School, an Italian student at the Johns Hopkins University and began to take lessons with him. We had an hour every afternoon and he breakfasted and spent Sunday mornings with me for seven weeks.

On the Italian ship I avoided Americans and pestered the steward and stewardess with Italian questions. Two days before landing I asked the purser if he could suggest someone to translate my paper into Italian. After reflection he said he had the very man, *il capellano*. I discovered that he meant the chaplain, a Catholic padre who had served as a stretcher-bearer in the Italian Army and had some medical knowledge. We worked steadily for eight hours each day translating a two-page introduction into Italian and writing a description of each of my one hundred lantern slides. Before we landed in Naples I showed the paper to an Italian surgeon who was returning from a congress. He remarked that it was beautiful Italian, but a trifle religious in phraseology. After his corrections I set to work to memorize it.

Ambassador Garrett had invited me to stay at the Palazzo Rospigliosi. I had a delightful two days there, but he and Mrs. Garrett kept me so busy with charming social functions that I had very little time for my manuscript.

About five hundred members of the Accademia Lancisiana di Roma were assembled when I was introduced by the president. I read my two-page introduction and then the lights were turned out for my lantern slides. As no provision had been made for a reading lamp, I was forced to demonstrate my slides extemporaneously. Fortunately many of the terms were medical Latin. At the end of an hour the ordeal was over. The audience treated me very kindly, and the president spoke at length, but so rapidly that I did not catch all he said. Apparently it was quite complimentary. Then I was called upon to reply. Having nothing memorized, I was terrified at the prospect, so, feeling utterly unable to make an adequate reply to his kind remarks, I simply stood up, threw out my hand in the Fascist salute, and said, *"Viva il Duce!"* The entire audience sprang to attention in the Fascist salute.

During one of my commitments to the hospital for some ailment, a Swedish nurse was assigned to my case. She was a charming girl, and it occurred to me that I might profitably spend some time studying her language. We secured the Berlitz book on Swedish and had several lessons a day. I was amazed to find how many Swedish words resembled many typical Scotch words and also some of the English language. This comparative etymology was interesting, but I found the language very difficult and did not make much progress. I kept at it, however, and would often tell the group of doctors who frequently collected in my room that they must go because I wanted to have some time with my Swedish. Once one of them, looking suspiciously at my charming nurse, asked how I spelt "sweetish."

Before a trip to the Grecian Archipelago with the John W. Garretts I thought it would be amusing to see if I could learn to speak modern Greek. I had spent some eight years at school and college in a futile effort to master the ancient language. I hoped that my many years of drudgery might be of some assistance in learning something of the modern language. I again applied at the Berlitz School, but found that this course had never been put into Greek. There was a young Spartan studying economics at the university, and he was glad to give conversation lessons. I commissioned him to prepare a Greek version of the Berlitz book. In a week or two he had completed this, and we began with lessons daily and on Sunday morning. I was amazed to find how similar the modern is to the ancient language, the principal difference being pronunciation. My instructor insisted that the modern Greek pronunciation was almost the same as that of ancient times, but that the universities had adopted the German pronunciation of Greek words, as they had of the Latin—I had been told the same thing by Roman scholars. As soon as I comprehended the fundamental differences in pronunciation it was much easier to understand his conversation.

In about three months we finished two of the Berlitz books that had been put into Greek, and I was very hopeful of being able to understand the language sufficiently to converse, but, as I have noted elsewhere, I found that in most of the Greek Islands the inhabitants spoke a patois that made conversation impossible. My only recompense was the hour I had with a pretty girl in Crete.

She was a clerk in a tourist office. She was alone in the office at midday, and when I said that I had been studying modern Greek for several months and would like to see if I could understand her, she seemed amused and invited me in. I asked her to speak very slowly and tell me of her life in Crete. It was possible for me to understand much of what she said. She told me why she had never married. They have an inflexible rule in Crete that a girl must bring an appropriate dowry with her. Although her sweetheart was anxious to marry her, the family insisted on the dowry, and as she did not have 16,000 drachmae, the match was called off. She said that recently one of the ladies in the city had had to bring with her a dowry of 1,000,000 drachmae when she married a prominent merchant. In none of the other islands that we visited did I have any chance with Greek conversation. Was the hour with the Cretan girl worth three months' study. *Quien sabe?*

CHAPTER 29. BOB

ON THE football team of 1894 at the University of Virginia a dashing figure was the right end—a tall, handsome, dark athlete, Robert Worth Bingham of North Carolina (who was later to become Mayor of Louisville, proprietor of the great *Courier Journal*, and Ambassador to the Court of St. James). I was trying for the team, and we soon became fast friends. His father was the celebrated Colonel Bingham who commanded North Carolina troops in the Civil War, and as my father had commanded Texans, we quickly formed an offensive and defensive alliance against the Virginians, who were prone to belittle soldiers from other Southern states.

Bob's good looks soon won the favor of the great college vamp, a Mrs. Du Bose, a grass widow who had a fine stable of riding horses. Bob was soon elected to ride with her over the mountainous bridle paths of Albemarle, much to our envy.

Bob was a student in the Medical School, but did not return after his first year because he had to go to work. Afterward he studied law and made a fine reputation at the bar. Louisville was in the hands of a gang whose corruption had become so flagrant that the mayoralty election was thrown out, and Robert W. Bingham was appointed mayor by the governor. When he assumed office, Bob found graft and vice rampant. When Bob instituted reforms, the gang swore vengeance, and one day the ringleader appeared before the young Mayor with pistol in hand and told Bob that he was going to kill him, but before doing so he wanted to tell him just what he thought of him. But the gangster had not realized what an athlete he was dealing with. In the twinkling of an eye, the gangster was on the floor and Bob had the pistol. Then he kicked the gangster out. They left Bob alone after that. The reforms he introduced were great, one of the most notable leading ultimately to the construction of a fine City Hospital and the reorganization of the Medical School.

About this time Bessy's cousin, Pendleton Beckley, invited me to become a member of the Juniper Hunt Club, to which Bob also belonged. This club had twenty-five thousand acres on Lake George, about a hundred miles below Jacksonville, Florida. My first visit was right after Christmas. We camped at the headwaters of the Juniper River in a dense forest. With army tents and cots everything seemed wonderful when we got into our pajamas and went to bed. Before long we were piling on our overcoats, and then we got into our clothes. As everyone was still frozen, we spent the rest of the night grouped around a blazing campfire. I learned for the first time that a Florida swamp can be colder than Greenland's icy mountains, and the only way to keep warm is to bed oneself on straw on the ground.

Bob and I found a wonderful guide and made him our own. Mel Long was perhaps the best deer-tracker in the world. As he started off one morning there were thousands of tracks in the firm sandy land. Soon Mel's sharp eye picked out one track that he said had been made recently by a fine buck. With remarkable speed he followed this track in and out among the bushes and the saw palmetto. Soon the trail led to a dry swamp thickly studded with trees. There was a heavy blanket of leaves and not a track could be seen, but Mel kept on, and when we reached the clearing on the other side, sure enough, there was the same fresh big, clear deer track. Before long Mel informed us that the buck was in a thicket ahead, and if Bob would go on one side and I on the other, he would flush the deer for us. Out came the buck, bounding over the shrubs, and Bob brought him down. Mel explained that broken twigs, freshly upturned leaves, a bit of hair rubbed against a tree, gave him sufficient clues to follow this animal for a hundred yards through the dark thicket.

Each day the club members would split up into numerous parties. Late in the afternoon they often returned with deer, bear, ducks, quail, or coon. One of our party specialized on rattlesnakes. Others took to the lakes and returned with good catches of black bass. At night we would gather around a great campfire. The stories and songs were wonderful. The two weeks slipped by very fast.

The following year we chose a higher and drier camp. One member remained in the camp each day as captain and tried to outdo his predecessor by adding some valuable feature to our comfort or pleasure. When my turn came, I wanted to do something unusual and decided to clear the great palmetto logs out of a near-by pool, which I thought would make a wonderful swimming-hole. With a dozen darkies I entered the water, and before long we had removed the fallen timber. Off to one side of the deep pool was a dark hole. Wishing to probe its depths, I dropped down and stuck one foot into it, but did not reach its limits. Paddling to the surface, I got out, and was drying myself when I noticed a great commotion in the hole I had just investigated with my foot. Out came a huge alligator. Terrified at what might have happened to me, I was too paralyzed to act, but Pen Beckley had arrived with a rifle; he killed the monster, and we dragged him out. He measured fourteen feet long and his mouth was big enough to have swallowed not only my leg, but me.

A little later the club had a nice house on the shore of Lake George. "Uncle" John and "Aunt" Mary not only were wonderful cooks but had lovely voices. With our portable organ on the beach and the gang around a fire, the spirituals that Mary and John sang in the moonlight, and for which we formed an enthusiastic chorus, were marvelous.

One spring Bob and my other Kentucky friends invited me to come out the first of May to fish in Lake Erie with the Ananias

Club. No more appropriate name could have been found. Each year this group went to Sandusky, Ohio, where a steamer took them to the Little Bass Islands near the Canadian shore of Lake Erie. In the Ananias Club were some of the most distinguished men in Kentucky—judges of the Supreme Court, leading lawyers, physicians, bankers. After a large breakfast of eggs, bacon, ham, sausage, waffles and molasses, hominy, and other Southern provender, we were off on the steamer for the fishing-banks. Towed behind were fifteen rowboats, into each of which climbed two club members and a guide with rods, reels, and two quarts of whisky. Early in the morning the fishing usually was slow, so we had a drink for good luck. When the first fish was caught, this was celebrated by another drink. If one had the hard luck to lose a fish, this catastrophe required the solace of a drink. Before the morning was over, libations were made to celebrate the greatest number of fish, the largest fish, the smallest fish, and several drinks were added just for good luck.

At noon we came together for lunch. The cooks prepared a marvelous meal with fried bass, and bacon that they toasted next to a slice of bread. Food never tasted so wonderful. The afternoon catch was generally not so good as the morning one, because many of the fishermen went to sleep. The homeward trip across the lake gave an excellent opportunity to get ready for the steaming dinner awaiting us. This was a very formal event. The club president, Charles Ballard, was an orator. His introductions were matchless. Every member was given a chance to tell a story, sing a song, do a dance, or otherwise distinguish himself. I joined these bons vivants year after year until the war took many of us into the army and put an end to the Ananias Club, along with many other good things in life.

One of the most amusing members was Dr. Clint Kelley, who was very fond of cockfights. His wife was a religious woman and hated this propensity of the doctor's, so he had to keep it quiet. One night a fine fighting gamecock of his had been sadly mauled, and to resuscitate him Clint hugged him to his bosom. His wife, seeing the feathers on his clothes, accused him of cockfighting. Nothing daunted, Clint said: "My dear, how wrong of you to accuse me. I have just been attending a German woman who gave birth to a baby in a large feather bed, and I must have got a lot of the feathers on my clothes."

Bob's early married life was saddened by a great tragedy, the loss of his young wife in an automobile accident. Left with three small children, he became the most devoted parent I have ever known. His life with Robert, Henrietta, and Barry was beautiful to behold. But his home sadly needed a mistress, and in 1916 I was delighted when Bob told me he was going to marry again.

He asked me to be best man at his marriage to Mrs. Mary Keenan Flagler, widow of the great railroad-builder Henry Flagler. I joined him at the Plaza Hotel, and after celebrating briefly at the bar we went to the barbershop to get polished up for the very distingué dinner that was being given Bob and his fiancée by the Pembroke Joneses. When I started to dress, I found that the maid at home had failed to put in my evening clothes. I telephoned for the head valet to come to my room and when he arrived, he said: "Hello, Dr. Young. I'm glad to see you." He had been the valet of one of my friends. "Well, if you are, show it by getting me a dress suit and a white waistcoat and tie." Somewhat flabbergasted by my request, after a moment's hesitation off he dashed, and in a few minutes was back. The trousers were just right, the waistcoat and tie were perfect, and the coat fitted beautifully. He admitted that he had taken them from the room of a Chicago millionaire who was away for the week end. Bob had explained my failure to arrive on time by saying that my train was late, but I frankly told Mrs. Jones that I was late because I had left my evening clothes at home and had on stolen clothes. At this announcement, Mr. Jones gave a yell, and proceeded to turn my pockets inside out searching for a name. Finally, inside the trousers, we found "Otto Schmidt," and during the rest of the evening I was toasted as "Schmidt" or "Otto."

After dinner Mr. Henry Walters, who lived with the Joneses, took me to his apartment and showed me some of the masterpieces that now hang in the Walters Gallery in Baltimore. Mary Lily Bingham died a few months after marrying Bob. In August, 1924, at St. Margaret's, Westminster, London, Bob and Mrs. Byron Hilliard of Louisville, Kentucky, were married.

I had just returned to Baltimore after a medical meeting when I found a telegram from Bob saying that Claire Sheridan, the famous British sculptor, had arrived in New York. He had commissioned her to make a bust of me. Her time was limited, and he asked me please to arrange for her to begin at once. I telephoned Bob that I was leaving in five days for a cruise; I had been away; I was head over heels in work; I could not possibly do it. The next day, Monday, a telegram arrived saying that Miss Sheridan would arrive on an afternoon train and please to arrange for the sittings at once. At the hotel I told her how impossible it was, but she said she was a quick worker, and as I had to eat sometime, she would do her work while I ate in her sitting-room. We began at lunch on Tuesday and by Thursday evening she had almost finished her work. Mr. Park, a New York friend, was called in to express an opinion. He said, "Miss Sheridan, Dr. Young is a serious surgeon, but you have him telling an army story." She replied that she had heard nothing else. With a few strokes she cut out the jocose lines, and when the family were called next day to inspect it, they expressed satisfaction. Bob sent the bust to the University of Virginia a few months later, where it was unveiled. They insisted on my being present, and I sat through the ordeal while Dr. John H. Neff made a meticulous analysis of my contributions to medicine. When at long last the function was over, a young woman came up and said, "I hope you appreciate that I have come fifty miles to see your bust unveiled." Whereupon, with a bow, I said, "I would go a thousand to see yours."

Soon after his inauguration, President Franklin D. Roosevelt sent to the Senate the name of Robert Worth Bingham to be Ambassador to the Court of St. James. Bob was critically ill at the time. A surgical operation on an abscess barely saved him from septicemia. Before he was well he insisted on going to his post in London.

A little later I received a cable saying that he was very sick, and on going over I found that the sepsis had settled in his kidneys. He was suffering from an acute nephritis (Bright's disease). As it was impossible to accomplish much for him in London, I begged the family to let me take him to one of the great French watering-places, but was told that it would be considered a great insult to the British to take the American Ambassador to France for treatment.

On investigation I discovered that a group of Australian doctors had organized a splendid clinic at Ruthin Castle, Wales, and there I hastened. The director, after serving in the British Army, had decided to locate there, and had added to his staff other Australians —clinicians and laboratory men, all experts in their work and well abreast of modern medicine. They were well prepared to carry out the thalein test and other methods that we employed at home. Thither I took Bob, and in a short time he had so greatly improved that he was able to stroll out on the beautiful grounds with Lord Derby, who also was a patient. The intimate friendship which they formed was of great value to the Ambassador later. Within two months Bob was able to go to Scotland, take his place in the butts, and bring down as many grouse as anyone.

With complete restoration of his health, Bob was invited more and more to take part in shoots: grouse in August, partridges and pheasants in the fall. Here his wonderful marksmanship gave him a great reputation. At one shoot I remember Bob bagged on the first day one hundred and ninety pheasants, on the second day two hundred and twenty, and on the third day about two hundred and fifty. With eight guns present, he had killed about a third of the birds.

This did not surprise me, as I had been with him in a duck blind at the Cedar Point Club on Chesapeake Bay. When the members of the club discovered that Bob had only a twenty-gauge Purdey with him, one after another explained that he could not kill ducks with a popgun like that, the shells of which contained only half as much powder and shot as the club members used in their No. 12 automatics. When they insisted that he use one of their own guns, Bob explained that he had a peculiar drop to his shoulder and the proferred guns did not fit him, that he would have to make out as well as he could with the little Purdey. We had not been in the blind long before two canvasbacks, traveling high and fast, came from behind on Bob's side. He upped with his popgun and brought them both down. Ducks soon began coming in rapidly, and so many fell that in a little while Bob was shooting only the canvasbacks. Finally he singled out drake canvasbacks to shoot at. By half-past eight we had picked up forty-five ducks. Bob had killed the majority. We got back to the clubhouse, and had to wait three hours before the other members with their No. 12 automatics and pump guns came in.

On one occasion, while shooting quail, I saw Bob with an automatic bring down five on the rise of the covey. When I first shot with him in Scotland on Lord Airlie's moors, Bob's record for birds passing and going away was high, but the fast incoming birds he frequently missed, while a kilted Scot in an adjoining butt had no difficulty with them. Returning to his home in Kentucky, Bob put up four telegraph poles in a field ten feet apart, thus forming a square, and erected platforms at ten-foot intervals. In front of each of these platforms he put a steel plate, and behind it a trap and a Negro. As Bob marched down the field, pigeons from these traps were shot at him, high and low, and before the summer was over he had so mastered the incoming shots that when he returned to Scotland he outshot the Scot.

We were always amazed at the wonderful amount of game we found all over Great Britain. Mr. Bernard Baruch's place was not far from Bob's, and they often killed ten thousand brace of grouse in a season. King George V, one of their greatest shots, is reported to have killed over twelve hundred grouse himself in one day's shoot. "The MacIntosh" is said to have killed two hundred more than that.

It was delightful to visit Bob at the American Embassy, to behold his great popularity and his wonderful success in dealing with the British, politicians and aristocracy alike. His son Barry had married a cousin of Wallis Warfield, and they and Henrietta Bingham, Bob's lovely daughter, were close friends of the Prince of Wales and frequently went to parties with him and had him at the Embassy. During Bob's first weeks of illness his wife took over the heavy social duties and acquitted herself wonderfully. Her charm and remarkable savoir-faire gave her a unique place in diplomatic circles. Occasionally I went as her escort, and one evening I was greatly pleased when, sitting next to George Bernard Shaw, she replied very sharply to him on one of his sallies against Americans. Never have we been represented by more patriotic Americans, who were quick to call down those who belittled our country, than the Binghams. In such great esteem was Bob held that he received the degree of L.L.D. from the universities of London, Edinburgh, Oxford, Cambridge, and St. Andrew's. I believe he is the only American citizen ever to be so honored. One evening he and King George were the only two who received honorary membership at one of the great social organizations. The freedom of the city of Barnstable, from which his ancestors had come, was also given him at a great celebration. Everywhere I went in England I was impressed by the great affection and esteem in which he was held.

Although greatly interested in his ambassadorial duties, every winter he longed to get back to his bird dogs. At Pineland Lodge, near Albany, Georgia, he had accumulated twenty thousand acres of fine bird country, built a charming lodge, and erected kennels for his seventy-five splendid setters. The shooting was wonderfully organized. We would start off in the morning with Bob driving a station wagon to some prearranged spot two or three miles distant. There in waiting was "Uncle" John with a dog wagon, in the back of which were six fine setters, and in the front three cocker spaniels. "Titsy" was there with three riding horses. Two dogs were released, and started in the proper direction. With his dog-trainer by his side, Bob and I followed the dogs in the wonderful swings they made through the fields and woods. Uncle John, with Titsy at his side, belabored the mules and kept up with us even though we crossed rough fields, gulleys, streams, and even logs.

When the dogs finally came to point, Titsy was there with us as we flushed the birds. With unerring eye he marked down the cripples and picked up our kills. The highly trained setters were good retrievers except in the briers, and into these they refused to go. Here it was that the spaniels were called in. With their tough wooly coats resisting the thorns, they plunged in, bringing out birds that otherwise would have been lost. Most amusing it was to see them follow a wounded bird into the hole of a burned-out stump. With their tails wagging, they forced their muzzles into the depths of the holes and finally brought out the bird. One day I said, "Titsy, where did you get that name?" "Well," said he, "when I was a baby I refused to be weaned and I kept on sucking and sucking until everybody got to laughing about it, and they named me Titsy."

Hawk Spectre was the chief of the kennel. He had won the national field-trial championship and had been graduated to the stud. His services there brought $100, and he was kept busy. Most of his pups had his wonderful form and carried their plumelike tails high above their backs as they stood rigid at point. Herbert Fishel and his wife were wonders at training these dogs. Bob's anxiety when one would get sick was touching. Some of them became infected with that terrible filaria known as heartworm. When we opened their hearts, we found them filled with a tangled mass of these six-inch hairlike worms, which looked all the world like a shredded wheat biscuit. In the blood it was possible to see the microfilaria as they wiggled among the corpuscles. Fortunately, a new drug had been discovered that, when injected intravenously, saved many of these fine animals.

A rash had developed on Bob's lower back, and in treatment of it he received an overdose of X-ray treatment. This resulted in a sore spot that prevented his riding horseback. Bravely he would go out on foot, until one day his farm-manager appeared with a contraption closely resembling a Roman chariot except that the wheels and the axles came from a Ford. As Bob stood behind the curving bentwood, with his strong Roman face he needed only a toga and a sword to be a perfect replica of Julius Caesar. Holding onto his gun with one hand and the frame of the chariot with the other, Bob would come dashing up to the point and take his place as we walked to the rise of the covey.

Soon after arriving in London on one of my visits to Bob I had to go to Belfast, where my old comrade Andrew Fullerton had persuaded Queen's University to give me a D.S.C. At a garden party in the lovely university grounds I met the Marchioness of Londonderry, whose husband was the Chancellor of the university. They invited me to dine at Mount Stewart, their country seat, some forty miles away. On the way down there I was amazed to see what appeared to be paintings of small snakes crawling up Her Ladyship's legs. I was so fascinated that I could not keep my eyes off them. As she made no effort at concealment, I finally said, "Marchioness, what have you got on your legs?" "Snakes," said she. "I had them tattooed on a few years ago. A celebrated Japanese artist arrived in London, and as skirts had become very short and legs very prominent, I decided to give them something to look at." Looking more closely, I said, "They are certainly very beautiful—as far as I can see." The snakes disappeared under her skirt and their heads were beyond the line of my vision. After a tour with her through the estate we had dinner, where for some reason the conversation constantly reverted to snakes, and I was able to amuse them with some of my experiences in Texas and the story of the girl and the boa constrictor in Trinidad. A couple of weeks later at a ball at Londonderry House, just off Hyde Park, my daughter Elizabeth and I were amused to see the snakes gaily weaving in and out among the dancers. The outer skirt was diaphanous, and the brilliantly colored serpents were clearly visible as the Marchioness danced. Calling on her a few days later, I met Ramsey MacDonald with a large portfolio. It had frequently been said that he reported regularly to Her Ladyship, who got, firsthand, many state secrets.

In November, 1937, Bob cabled me that he had not been well, wanted to come to Baltimore for treatment, and would arrive on the twenty-fifth. I had been invited by the Pan-American Airways to go to Bermuda on their first flight from Baltimore. As I had been down with a cold, I was glad to have this opportunity for a week in a balmy climate, of course expecting to be back before Bob's arrival. On the way over I got greatly chilled, came down with pneumonia, and did not get back home for three weeks. When I arrived, poor Bob was unconscious. As I bent over him, saying, "Bob, this is Hugh," a faint smile crossed his face and he gurgled some reply, but I fear he did not recognize me. In a few hours he was dead.

On his return to the hospital an abdominal incision had been made by Dr. William F. Rienhoff. An extensive infiltrating mass, known as Hodgkin's disease, was found. This irregular growth had spread up and down the peritoneal cavity, gradually strangling the vessels that went to his vital organs. Fortunately, the final stages were rapid. Severe pain came only at the last and was well controlled by opiates. The end came swiftly. I was grateful that he had not suffered long, but terribly upset because I had not been here to be with my old friend, who in his last illness had turned again to me in hopeful confidence.

CHAPTER 30. FISHING

MY FIRST experience with fly fishing was in the lakes and streams of northern Maine. A few years later I went with General Hugh McLean far up into New Brunswick, Canada, for salmon. The General represented Lord Strathcona, who owned about twenty miles of the Tobique River, a fine salmon stream. On this a few years before the General had built a princely lodge to accommodate Princess "Pat" (Patricia Ramsay) and her party, who had come to Canada to see the regiment that had been named for her. No such gorgeous lodge had been constructed before in the wilds of Canada. It had individual showers and hot and cold water in each room. After about ten days of very good fishing we traveled downstream and fished with the Tobique Club. There I met Robert Emmet, a grandson of the Irish patriot. He was an ardent sportsman; he did not allow the guide to gaff his salmon, but insisted on playing the fish until he could beach it, and go out and pick it up.

In 1919 I went with my son and three others to fish the lakes of the Timagami region in northern Canada. Some lakes were filled with speckled trout and others with small-mouthed black bass. We used frogs for the latter. I fastened a frog on the hook by its lower jaw—the regulation way. In a short time I got a strike, gave the fish time enough to swallow the frog, and then set my hook. The fish was a big one and I had to play it a long time before it finally tired and I could reel it toward the boat. I saw a ripple in the water around the line and expected to see a fish, but instead the frog came up the line hand over hand, like a monkey. I caught two more fish with the same frog. Each time it had been spit out by the fish and frantically climbed the line to get away from it. After removing the third fish I did not have the heart to use the frog again, so I bade the boatman go back to the marsh, where I placed the frog on a mossy bed while the guide cursed.

I shall never forget the first bonefish I hooked. I was off one of the Matecumbe Keys with Dr. Tom Otto of Miami. I used a bait of shrimp and crab, which was cast just in front of some tailing bonefish. I soon had a strike. I let the fish have the bait and nervously waited until it had carried it about two or three feet before I set the hook. In a flash it was off with speed such as I had never seen before. My light reel without break fairly burned my thumb through a stall. Away and away the fish went, as if bound for Cuba. Putting on more and more pressure, I finally stopped it after a run of about a hundred yards. Then it turned and started toward me. It took very rapid reeling to keep the line taut. Suddenly the fish stopped and I was unable to budge it. My guide, Preston Pinder, a noted fisherman, said that it had gone under a bunch of coral. So I reeled in as Preston poled the boat closer. Finally we were over the fish, but could not move it. Preston asked me to give him the rod. Bending the brim of his big straw hat while holding the line taut, he sawed on it with his hatbrim as if with a fiddle bow. I asked what he was trying to do. He said the vibration of the taut line would make the fish so nervous that finally it could not stand it any longer and would come out, and sure enough it did. After a fight of over half an hour I finally boated it. It weighed nine pounds—a big one for a bonefish.

One of my best guides was a woman. She had been brought up by a fisherman father on one of the Florida islands. He had no sons, and had taught his daughters to row, scull, and pole. The man I had expected to take me could not go and his wife said that she could recommend her sister, who on weekdays was a masseuse in

Miami. Before long we saw ahead of us in the receding tide a large
school of bonefish with their tails out of the water as they dug in the
coral sand for the crabs on which they live. She poled the boat into
a fine position on the tidal side of the fish and anchored. A long cast
placed the bait of shrimp and crab a short distance from the fish
without disturbing them, and the tide carried the bait to where they
were. I landed a good fish. We hunted and hunted for another school.
At last my guide said a good chew of tobacco always brought her
luck, and she bit off a big piece. She proved to be an expert spitter.
After a time we caught some more fish. When we had been out about
four hours, my guide calmly remarked: "Please look the other way.
I've got something to attend to." Besides being a good guide, she
was pretty.

On the Potomac above Piney Point are three lumps of stone on
which rock or striped bass are always present. Tom Trott, our guide,
was one of the few who could fish these lumps accurately. Walter
Denny, Al Koeneke, and I had many a fine day's fishing with Tom,
but the best was on two moonlight nights. On one of these the tide
began to flood just as the moon came up. Tom threw out an anchor
over the biggest lump. He had telephoned us that the fish were
taking only soft-shell crabs and told us to bring as many as we
could get. Placing our hooks through the abdomens of the crabs so
as not to kill them, and casting them wriggling out into the water,
we caught in one evening over fifty fish weighing from six to twenty
pounds. With light tackle one had to be careful in bringing in these
big sporty fish. On the following evening we had a similar experience,
but had to stop because we had used the last of our twenty-one
dozen crabs. After filling our large boxes with fish for our families
and friends, we turned over the remainder to Tom, who sold them
for over $50. We all agreed that this was the finest fishing we had
had.

The Chesapeake Bay offered such wonderful sport that I finally
bought a forty-two foot Dawn cruiser. With three or four companions we would start off on Friday afternoon, and often con-

tinued down past the mouth of the Potomac, going into Tangier Sound and up to Crisfield for anchorage during the night. Before we returned on Sunday we usually had fine catches of rock, trout, hardheads, and sometimes bluefish. A famous place was the southwest Middle Grounds, a long strip of shoal banks where the Potomac empties into the Chesapeake. Coming down one afternoon at the upper end of the Middle Grounds, we saw ahead a great number of gulls on the water. This indicated that fish were nigh. Another sign was a large slick covering perhaps five acres in that region. These slicks come from fish on the bottom who are chewing over their food and emitting the oil. Seeing these two positive signs of fish, we anchored. Before long there was a mass movement of gulls to the east and down they dashed into the water. As we rushed up, a great school was literally tearing the water up as they caught the small fish on the surface and threw the fragments into the water, where they were caught by the birds. In an hour we had boated at least a hundred and fifty fine bluefish. Then the sport ceased as suddenly as it had begun. We moved on down the bay to the wreck of the battleship *Texas* off the mouth of the Rappahannock, which is always a fine place to catch small fish. With a captain who was a good cook we lived high on these excursions, which were splendid for the health and vigor of all of us.

A group of us got together and purchased a smaller boat for fishing off Gibson Island. With Sam Whalen, an expert guide, for a number of years we had splendid sport in the broad waters of the bay north of Kent Island and immediately in front of my bungalow, where there was a narrow winding shoal known as Snake Ridge. We could always find good fishing of some sort. At times it was rock, at others hardheads, at others perch and Norfolk spots. We were usually certain of making a good catch in a few hours. With my dear friend Warren Buckler, I usually would go down on Wednesday morning. By arriving at the hospital at eight o'clock and doing one or two operations, it was possible to get down to my bungalow at Gibson Island and reach the fishing-grounds in the bay between eleven and twelve o'clock. We almost always had good afternoon fishing and were usually back for seven o'clock dinner. Where else in the United States could doctors look after their practice and at the same time get such splendid fishing and be back in time for an evening at home? We also spend almost every Sunday fishing.

The striped bass, or rockfish, is as changeable and fickle as a woman. One week they may take the artificial lure known as the Huntington drone; another week they may refuse these and take only feathers; the next week they may not take anything. Once toward the end of the season Walter Denny and I, fishing with Tom Trott, found that they "bit" greedily at eel skins. This is a very ingenious bait. The fisherman skins the eel, cuts off the head, and replaces it with an aluminum one containing two large red eyes. Through the center of this runs a wire to which a hook is fastened that comes out through the belly of the eel. When trolled through the water, this eel wriggles in a most lifelike manner. We had been fishing all day with very little luck, having tried various lures without success. Late in the afternoon a squall came up; there was a heavy wind and a violent downpour of rain. The squall disappeared as quickly as it had come, and immediately the water was filled with rock, which were greedily eating up a large school of shiners on the surface. We cast out our eel-skin baits and trolled through the school. In half an hour we had boated nearly forty fish weighing between six and twenty pounds. Then suddenly the fishing was over. This fickleness makes fishing perpetually interesting. It is a constant matching of wits between the fisherman and the fish. Those fly fisherman who are inclined to look down upon trolling as unsportsmanlike only have to come down, try it themselves, and see how many more fish an expert in bay fishing will get, to realize that there is a great deal of skill in it.

On a trip to Alaska several years ago I had some excellent fishing in White Horse Rapids, that celebrated strip of fast water down which the Yukon gold-seekers went in their fragile craft, many of which were dashed to pieces against the treacherous rocks. On inquiry I found that the grayling, the sporty arctic fish was there in great numbers. One of the inhabitants was a great fisherman, and supplied me with rod, reel, proper flies, and hip boots. It was necessary to wade out into the rapids and cast into the fast water. The fish bit only in the evening and we did not begin to get strikes until about eight o'clock. The fishing continued good until ten o'clock, when the northern twilight disappeared and darkness came on. The grayling were fast and hard to bring in. Several times I had to follow them out, and in so doing slid off some of the slippery rocks and got my boots full of water; but the fishing was fine.

I left the ship at Prince Rupert, where a friend had arranged for me to have some fishing at Lac Trembleur, which he said was only a short distance up the Canadian National Railway—I found it was four hundred miles, and then had to travel eighty miles by truck before I reached an outpost of the Hudson's Bay Company on Stuart Lake. From there we had to travel by fast motorboat about thirty miles up the lake and through rapids so difficult that we had to stop and get an Indian guide. Finally we reached Lac Trembleur, a narrow piece of water between two precipitous hills and so deep that no one has ever reached bottom. It was so named because it constantly trembles as a result of its peculiar geologic formation, of volcanic origin. I could fish for only a day and a half, as I had to hurry back and catch another boat, but during this time I caught five rainbow trout, the largest weighing nine pounds. They are great fighters, and on being hooked go at once for the bottom. It took hard reeling with light tackle to get them up to the surface, and then a grand fight finally to net them. Owing to the wide range of their activity it was about as sporty fishing as I have ever had and the five fish were well worth the trip of a thousand miles.

IT IS not easy for one to talk about his personal life. I have already told several times of the musical Colston family into which I married. Bessy, the youngest daughter, was lovely and charming. She inherited a pretty voice from her mother, and also her great love of reading. Affectionate and fond of companionship, and with a host of friends, she was very tolerant of one so wrapped up in his profession and wedded to his work, and was very happy with her brood of four, on whom she bestowed great love.

When only forty-eight, Bessy died of septicemia. The blow was doubly crushing to me because we had cured so many patients with blood poisoning, but were unable to save her. During the fall of 1927 she began to complain of slight pains in various joints, and a little fever. As this continued for several days, I had a blood culture taken, and was horrified to find that the *Streptococcus viridans* grew from it. I knew that she had an old heart lesion that had come as a result of inflammatory rheumatism during her childhood. I had her heart examined at once. The murmurs (blowing sounds) caused by a leaky valve in the heart that had long been present were apparently not accentuated. We hoped against hope that the organisms in her blood would not settle on the roughened areas on her heart valves, and that the blood-stream infection might be eliminated. But the fever continued, and soon the heart sounds became worse. It was evident that the infernal bacteria had begun to pile up their

MRS. HUGH HAMPTON YOUNG AND HER CHILDREN IN 1910

After a portrait by Eric Haupt

exudate in her wounded heart. In the meantime I had frantically searched the medical literature of the world, but had met with almost no encouragement. The disease was admitted to be about 100 per cent fatal. We had at hand a number of antiseptics with which we had apparently cured some cases of blood-stream infection far more fulminating in their symptoms than Bessy's. As the medical men all said that the prognosis was surely fatal, we decided to try intravenous injections, first of neosalvarsan, which had saved a number of patients with streptococcus septicemia of other types, but without success. As she steadily went downhill, it seemed desirable to try another intravenous antiseptic, but the septicemia persisted. The blood content of red cells had continually dropped, and was now only about 50 per cent of normal. It was decided to give her a pint of blood from her brother. Although the two bloods matched perfectly, a violent reaction occurred during which numerous particles were thrown off from the great mass of exudate that had formed in her heart, and were quickly transmitted to terminal arteries, where the emboli blocked the circulation to extremities and brain, and she soon passed away.

This condition, known as *endocarditis lenta* on account of its few symptoms, its slight discomfort, and its soothing character that leads one to hope that it may soon disappear, is probably the most fatal of all diseases. In Bessy's case it came from a dead tooth that gave no symptoms, and no evidence of an abscess at its root. Very soon after the demonstration of a blood-stream infection in her case this tooth was extracted, and from its root a culture was taken that showed the dreaded *Streptococcus viridans*. This was the focal abscess from which the green streptococcus had from time to time penetrated into the blood, and, settling in the heart, had piled up a mass of exudate that finally was almost as large as a Seckel pear.

I have given Bessy's case as a warning to all with valvular heart disease to be sure that no chronically infected teeth are present. It is the duty of physicians to warn patients with chronic valvular heart disease that they must give great care to their teeth; that a chronic abscess at the root of a tooth must be prevented at all costs, either by local treatment or by extraction; that dead teeth are dangerous. It is likewise the duty of dentists when they find devitalized teeth or discover apical abscesses to find out whether such patients suffer from valvular heart disease, and if so, to take no chances with a chronically infected tooth. The dental operation must be radical, and vigorous antiseptic applications made. Had these precautions been taken in poor Bessy's case, her untimely death might have been averted.

Bessy's early death left me with three unmarried children, but they had been so well brought up by their mother that I had few worries, and had the great pleasure of seeing them all happily married. Now I have nine grandchildren, who give me great delight.

Baltimore is a charming place in which to live. When I came here, although thirty years had passed since the Civil War, the reigning families were Southern in both connections and sympathies. During my first four years I was immured in the hospital. Then I opened up my office on Charles Street. Each Sunday after church everyone joined the Charles Street parade. The first money I made in practice was spent on a frock coat, striped trousers, a high hat, and a gold-headed cane, so as to be properly attired on Sunday. My office had large windows, and it was a popular place from which to gaze on the beauties in their bustles as they passed up and down the street.

One Sunday I received an urgent call to go to the home of Captain Colston. As I went down Charles Street in my very formal attire with my ungainly surgical bag in my hand, I made an incongruous picture on my way to reach the patient two blocks away. I found Mrs. Colston with an abscess of the gum that was causing her great pain. Concealing my scalpel from her gaze, I gave a jab that cured her, but she upbraided me sharply for not having warned her what I was going to do. I nearly lost my entree into the family. After a few weeks Mrs. Colston wrote me requesting my bill. Not knowing my designs on her daughter, a little later she wrote me a more urgent note, to which it is said I replied, "I'm very sorry I

FRANCES KEMPER YOUNG
(Mrs. William Francis Rienhoff, Jr.)

FREDERICK COLSTON YOUNG
(married Nellie Croxall Biays)

HELEN HAMPTON YOUNG
(Mrs. Bennett Crain)

ELIZABETH CAMPBELL YOUNG
(Mrs. Warren Russell Starr)

At MacCallum Rienhoff's Christening Party in 1932

Their grandfather with (*left to right*) Bennett Crain, Jr., Hugh Hampton Young II, Betsy Colston Young, MacCallum Rienhoff, Hugh Young Rienhoff, William Francis Rienhoff, Jr.

cannot send you a bill, because I have no license to practice dentistry."

Through the many sons of old Baltimoreans I had known at the University of Virginia, I had been properly introduced in the city, and my in-laws greatly widened the scope of my acquaintance. After Father died, Mother came to live with me in 1902. Old Southern families immediately rallied around her and helped to to assuage her great bereavement. Mother took great delight in my children as they came along, and showed an ever helpful interest in their development.

Since 1910 the Chesapeake Bay has been the scene of a great part of my outdoor life. In that year Mr. Carroll T. Bond, now chief justice of the Maryland Court of Appeals, asked me if I would like to help an old ex-Confederate, Captain Jefferson Cook, who owned large properties on the Bay and the Magothy River about twenty miles from Baltimore. Captain Cook had outfitted blockade runners to the Confederacy during the Civil War. He had a small mortgage on his farm and begged Carroll Bond to find someone to take enough of the land to lift the mortgage. I was not particularly interested in water-front properties, but agreed to see him. When I saw the lovely site on the Chesapeake Bay and Magothy River that formed the lower peninsula of Captain Cook's farm, I was fascinated with its beauty and asked him: "How much land will you give me if I lift the mortgage"? "As much as you want," said the Captain. So I drew a line across the peninsula, the deal was closed, and we measured the acreage later.

Here I built a bungalow. To one of the numerous parties that we gave there came Mr. W. Stuart Symington, Jr. He expressed amazement at the beauty of the spot and asked who owned Gibson Island adjacent. After his fourth julep he said that he was going to buy it and make it a haven for yachtsmen and golfers. And so he did, in a grand and a glorious way, without regard to expense, so much so that he went broke and dragged along with him his sympathetic brothers. But in the meantime he had organized the Gibson Island

Club with splendid golf links. He did not live to see the organization
of the yacht squadron that has played such an important rôle in
maritime activities and afforded Baltimoreans (and many others)
a chance to enjoy the incomparable Chesapeake Bay.

The Johns Hopkins Hospital staff was comparatively small, a
closely knit organization in which the great men showed the kindest
interest in the youngsters, a truly delightful atmosphere in which to
work. Dr. Welch, the father of the Medical School, was omnipresent.
His advice and assistance were sought by the political leaders of
city, state, and nation, and to the entire medical profession he was
known as "Popsy."

In 1912 I received a letter from Dr. Welch in which he said: "I am
very much pleased to hear that you have been appointed chairman
of a subcommittee to make recommendations about the national
health organization. . . . I think that you may gain immortal re-
nown by straightening the tangle. . . ." This was the beginning of a
campaign in which I took a very active part. Here again Senators
and Representatives who had been patients at the Brady Institute
often formed the "spearhead of attack" to persuade the Congress
to pass legislation that the medical profession considered of great
importance. Dr. Hugh S. Cumming, then Surgeon General of the U. S.
Public Health Service, likes to tell of an amusing occurrence when
the bill to create a National Health Institute was before the Appropriations Committee. Favorable action was blocked by Senator
Couzens of Michigan. At a meeting of the committee in which a
hearing had been granted on the measure, Senator Couzens had just
expressed himself very forcibly against the bill when I arrived, and
was called on to speak. Immediately afterward Senator Couzens,
who had recently spent some time with us at the Brady, withdrew his
opposition, and the splendid Hygienic Institute resulted.

There was hardly an important movement in which Dr. Welch
did not take an active part. I have recounted how he soon pushed
me into various outside activities. I found that being associated
with important movements of all sorts brought new and varied
interests and personalities into my life. For one reason or another,

when I once got interested in some work I stayed on, so that now, after many years, I am still on the State Mental Hygiene Board, the boards of the War Memorial, the Baltimore Museum of Art, the Aviation Commission, the Lyric Theatre, the Baltimore Opera Club, and the Gibson Island Club and Yacht Squadron. I have tried to resign from many of these boards. The chairman of one of these said he wanted to keep me on "for emergencies." For ten years I have been "Civilian Aide to the Secretary of War."

One might ask whether such distractions do not interfere with one's clinical and scientific life. While the answer is undoubtedly yes, the broadening of interests and the contacts with important men in many walks of life are well worth while. The chairmanship of the State Aviation Commission has brought me in close touch with some of the flyers who have made aviation history. My musical interests have made for me charming friendships with great singers at the Metropolitan, and with other musical artists. While commodore of the Gibson Island Yacht Squadron I was instrumental in inaugurating the ocean race from New London to Gibson Island, and I was brought into intimate contact with many of the important figures in yachting. As chairman of the Mental Hygiene Board I have learned to know well the fine group of self-sacrificing men who spend their lives with the insane. At the War Memorial I have been brought close to the fifty societies of veterans of various wars, many of whose records are inspiring. As vice-president of the Baltimore Museum of Art, acquaintance with another large group of interesting men and women has ensued. It has led me into close association with Dr. David M. Robinson, whose archeological explorations at Olynthus, Greece, excited my interest so much that when he was unable to continue owing to lack of funds, I found it possible to secure the support of a group of my wealthy friends. Their contributions kept Dr. Robinson's explorations going for several years and led to discoveries so noteworthy that their description and illustration occupy six large volumes, one of which he kindly dedicated to me.

One of my great delights has been the annual dinner of the Baltic

Society—composed of the survivors of those who crossed on the
S.S. Baltic with General Pershing. The Commander in Chief treats
his old staff officers with charming cordiality. Between the highest
ranking officers of the A.E.F. and their junior comrades-in-arms
there is now a delightful camaraderie—jovial joshing of great
superiors by their erstwhile inferiors is encouraged, and we even
make bold to poke mild fun at the great Commander in Chief.
At one of the dinners I was incited to tell of some of his conquests
among the ladies. On my way to Paris a lovely lady to whom I
had been talking for some time finally said "Don't tell anybody,
I'm going to marry General Pershing." The next day at the Hotel
Ritz in Paris a lady next to whom I sat at a dinner given by General
Dawes, whispered to me, confidentially, "I'm going to marry General Pershing." On my way back across the Atlantic a perfect Juno
from Boston said, "Don't dare breathe it, but I'm going to marry
General Pershing."

Early in my professional life in Baltimore I formed a close friendship with Albert Cabell Ritchie. His personal charm and brilliant
mind made him one of the most delightful companions. As he rose
rapidly in public affairs and became Governor of Maryland his
eloquent and frank discussion of national affairs soon marked him
as presidential timber, and he was called far and wide. It was my
great pleasure to accompany him on some of his travels, and to
participate as a delegate at national conventions before which
Maryland placed the name of her adored son for the Presidency.
And in 1932 he missed the nomination by a very close margin when
Texas, the pivotal state, was switched to Roosevelt by a vote of
53 to 51 with sixteen Ritchie men absent from the caucus of the
delegation. Ritchie had asked me to be liaison man with the Texans,
and it broke my heart when my native state, which seemed safely
in his column, was thus taken from him.

Interest in music in Baltimore has been greatly stimulated by the
Garrett concerts that are given at Evergreen. For sixteen years the
John W. Garretts have sponsored spring and fall festivals of

classic music by the Musical Art Quartet, whom they install in a bungalow on their estate. This splendid string quartet, often assisted by Mr. Frank Sheridan at the piano, has played evenings or afternoons to music-loving friends of the Garretts in their "Little Theatre." This home of the distinguished diplomat and his charming and colorful wife is a Mecca to which come diplomats, statesmen, litterateurs, artists, and professional men of all sorts. Here it has been my privilege to meet some of the most distinguished men of the world.

Mrs. Young from the start encouraged me to take an interest in international medical societies, and to travel widely. For many years she accompanied me to the triennial meetings of the International Association of Urology. We formed close friendships with charming people from many countries. These trips frequently were extended to travel widely. In other years we voyaged to distant lands, often accompanied by our children, one of whom was less than two years old when she first crossed the Atlantic, which I have traversed thirty-eight times.

But my real life—my greatest happiness and my most thrilling experiences—has been at the Brady Urological Institute. With the building of this complete surgical unit, and the attraction of keen young men and women to head the various departments, an opportunity was afforded to carry out my dreams of developing a clinic of far-reaching influence in urology. I have already spoken intimately of the work of the staff of the Brady Institute and the splendid positions its graduates have won in the urological centers of the country.

I have referred to the machine shop that we fitted out in the Brady Urological Institute. It has been a constant joy to me and to the other members of the staff. Its proximity has made possible the immediate carrying out of new ideas for instruments and apparatus, many of which would never have been constructed had it been necessary to leave the hospital and go to some strange mechanic in another part of the city. Each man who has an instrument or a piece of apparatus that he wishes to have constructed in our machine shop is required to furnish a good working drawing. In this way the principles of mechanical design and construction have been inculcated. Many of these men have demonstrated the value of this training by subsequent inventions.

One summer while I was convalescing from some nose and throat operations in a sanatorium near Colorado Springs I found the doctors trying to empty lung abscesses by having the patient hang head-down over the end of a table. This procedure, which was apparently the accepted method at most sanatoria for the tuberculous, struck me as being very unsatisfactory. I obtained permission to go to the city, went to a steam fitter, and with him designed a table of tubular steel and parts from a Ford automobile, with rotating frames, by which the patient could be quickly placed in any position desired to empty a cavity in either the right or the left lung, and at the slightest sign of weakness could be quickly restored to a horizontal position. This postural table is now widely used.

At another time, when a specialist hammered away with a chisel for a long time to remove a "spur" in my nose, it seemed to me that a power drill could be devised to do the work more efficiently, more quickly, and more safely. We made up an apparatus in our shops, and presented it to the other department. It was a great pleasure to hear later that this drill had been used on one of the DuPonts.

I have mentioned these details to accentuate the importance of mechanics to medicine, and particularly to surgeons, as well as the desirability of cultivating the inventiveness and mechanical skill latent in our assistants. Several of these whose early education I have directed went through courses in mechanical design, drafting, and machine-shop work with great benefit.

I was one of the charter members of the American Urological Association, and have taken an active interest in this important national society. As editor of its *Journal of Urology* I have concerned myself greatly with the development of this fine branch of medicine.

The urological experiences in which I have been intimately concerned have already been given in considerable detail, but it may not be amiss to refer here to my more recent life as a urologist. The patients who come to the Brady Institute often present problems of great and perplexing interest, the elucidation of which requires every branch of the large organization that we have assembled. When an apparently satisfactory diagnosis of the hidden lesions of these deep organs has been arrived at, the question often arises as to whether it is possible to effect a cure by surgery. Not infrequently the operative problem is entirely new. Many patients arrive with cardiovascular and kidney disease. Immediate operation would often prove fatal. Only by the most meticulous preparatory treatment and the use of all the multiple agencies of medical diagnosis can a surgeon tell whether he is justified in daring to operate. In these clinical studies and operations I have had the co-operation of the splendid group of men of the staff of the Brady Urological Institute, and that of consultants in other departments of the hospital. In my early days medical consultants were apt to say that very old men could not be operated upon. With the progress of time I have shown that even very desperate cases—even those patients who have had several attacks of apoplexy, and other serious complications—may be safely guided through grave surgical procedures.

No recital of surgical triumphs would be complete without acknowledging the great debt of gratitude that we owe to the nursing profession. Through many long hours each day these faithful women administer to their patients, many of whom are in a desperate condition, not infrequently hanging between life and death. The nurses today are well educated, superbly trained, and very intelligent coworkers with the medical profession. Their devotion to duty, their keen appreciation of the progress of a patient, their quick recognition of important changes in the patient's condition, are of the greatest possible assistance to the surgeon. Without the wonderful work of the nurses, and that of the house officers, it would have been impossible for us to have had a hundred and ninety-eight consecutive perineal prostatectomies without a death, and two hundred and twelve consecutive cases in which one kidney was removed without any fatality.

Life at the operating-table is often very thrilling. Brought up as I was by men who had seen so much excitement in battle, for many years I was grievously disappointed that I could not follow in their footsteps; in fact, during the World War I tried to transfer from the medical corps to the infantry—but the surgical amphitheater is a perpetual battle ground and therefore more than compensates.

Military leaders have often remarked on the great anxiety that they felt after sending their troops into battle, uncertain whether the result would be victory or death. Such is not infrequently the case with a surgeon. Recently a man came to me who had an early cancer that I was confident I could cure by a radical operation, but he had a very bad heart, and the medical consultants thought that he would not stand the extensive operation that was necessary. Was I to leave him to die of the cancer, or operate with the chance of killing him? I decided that it was my duty to operate. In order to see whether his heart would stand the strain of the position in which it was necessary to place him for the operation, I suggested that we take the operating-table to the patient's room, and put him in the elevated position with his thighs high in the air. Much to my delight, he went through this ordeal well. The operation was carried out without disaster, and the wound eventually healed. The patient left the hospital with every prospect of a cure.

Many years ago a man of ninety who had been an intimate of President Lincoln arrived with a prostate so greatly enlarged that it could be palpated through the abdomen. It was almost the size of a pineapple, and he was suffering greatly. The newspapers gave great publicity to his presence in the hospital. I had not been in practice long. If this patient died, the whole country would know about it, and it would hurt me professionally. Nevertheless, I decided to undertake the operation. Happily, he lived for several years after it.

Another man, well over eighty, had a huge diverticulum much larger than the bladder, and filled with foul secretion. He was the president of a railroad, and much in the public eye. The operation to remove the diverticulum would be very extensive and dangerous. Would it be better to leave him alone? I decided that I should take the risk, and again luck was with me. He lived many years in comfort.

Another desperate case was that of Hilary A. Herbert, Secretary of the Navy under Grover Cleveland, and greatly honored as the founder of our modern navy. From long-standing prostatic obstruction, and great back pressure, his kidneys were markedly impaired, and he was very uremic. Even with catheter drainage the kidney function failed to improve, and his suffering was great. Should I risk the chance of his dying from the operation? Would his almost completely destroyed kidneys stand the procedure, and if so, would they ever improve? Mustering up my courage, I carried out the operation as quickly as possible. For several days afterward it was touch and go, but eventually he rallied, and he left the hospital improved. Before long his kidney function returned, and he lived for several years in comfort.

Two patients arrived suffering with tremendous hypertension, the blood pressure ranging between 260 and 280. Frequently during operation the hypertension increases. Should I refuse to operate, and leave them to eke out their lives in pain? Again the chance was taken. During operation the blood pressure in each of these cases rose to over 300. I was in constant dread lest some artery rupture. I worked as fast as I could to shell out the prostatic enlargement, and got the patient off the table in a short time. Again nature was kind, and both men recovered. In each case the blood pressure fell during the ensuing years.

Another case that taxed my fortitude was that of a small child with a tumor of the kidney so huge that it was several times the size of the infant's head. The child could not have lived much longer with this rapidly growing neoplasm. The operation to remove it was very extensive, and unusually shocking. Blood transfusions were started beforehand, and kept up during operation. As little anesthetic as possible was given, and the operative procedure was carried out as fast as I could make it. Fortunately the child went through it all right, and he had no recurrence of the tumor.

Another case was that of a boy with a malignant tumor of the testicle. In these cases, in order to obtain a radical cure it is necessary to carry the incision far up through the abdominal wall, from the groin to the ribs and back, raise up the peritoneum, and follow the lymphatics and glands not only into the deep pelvis, but up along the great blood vessels behind the abdominal cavity, up to and beyond the kidneys. These lymphatic structures lie upon the aorta and the vena cava. The dissection to remove them while the pulsation of a great vessel goes on is delicate in the extreme. With baited breath the assisting staff looked on while the operator dissected off the lymphatic chain. No general could ever be in greater suspense as his men go forward to battle than an operator under such circumstances, but to save the boy from certain death of malignant disease makes it very worth while.

It is especially important for one who leads a strenuous life to have periods of relaxation, complete change of scene, and absolute divorcement from intense mental interests. From this standpoint Baltimore is ideally situated. With the arrival of spring the trout streams of Maryland, Virginia, and Pennsylvania that can be reached in an hour or two offer excellent fishing. A little farther, in the mountains of western Maryland is the Woodmont Rod and Gun Club, where well-stocked lakes and streams give fine sport for trout during May and June, and for bass during July. With the coming of summer the Chesapeake Bay and its tributaries offer the angler excellent fishing. In September railbirds arrive in great quantity on the Patuxent marshes, only forty minutes by automobile from my home. Here, with an expert pusher, at high tide one is able to get his limit of fifteen birds in an hour or two. With the receding of the tide I usually embark in a rowboat with a twelve-year-old Negro boy as my guide, and have excellent fishing for yellow perch, one of the most delicious of pan fish. In November duck-shooting, for which Maryland is so famous, arrives. One of the best of the clubs is the Cedar Point immediately across the Chesapeake Bay from Baltimore. We usually got there in the early evening, and sat down to a veritable banquet: oysters tonged from the flats near by, terrapin from our own protected marsh, canvasback ducks, wild rice, corn bread, and other specialties of the Eastern Shore. Breakfast before daylight made it possible to reach the blinds by sunup. Usually one does not have to wait long for the ducks. I have described how Bob Bingham amazed us all with his marksmanship one morning at this club. In November and December again the Woodmont Club offers sport that is hard to resist. Wild turkeys and pheasants are at hand the latter part of November, deer during December, and other game during the remainder of the winter. In the inclement months of January and February I frequently am able to steal away by plane, and join one or more friends in Florida: Mr. George A. Bacon at Sarasota, where grouper, king, and tarpon abound; Dr. and Mrs. E. Clay Shaw in Miami, whose home I use as headquarters from which to fish in the adjacent waters with Dr. Thomas O. Otto, Mr. John Oliver LaGorce, Mr. James H. Cox, Mr. Edwin N. Belcher, and Mr. William Burdine, with all of whom I have had cruises in their yachts or motorboats especially designed for Florida fishing, or down the Keys for bonefish along the flats, or big fish in the Gulf Stream with friends on Matecumbe Key; or out to Everglades City with Mr. D. G. Copeland for the dynamic baby tarpon on the lightest tackle for fly fishing; with Dr. Louis C. Orr, and Mr. Alfred Harcourt I have had wonderful fishing in the inland waters for bass, and other small fish. A surgical life in Baltimore, if properly interspersed with sport on water or in the field, is hard to beat.

For many years I have been a great believer in setting-up exercises that I learned when a youth in the Maverick Rifles. I have rarely failed to go through some of them in my bathroom each night and morning. As the years have gone by, I have modified and simplified the exercises, and have included finger and forearm movements too, believing that if pianists find it necessary to go through long exercises daily to keep their fingers fit, a surgeon should also. My routine night and morning now consists of a dogtrot on the bathmat for a hundred counts, then a combined arm and forearm movement in which I massage my abdomen, thus exercising my shoulder and chest muscles. At the same time I take deep inspirations at every count of four, and also exercise the neck muscles by throwing the chin up and down. At first it was difficult to do these five things at one time. Perhaps they have helped in preventing the development of a pendulous abdomen and a dewlap, as well as increasing my lung capacity. Every moment is utilized. While sitting, I generally carry out my finger and forearm exercises. It is interesting to note that by concentrating on these, other movements are co-ordinated very satisfactorily.

The great sculptor Gutzon Borglum said, "My own fingertips are more accurate than my eyes in the information that they have conveyed to my mind." This statement applies equally well to surgeons. In my lectures to students and talks with assistants, I am prone to stress the importance of developing a *tactus eruditus*, a delicate touch of the fingertips so erudite as to convey accurately to the brain what is felt. In the depths of a surgical wound, sensitive fingers are often called upon to furnish information on which vital decisions are made, and surgical procedures are carried out. It is all-important that every surgeon should keep his fingers supple and sensitive.

In my early life as a urological surgeon I found my interests largely taken up with the maladies of the aged. It was interesting to prove that there was no age limit to urological surgery, that men well up in the nineties are quite amenable to grave surgical operations. In this work with old men it is delightful to find how many of them are vigorous far beyond the sixties and to be able to refute the unfortunate statement that was quoted by Osler that a man is capable of no important work after forty, and that he might well be chloroformed at sixty. It has interested me greatly to take part in the effort to persuade industrialists that there is no justification in excluding men past middle age from their organizations. It has been a pleasure to observe the recent demonstrations that in many plants the older men often do more and better work than the younger, and are generally more steady and trustworthy.

In 1930 I missed going to Vatican City on an interesting mission. A legate from Cardinal Mundelein came with a letter asking whether I could arrange to go to Rome to operate upon Pope Pius XI. Several weeks latter word came to me that permission had been denied by Signor Mussolini.

In recent years the development of endocrinology, the production of glandular extractions with which the genital tracts are so closely associated, has brought new and great interests to my work. Men, women, and children presenting piteous abnormalities and sad psychic states have come to us. A big, new field has been developed in urological surgery. It has often been possible to cure these pitiful patients. Transforming unhappy children and sending them back normal to their frantic parents has been the greatest gratification of my life. The use of glandular extracts (hormones), although a very new field of urology, has already accomplished amazing results. These rapid strides have brought with them the necessity of greatly broadening the work of our laboratories, and have added much to the cost of maintenance. Pari passu has come the necessity of obtaining more and more funds. One of my most important occupations has been to persuade wealthy friends and patients to endow this work. I have already indicated how remarkable has been the response, and named some of the many who have contributed generously. They have to date given over $2,000,000. Most of them, I hope, have got some of the satisfaction from their donations that James Buchanan Brady was so proud to acknowledge from his.

The urge to pursue interesting problems and to write and lecture about them has been an ever present motive force. In fact, if two or three weeks go by without my becoming engaged in the preparation of some manuscript I have a distinct feeling of unrest. During the many minor illnesses that have confined me in bed, I have taken advantage of the freedom from outside annoyances to dictate papers. Since beginning practice, I have written over three hundred individual papers and the following books: *Studies in Hypertrophy and Cancer of the Prostate; Young's Practice of Urology*, a two-volume textbook, in conjunction with David M. Davis; *Urological Roentgenology*, with Charles A. Waters; and *Genital Abnormalities, Hermaphroditism and Related Adrenal Diseases.* A number of years ago Dr. Thayer put me to bed for four months on account of a heart that he said I had overstrained on a strenuous canoeing trip. This long period of enforced confinement passed very quickly when I began dictating papers, eight of which were completed during my incarceration. Last fall I had the misfortune to come down with that common and very annoying malady known as shingles. On the insistence of my secretary, Miss Bertha M. Trott, I started to dictate the autobiography that I had been promising Mr. Alfred Harcourt for several years, so that the readers may either thank or curse the shingles, as they see fit.

Need I say more to show how much I have enjoyed the life I have led, or what a thrilling time I have had in my professional work? But there is still so much to do, so much to live for.

INDEX

This index includes: *Personal names.* Every name whenever mentioned, with "ref. **to**" when there is little concerning it. Names in quotation marks are "assigned" names or nicknames. *Place names,* including World War battles. Only when special attention is given to them; countries (not cities and towns) when the author visits them.

Abel, Dr. John J., 92, 94, 242

Abercrombie, Roland, 234

Acriflavine, 253

Adam a hermaphrodite? 201

Adams, Franklin P., 324

Adrenal glands affect virilism, 205–09 (illus.)

Aegean, H. Y.'s cruise to the, 466–68

Aesculapius, 467

Agnew, Thomas and Sons, 446–47

Airlie, David L. G. W. Ogilvy, earl of, 511

Albarran, Dr. Joaquin, 89

Albert, duke of York, ref. to, 394

Alexander, Samuel T., 104–09 (quoted); daughter of, 109

Alfonso XIII, King of Spain, ref. to, 495

Allatoona Pass, battle of, 12–13

Allen, Mr. and Mrs. Fred, 455–56

Allen, Raymond P., 228

Allenby, Gen Sir Edmund, 462–63; wife of, 463

Alsace-Lorraine, H. Y. in, 355–57, 360–61, 381–82, 388–89

Alyea, Dr. Edwin P., 245

American College of Surgeons, 457–61

American Commission for Relief in Belgium, 381, 383

American Expeditionary Force: the first divisions of, arrive in France, 307; returns home, 341–42; First Army, 373, 379; Second Army, 379; Third Army, *see* Army of Occupation; 1st Division, 286, 291, 307, 351–52, 362, 366, 371, 374–76, 380, 382, 386; 2d Division, 307, 349, 351, 362, 366, 368, 372, 382; 3d Division, 339, 351, 362–65, 385–86; 4th Division, 351, 368; 5th Division, 371; 26th Division, 343–49, 351, 353–55, 364, 368–69, 371, 380; 28th Division, 362–63; 32d Division, 355–57; 35th Division, 361; 42d ("Rainbow") Division, 338–39, 369–71, 374–76;

49th Division, 371; 77th Division, 358, 375; 79th Division, 374; 82d Division, 357, 371; 89th Division, 376; 90th Division, 371; 92d Division, 361–62. *See also* Liquors, alcoholic; Skin diseases; Venereal diseases; names of persons.

American: Legion, ref. to, 442–43; Medical Ass'n, ref. to, 238; Red Cross, *see* Red Cross; Surgical Society, 88; Urological Ass'n, 248–50, 473, 530

American Medical Service for the Civil Population of Eastern France, 294–99; ref. to, 322; mess for the staff of the, 322–27; end of the, 390

Ames, Joseph S., 437

Ananias Club, 506–08

Andrews, Margaret, 434

Andrus, Dr. Edwin Cowles, 117

Anesthesia: discovery of, 69–73; early practice of, 58–59; improvements in, 68; H. Y. gives, 59, 68–69, (tiger) 209–10

Anthrax, a rare case of, 50–52

Antiseptics, 252–63

Anus, imperforate, 198–200 (illus.)

Aphrodite, 201–02

Archer, George, 228

Archives of Surgery, 181

Ark, the, and the *Dove,* 447

Armijo, Gen. Manuel, 8

Armistice, World War, 378

Army of Occupation, World War, 340–41, 379–80, 388–90

Artigue, Capt. d', 285

Ashford, Dr. Bailey K., 286, 296

Australian troops (World War), venereal diseases in the, 273, 332–33

Austria, H. Y. visits, 454–55, 465

Austrian, Dr. Charles R., 173

Aviation: H. Y.'s interest in, 420–22, 482–87, 527; his flights, 483–84, 487–90, 493–94

INDEX

Windsor, Duke of (Prince of Wales; Edward VII), ref. to, 512; Duchess of (Wallis Warfield), ref. to, 430, 512
Winship, Gov. Blanton (Puerto Rico), 472
Winterode, Dr. Robert P., 410–12
Wolf, Robert, 214–15 (quoted)
Woodmont Rod and Gun Club, 534
Woods, Mrs. Arthur, 466, 468
Workshop, H. Y.'s as a boy, 29–30. *See also* Machine shop.
World War: H. Y. in the, 264–390, 485–87; Memorial, Maryland, 442–44
Wright, Orville, 484; with Wilbur, 483, 485

X-ray burns, 212–13
X-ray pictures, 155, 158, 165, 170, 174, 177

Y.M.C.A., (World War), 289
Young, Albert, 449–50
Young, Bessy Colston (Mrs. Hugh Hampton), 496, 522, 524, 529; marriage of, 496; illness and death of, 522–24; ref. to, 150, 213, 221–22, 244, 370, 377, 438–39, (on trips) 218, 453–55 *passim*; por., 522
Young, Charles Kemper, 10–11
Young, David (H. Y.'s greatuncle), 10; wife of, 37
Young, Frances Hampton Gibson (Mrs. Hugh Franklin; H. Y.'s grandmother), 6
Young, Frances Michie Kemper (Mrs. William Hugh; H. Y.'s mother), 3, 10–33 *passim*, 50, 525; marriage of, 18; quoted, 22; por., 4
Young, Col. Hugh Franklin (H. Y.'s grandfather), 4–10, 16–18, 21, 24, 26, 33; death of, 34; quoted, 7–9, 33; wife of, 6; por., 4
Young, Dr. Hugh Hampton: ancestry of, 5, 429–30; birth of, 18; childhood and youth of, 18–46; marriage of, 496; wife of, *see* Young, Bessy Colston; children of, ref. to, 213, 218, 420, 453, 462, 473, 514, 516, 524, 525, 529, pors. of the, 524; grandchildren of, ref. to, 22, 524, pors. of the, 525; bust of H. Y., 509; pors. of H. Y., frontispiece, 264, 526
Young, Dr. Hugh Hampton: education of, 20–21, 31–32, 34–37, 40–46; chooses a vocation, 33, 39, 42–43, 50; studies medicine, 42–46; practices medicine, 47–48; at Johns Hopkins Hospital, 49–

77; fails to get position as bacteriologist, 52; gets one, 56; fails to get professorship in pathology, 55; app't'd head of Dep't of Genito-Urinary Surgery, 76–77; practices in Balto., 78–80; vacation for illness, 80–82; operating in Mexico, 82–85; developing a specialty (urology), 86–208; experiences of, with J. B. Brady, 216–37; Director of the Brady Urological Institute, 86–215, 221–63; in the World War, 264–390; 485–87; made Director of Urology A.E.F., 281; consultant for Pres. Wilson, 398–403; state and civic interests of, 404–52; cruises and trips by, 453–81; interest of, in aviation, 482–94; study of languages by, 495–503; friendship of, with R. W. Bingham, 504–15; fishing and hunting, *see* those headings; summing up by, 522–38
Young, Dr. Hugh Hampton: books by, 538, (ref. to) 150, 209, 259; degrees and honors rec'd by, 44, 488, 514; positions held by, 56, 76, 281, 408–09, 413, 418, 420, 430, 439, 443, 449, 461, 471, 527
Young, Dr. Hugh Hampton, reports, papers, and articles by: medical and surgical, 51, 75, 79–80, 82, 110–11, 120, 121–22, 129–30, 139–40, 146, 150–51, 167–68, 179, 181, 255, 257–58, 473, 494, 496, 500–01, 538; on the Maryland World's Fair exhibit, 432–34, 435; World War, 288–90, 335–36
Young, Dr. Hugh Hampton, quoted, 7, 42, 48, 50, 56, 57, 69, 76, 84, 120, 190, 212, 267, 270, 276, 281, 313, 314–15, 324–25, 357, 401, 405, 409, 415, 428–30, 436–37, 470, 508–09, 524–25
Young, Rev. John, 20
Young, Dr. John (H. Y.'s greatuncle), 10
Young, Newton (H. Y.'s uncle), 17
Young, Gen. William Hugh (H. Y.'s father), 3, 10–29, 33, 50; ref. to, 72, 525; birth of, 6; marriage of, 18; in the Civil War, 11–15, (ref. to) 481, 504; quoted, 39, 42; por., 4
Young's punch, 119, 216–17; illus., 119, 121; small, 138–40 (illus.); operation, 118–34 (illus.), 217

Zinsser, Dr. Hans, 336–37